BRE Digests   **Building Defects and Maintenance**

BRE Digests

Building Defects and Maintenance

Essential information from
the Building Research Establishment

ⵁ **THE CONSTRUCTION PRESS**
LANCASTER   LONDON   NEW YORK

Published in 1977
by
The Construction Press Ltd
a company within the Longman Group.

Second impression 1978

The Construction Press Ltd
Lunesdale House
Hornby
Lancaster LA2 8NB
England.

Longman Group Ltd
5 Bentinck Street
London W1M 5RN.

Longman Inc.
New York.

Printed in Great Britain.

ISBN 0 904406 45 8

Foreword

This book and its companion volumes bring together in a bound and edited form the monthly publications of the Building Research Establishment known as the BRE Digests. Respected throughout the construction industry, the BRE Digests have earned a reputation for authoritative information presented in a readily understood manner. Each Digest takes a subject of particular building concern and provides an analysis of the most important and useful relevant information available about it.

The first edition of this series of volumes presented the BRE Digests in a format which has proved to be outstandingly useful and successful. They were originally published in 1973 with a somewhat uncertain expectation of likely demand, but three printings were required to fill the orders that started to arrive from almost every country in the world.

Since the publication of the first edition, however, about 40 new Digests have appeared and many of the earlier ones have been revised and updated. This new edition therefore will meet a very real need in the many offices and colleges where it is essential to be up to date. These volumes contain all current Digests up to and including that issued in February 1977, with the exception of No. 149.

The editorial format of the first edition has been retained, with the series contained in four volumes on Construction, Materials, Services, and Defects and Maintenance respectively. Each volume includes a comprehensive index to the whole series, thereby making easy cross-reference from one volume to another.

New BRE Digests are published at monthly intervals by HMSO and these may be purchased either singly or on a subscription basis through any supplier of HMSO publications or direct from their London bookshop:

HMSO
PO Box 569
London, SE1 9NH.

ACKNOWLEDGEMENT

We have pleasure in acknowledging the co-operation of both the Building Research Establishment and Her Majesty's Stationery Office in granting us permission to publish the BRE Digests in this volume.

Contents

1 Design and Appearance

Design and appearance —1

From time to time a Digest has dealt with a particular aspect of the behaviour of materials when used in juxtaposition and in specific conditions of weathering— for instance, the effects of moisture penetration and attack by alkali and sulphates on stone, brickwork, mortars and renderings, the effect of the washings from limestone walls on sandstone plinths and pavings, the failures of paints or the corrosion of metals. Such effects have usually been discussed primarily in terms of prevention and cure, rather than in terms of appearance and architectural detailing. However, the appearance of many of the buildings erected in the last two decades suggests that the reasons for certain details used in the past are not widely under- stood and that, in certain cases, even elementary safeguards have been neglected, resulting in much preventable shabbiness quite early in the life of the building. This Digest and the next discuss some important design details on which the ability of a building to retain a satisfactory surface appearance depends. The present Digest is concerned particularly with the appearance of Portland stone; the next will illustrate the appearance of other facing materials.

Until the 1930s there was little temptation for an architect in this country to depart from traditional practice; he could generally rely on inherited specifications to produce, in very broad terms, known effects of time, wear and weathering on the materials of his region. Now, however, designers and builders are faced with an immense building programme, in which the choice of new materials or old materials used in new ways becomes ever more bewildering. The repercussions of this choice on design details must be carefully thought out.

The first five illustrations are of buildings 50 years old or more. In Fig. 1, the appearance of the base of an historic building has been spoiled in two ways. First, streaking has been produced by rainwater washings from a limestone wall over a sill-course not undercut to form a drip; soot has been washed away in irregular stripes, resulting in a 'seismograph' pattern which destroys the effect of horizontality, unity and solidity desirable in a plinth. Secondly, decay of the sand- stone base-course has been caused by the washings from the lime- stone wall above (a defect common in sandstone pavings at the base of limestone walls), and the appearance of solidity at the base is further impaired.

Figure 2 shows a well-known and particularly effective example of the way in which certain elements of a composition can be 'acciden- tally' emphasized by the rain-washing of limestone, to the enhance- ment of the general effect. Figure 3 shows a similar effect, but here the stone below the exposed copings (without damp-proof courses) and around the porch has suffered from moisture penetration, which also affected the interior of the church. Only under the eaves of the main roof is the stone free from the effects of dampness—an example of the value of eaves in the preservation both of the fabric and of the original appearance.

Fig. 1

Fig. 2

Figure 4 shows a limestone plinth badly pitted by moisture rising from a basement area in which the junction of the asphalt paving with the damp-proof course in the wall was defective.

Many limestone façades in London, even where facing south or south-west, as in Fig. 5, do not become bleached by rain over their lower portions because they are sheltered by nearby buildings. In this fairly typical example, the transition from the soot-darkened stone of the lower storeys to the bleached stone of the attic storey is sufficiently well defined almost to give the illusion in bright sunlight that the attic was built with a different kind of stone.

The search in the 1930s for a new architecture brought in its train a fashion for 'modernism' which was frequently expressed by the avoidance of pitched roofs and the use of cement-rendered walls. The flat roof construction increased the exposure to the weather of the walls—and these were often built of brickwork containing soluble salts. Some of these early experiments in modern architecture are now familiar by their dated and frequently shabby appearance, brought about by the too-hasty abandonment of traditional practices based on long experience.

Typical of the effects of soluble sulphates from damp brickwork on cement-sand renderings applied in the 1920s and 1930s are the examples shown in Figs. 6 and 7 of exposed wall heads with no damp-proof capping; in Fig. 7 can be seen characteristic horizontal cracking formed by expansion of the sulphate-attacked mortar in the bed joints.

These early examples of 'modernistic' design in this country were mainly buildings of domestic or commercial character. Civic and

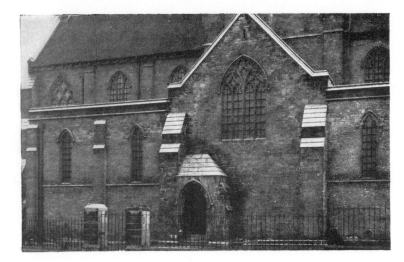

Fig. 3

Fig. 4

government buildings, banks and large office buildings, though usually of framed structure, were still being clothed in the 'free classical' style considered to be a symbol of status and durability. The appearance of such buildings could be marred later by the mode of weathering of some of the very features that were designed to contribute to their impressiveness; thus Fig. 8 shows the unsightly staining of masonry caused by lime-washings from a massive block of sculptured limestone in an exposed position above a main entrance. In Fig. 9 is shown a reasonably neat end wall to a north-light industrial building of the inter-war period, where appearance has been spoiled by dampness penetrating the brickwork from the coping. The wall has dried out below the level of the roof slopes, which have been accentuated (instead of being masked) by the pattern of dampness and efflorescence in a much more untidy way than if the profile of the wall had followed the slopes. Pattern-staining from the ledges and braces of the doors adds to the impression of untidiness. (Other discolourations are the remnants of war-time camouflage.)

It is surprising that so many post-war buildings, be they of traditional or non-traditional design, exhibit faults that could have been avoided by simple precautions against the effects of dampness on Portland stone. One of the commonest of these faults is the damage caused to plinths arising from a lack of proper damp-proof coursing above the system of basement tanking. Frequently the vertical tanking applied

Fig. 5

Fig. 6

Fig. 7

Fig. 8

to basement walls and the horizontal tanking over 'vaults' appear to be unconnected or inadequately connected with the damp-proof course in the walls above, or else the pavement is finished at a level higher than that of the damp-proof course in the wall. Figure 4 shows a Portland stone plinth damaged by moisture rising through a faulty damp-proof course in a building erected before the 1914-18 war. That a similar fault should arise in a building dating from 1952 (Fig. 10(a)) and in those illustrated in Figs. 11 and 12, is a clear indication that sufficient attention is still not being given to this matter.

Figure 11 shows details of a modern office building completed in 1958, where there appears to be a lack of continuity of damp-proofing between the basement tanking and the damp-proof course. Rain splashings from the pavement have contributed to the unsightliness of the plinth (Fig. 11(a)), but the surface of the stone is, in parts, already starting to scale, as can be seen from the crack visible in Fig. 11(b). There is something to be said for the use of a harder and more impervious stone than Portland for plinths in situations such as these. The marble skirting shown in Fig. 11(b) is too low to mask the unsightly effects of the rising moisture.

Fig. 9

Figs. 10 (*a*) and (*b*)

In the office building illustrated in Fig. 12, dating from about 1958 and faced with Portland stone, the plinth was so rapidly affected by rising dampness that remedy was sought in the form of a siliconate injection into holes drilled in the plinth and subsequently plugged, but the appearance was not improved. The holes can just be seen in the photograph, close to the pavement. Higher up, the unsightly effect of the washings from the flush limestone window sills is obtrusive.

In Fig. 10, the 'seismograph' effect is accentuated by the design of the top of the plinth which, though aesthetically good in itself, does not allow the washings from the limestone sills to be thrown clear. The resultant streaking over the soot-laden portion of the plinth can only be described as a disfigurement of a type that the architect certainly would not have wished as a feature of 'weathering'. The rapidity of the damaging action of dampness from below or behind a Portland stone plinth can be gauged from Fig. 10(*b*), a close view of the same plinth, showing patches of deep pitting and scaling after only 11 years' exposure.

Figure 13 provides a striking example of how water can affect designed appearance. The wide projections at the base of this large Portland stone building were presumably intended to impart an appearance of massive strength and imposing dignity. The stone in the plinth was grooved vertically to give variety of texture. Water has gushed from the wide ledges, staining the face of the ashlar and so markedly bleaching the quoin that the impression of strength has been spoiled at the very point where it should tell most—at the corner of the building. The grooving of the plinth in rather wide 'batts' has accentuated the vertical streaking.

Figs. 11 (*a*) and (*b*)

Fig. 13

The Portland stone ashlar shown in Fig. 14(a) was used to face the ground-floor walls of a tall office building which is surrounded at first-floor level by a podium for pedestrians. The paving of the podium is of concrete flags over a layer of asphalt that was intended to ensure watertightness below. Either faulty design or bad workmanship, or a combination of both, has resulted in such disfigurement of the ground-floor ashlar as that shown here, owing to leaks from above, and this within but a year or so of completion of the building. Figure 14(b) shows a staircase giving access to the podium: the ground-floor ashlar is stained by dampness caused by the lack of a raised edge to the landing, thus allowing water to run over the edge.

The disfigurement of and damage done to Portland stone by dampness is by no means confined to the lower parts of buildings. Badly stained parapets (Fig. 15), caused by faulty damp-proofing, can be seen in numerous buildings erected recently. If cornices and eaves are to be rejected even on plain rectangular buildings where a pitched roof would present no difficulty, then the flat roof and parapet should be so constructed that moisture cannot penetrate into the wall. A continuous damp-proof course under copings is essential.

Canopies, too, seem frequently to provide a source of disfigurement arising from the lack of precautions against the entry of moisture into the fabric. In Fig. 16(a), dampness rising from the top of the canopy has stained the stones immediately above it. In Fig. 16(b), an entrance to a business premises, dirty water has run down between the canopy and the return wall on to which it abuts, leaving very ugly streaks to mar the appearance of the entrance. Above this canopy can be seen a dark vertical stain where water, carrying soot with it, has run through a joint in the window sill immediately below a mullion—a very prevalent form of disfigurement in modern buildings where the sills of continuous windows are joined at the mullions. When such sills are of slate, as they frequently are (though not in this case), the ends of the sections could be rebated and bedded in mastic instead of a straight cut with pointing in mortar.

Figure 17 shows two examples, after about 12 years' exposure in London, of the alteration of designed appearance by the staining of Portland stone. In Fig. 17(a) the 'pattern design' as it left the drawing-board, of a wall facing north-east on an open site, has already been affected to a marked extent. In a further 12 years, unless the façade is washed (or masked by adjoining buildings) the original pattern will have been quite changed. In Fig. 17(b) (a free classical design) staining by water dripping from the astragal moulding under the slight cornice over the soot-covered ashlar below has marred the appearance of a very well proportioned entrance. The wall faces west in a narrow

Fig. 12

Figs. 14 (a) and (b)

Fig. 15

Figs. 16 (*a*) and (*b*)

passage and is unlikely to receive sufficient rain to wash it clean. The peculiar pattern and obtrusiveness of this disfigurement seem disproportionate to its cause. In both Figs. 17(*a*) and (*b*) the original appearance could be restored by cleaning the stone.

The curtain-walling of the seven-year-old building depicted in Fig. 18 has mullions faced with Portland stone, of which the particular pattern of staining seems to indicate that rainwater has somehow penetrated into the mullions, and has leaked out again through the joints between the stones, washing away the soot and leaving white patches on drying off. The resulting appearance of the stone contrasts unfavourably with that of the curtain walling itself, which can be quickly restored to its original brightness by regular washing carried out in conjunction with external window cleaning.

Figs. 17 (*a*) and (*b*)

Fig. 18

Figs. 19 (a) and (b)

Figure 19 shows a low retaining wall with Portland stone and apparently quite unprotected from the entry of moisture. Its poor appearance only a year or so after completion requires no further comment. The pattern of distribution of the patches of dirt and bleached areas about the joints resembles that seen on the stone mullions in Fig. 18, and can be seen in detail in Fig. 19(b). Judging by examples of Figs. 10(b) and 11(b), pitting and scaling of the stone may be expected, in such conditions as these, in 5 to 10 years' time.

It will be seen from these examples that changes in appearance can happen in three ways. First, there are the preventable faults in design and/or construction where there is sufficient information available at the time to avoid them. Secondly, there is the unforeseeable behaviour of a material in a given situation where it could reasonably be argued that there was insufficient information generally available at the time, and where the change may be not wholly explicable in the light of existing knowledge. A third way in which the appearance can alter is through the process of 'natural' weathering, often as the result of micro-climatic influences, frequently unpredictable in detail.

While further research into the problems of exposure, the effects of wind and water distribution and atmospheric dirt might eventually provide designers with some further guidance towards more predictable appearances after weathering than has hitherto been possible, the reasons for the unwelcome visible effects on the fabric are now sufficiently known for them to be avoided in most cases.

Design and Appearance—2

Slate

Green slate, mainly from Lancashire and Westmorland, seems to be almost as favoured for wall cladding today as it once was for roofing, but changes in appearance may be less tolerable in the new situation. In **1**, dirty water dripping from the sills on to the rough texture of riven slabs has produced an unusual staining pattern, the overall effect being worsened by paint flaking from the concrete.

In another office block of about the same age (5–6 years) sawn slate was used (**2**) and, though the sills have prevented dripping on to the slate, weathering has exaggerated the original variations in tone that may have been present in slabs obtained from different quarries. The slabs on another building of similar age (**3**) have weathered more evenly, though gaps in the sill have allowed water to seep through and cause staining.

Brickwork

The appearance of good brickwork, though less affected than that of many other building materials, can be spoiled in some situations. In **4**, staining and efflorescence have been caused by water dripping from a flat roof having no projection beyond the wall face. The roof to the adjoining bay has a projecting edge with a drip under it; on this bay staining is insignificant. Similar discolouration and efflorescence can be seen in **5**, where the concrete treads of external stairs are level, so allowing water that collects on them to soak into the brickwork.

Washings from limestone features cause frequent disfigurement of adjacent areas; the 'moustache' effect (**6a**) is a familiar example. Here the white streaks below the ends of

1

2

3

4

5

6a

6b

Where glazed materials cannot be kept clean, appearance depends largely on the effects of fortuitous washing of dirt deposited from the atmosphere by rain, as in **7b**, where the ground storey is faced with dark green glazed terracotta, and the upper storeys with cream-coloured blocks.

Timber

The natural resistance to decay of timbers such as teak and western red cedar has often led to the incorrect assumption that little or no maintenance is required. The western red cedar panels in **8** remained untreated for five years. Annual application of a linseed oil/paraffin wax mixture containing a fungicide is the minimum necessary to preserve appearance.

Metals

Some metals, e.g. copper, oxidize attractively upon exposure, whereas others such as aluminium alloys may become unsightly. Aluminium used externally requires anodic treatment, followed by periodic washing, to maintain appearance. Where the aluminium has not been anodized, more frequent washing is necessary, depending upon the extent of atmospheric pollution. If this is neglected, dirt particles may cause disfigurement by pitting, as in **9**.

Cast stone

The appearance of cast stone can be marred by streaking and staining; **10** is typical of this, though here it is relatively free from the crazing which sometimes occurs. Water has dripped over the surface from a ledge, the flashing being inadequate to throw it clear of the stone.

7a

7b

window sills show prominently. In **6a**, a throat under the sill is returned at the ends to meet the wall face, thus largely nullifying the value of the projection. **6b** shows a building in which this type of disfigurement has been largely avoided by setting the wooden window frames slightly in recess of the wall face, with a lead flashing at the sills extending about 100 mm into the brickwork on each side.

Terracotta

Few buildings executed in smooth-textured brick and terracotta show evidence of the defects already mentioned, especially where careful detailing has been followed by regular maintenance, as in **7a**.

8

9

10

12

11

13

Concrete

Crazing and cracking in concrete introduce the risk that water may penetrate to the reinforcement, cause corrosion and lead to eventual disintegration.

11 shows crazed and cracked slabs on a building of fairly recent construction, and **12** illustrates uneven discolouration on the slabs of another building. In **13** the pattern of jointing on an end wall has been unbalanced by rain washing out the joints in the upper part and soot lodging on the lower joints, exaggerating them unduly. **14** shows stains beneath the edge of a flat roof where water has seeped under the coping, and to the right can be seen spots where rusting of the underlying reinforcement has occurred.

14

15

16

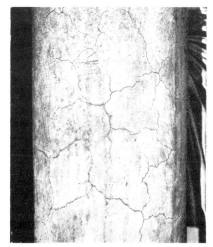

17

Concrete poured *in situ* may show additional defects, such as shutter-marks and irregularities resulting from different pouring operations.

The soffits of the wings of a penthouse (**15**) have become heavily stained in a polluted atmosphere, except at the edges. Unintentionally, an impression of crushing weight has thus been given to the superstructure. Cleaning to preserve the original appearance would clearly be an inconvenient operation.

In **16**, the concrete in a roof edge of unusual profile shows what appear to be shutter-marks over the arches, not removed by bush-hammering. These blemishes are accentuated by the many rust stains on the concrete, caused here perhaps by iron pyrites in the aggregate rather than by rusting of poorly protected reinforcement. Finishes of cement, aggregate and sand do not always 'weather' attractively, particularly in dirty atmospheres. If the mix or backing is unsuitable they are likely to craze and are vulnerable to sulphate attack.

17 shows a light-coloured terrazzo finish applied *in situ* to a ground-storey circular column. The crazing of the terrazzo, dirt from the atmosphere and children's scribbles, have combined to spoil the appearance in a short time. **18** shows a rendering down which water has flowed from a flat roof with no projection. The pattern of staining has been caused by water drying off before reaching the base of the wall.

18

Further reading

'A qualitative study of some buildings in the London area', *National Building Studies, Special Report 33*; and 'Qualitative studies of buildings', *Special Report 39*.

Changes in the appearance of concrete on exposure

D B Honeyborne BSc

The factors that cause major changes in the appearance of facing concrete may be internal or environmental. More often than not, they are a combination of both, for it requires some internal deficiency to give the aggressive elements in the environment an opportunity to bring about noticeable change; concrete of good quality will suffer little more from the normal environment than a slow dirtying in areas not well washed by the rain, or a staining from some other building material which could almost certainly have been avoided by better detailing.

This digest illustrates some of the undesirable changes that may occur with the passage of time if concrete design falls far short of that recommended on the basis of good practice.

The effect of design on the manner in which Portland stone, brick, wood and some other building materials change their appearance after years of exposure to the weather is discussed in Digests 45 and 46 *Design and appearance*. Natural weathering may or may not be considered to enhance the appearance of these materials, the quality of which is outside the control of either the designer or the constructor except to the extent that selection can eliminate the unsuitable. But the causes of deterioration of concrete are sufficiently well understood for it to be possible to avoid the most striking defects, and to minimise maintenance costs, for example, by careful design of the mix and by correct positioning of the reinforcement.

Normal weathering

The drying power of the sun and wind, rain, the oxygen and carbon dioxide that are naturally present in the air, and the sulphurous gases and dirt with which we have polluted it, all play a part in causing changes in facing concrete, though not all these changes have a marked effect on its appearance. There is surprisingly little published about the chemical and mineralogical composition of the surface of weathered concrete but it is possible to deduce broadly how it changes with time.

Hydration of the cement results in the formation of hydrated calcium silicates and aluminates and the remaining water becomes highly alkaline. At the surface this alkalinity is neutralised and the hydrated aluminates and silicates are very slowly decomposed by the carbon dioxide and sulphur dioxide of the air, and calcium carbonate, calcium sulphate, alumina and silica are formed. In good quality concrete this produces little change in appearance; the calcium sulphate helps to act as a binder to retain dirt deposited in sheltered areas but, because of its slight solubility, helps to keep rain-washed areas clean.

Quality control

Methods of designing adequate concrete mixes have been described frequently in recent years (*see* references 1–4). The advice given covers the use of some of the artificial aggregates as well as the natural aggregates. However, the designer will often be tempted to relax his specification for aesthetic or economic reasons. The following illustrated comments will help him to judge the risk involved in making departures from the ideal in any particular circumstances.

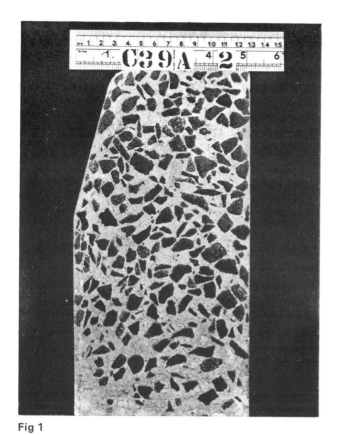

Fig 1

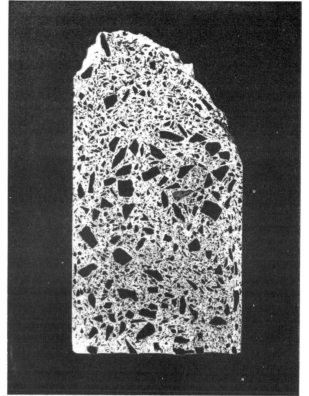

Fig 2

Fig 3

Poor grading leading to shrinkage cracking

As the water in a concrete mix reacts or dries out, the cement paste binding the aggregate together shrinks. In concrete with well-graded aggregate, for example, the kerb shown in section in Fig 1, this results simply in a general reduction in volume, without visible deterioration. If, however, the mix is poorly graded either throughout the mass of the concrete or as a result of segregation of the finer and coarser aggregates, considerably greater shrinkage may occur in the regions containing the finer fraction, resulting in surface cracking. The cracking is seldom very deep and where the exposure conditions are mild the cracks often gradually fill up again with a deposit of calcium carbonate (limestone). In severe conditions of exposure the cracks may lead to disintegration, as shown in Fig 2. Fig 3 shows surface cracking of a new concrete fence post, caused by poorly graded aggregate leading to excessive shrinkage of the surface.

Carbonation shrinkage

The carbonation of the products of cement hydration by the carbon dioxide of the air is accompanied by a tendency of the materials to shrink. The reason is not completely understood but the effect when the aggregate near the surface is not well graded is to produce surface cracks which may be distinguished from cracks caused by drying shrinkage because they take much longer to develop. The cracks illustrated in Fig 4 were photographed rather less than a year after casting, but developed after only a few months. Like the shrinkage cracks described above, they tend to be self-healing.

Action of calcium chloride

Calcium chloride is often added to a concrete mix to accelerate the rate of setting. When used in excessive amounts, generally or locally, it can lead to corrosion of the reinforcement as described later.

With unreinforced concrete, the addition of calcium chloride in amounts between 0·5 per cent and 2·0 per cent of the weight of the cement leads to a 50 per cent increase in drying shrinkage; greater proportions lead to very much greater shrinkage.[7] The shrinkage cracking referred to above can, therefore, become more serious when calcium chloride is used as an admixture.

Shrinking aggregate

Wetting and drying causes concrete to expand and contract. This movement is normally caused entirely by the expansion or contraction of the paste formed by the set cement and the finest aggregate, the coarser aggregates playing a negligible part. Such movements are, at most, of the order of 0·04 per cent. However, some aggregates, particularly some doleritic and basaltic types from Scotland, have a large wetting and drying movement on their own account, so much so that the total movement of the concrete can rise to 0·1 per cent. The movement can be even greater if calcium chloride is used to accelerate the set. Such movements are difficult to accommodate in buildings and give rise to cracking of reinforced concrete wall panels, excessive deflection of balcony slabs and other troublesome structural effects; but

Fig 4

the use of such aggregates can also lead to complete disintegration of the concrete, particularly when the mix design is not ideal. In these circumstances, the very high shrinkage of the paste of hydrated cement and fine aggregate leads to cracking (Fig 5) and eventual break-up of the concrete by frost and other agencies when such concrete is exposed to the weather. The mechanism of cracking is rather like that of normal shrinkage cracking but the movement is very much greater and the effects can be much

Fig 5 Frost damage following cracking caused by the use of a high-shrinkage aggregate

Fig 6 Rust staining caused by aggregate containing active pyrite

Pyrite staining

Over the past fifteen years or so there has been a growing incidence of the appearance of brown stains on the surface of facing concrete, associated with the use of Thames gravel aggregate; an example of this is shown in Fig 6. It has been found[10] to be caused by a rare form of the iron sulphide mineral, pyrite, which reacts with water and the oxygen of the air in the presence of lime to form a brown iron hydroxide. The hydration products of cement provide the lime. Although simple tests have been developed which will distinguish between this reactive form of pyrite and the normal unreactive form, it will normally be impracticable to examine a large enough sample of aggregate to ensure that this risk of staining is reduced to negligible proportions. Where such aggregate must be used for facing purposes and it is essential that staining be avoided, the problem should be discussed with the aggregate suppliers.

Reactive ironstone aggregate

Some ironstone in the Midlands is unsuitable for use as aggregate because it reacts expansively with lime formed during hydration of the cement. This can lead to disintegration, either directly, or by frost action following cracking caused by the expansion (*see* Fig 7).

more devastating. The shrinkage of the coarse aggregate contributes most to the overall movement of the concrete; the shrinkage of the fine fraction contributes most to the disintegration. The use of a non-shrinking fine aggregate therefore reduces the risk of disintegration.[9]

Digest 35 *Shrinkage of natural aggregates in concrete* describes a laboratory procedure for determining the drying shrinkage of concrete and makes recommendations for the use of concretes having various shrinkages.

Alkali-aggregate reaction

Disintegration of concrete can occur if the aggregate is of a type that will react chemically with the sodium or potassium alkalis released during hydration of the cement. The first stage of the reaction is the formation of a silicate jelly which often exudes from the surface (Fig 8). The reacting aggregate also expands and causes disintegration, either directly or by so

Fig 7 Cracking following expansion of a lime-reactive ironstone aggregate

weakening the concrete that it is susceptible to frost action (Fig 9). The degree of expansion is less with low-alkali cements. Fortunately there are no known deposits of aggregate in the United Kingdom that have any significant degree of alkali-aggregate reactivity, but a designer of concrete buildings for other parts of the world might run into serious difficulties if he does not get advice on the suitability of the available aggregates.

The subject is discussed in technological detail in National Building Studies, Research Papers 17, 20 and 25 (HMSO, London), now out of print but likely to be available on loan or for reference in many technical libraries.

Sulphurous gas attack

With poor quality concrete exposed to a polluted city atmosphere, but sheltered from the effects of frost, the calcium sulphate formed by the reaction of the sulphur gases in the manner just described is liable to develop a skin that blisters and peels off. The action bears a remarkable resemblance to the behaviour of poor quality building limestone or calcareous sandstone, for example the Headington stone of Oxford, exposed under the same conditions.

This effect occurs whether the aggregate is of crushed limestone or crushed sandstone, but the Building Research Station has no record of its occurrence with flint aggregate concrete.

Carbonation leading to corrosion of reinforcement

The steel normally used for reinforcement of concrete becomes rusty on exposure to air and oxygen. In concrete this rusting is normally inhibited by the high alkalinity of the uncarbonated concrete. In good quality concrete, carbonation penetrates very slowly

Fig 8 Exudation of jelly in laboratory specimens containing alkali-reactive aggregate

indeed, and steel at the normally recommended depth of cover should last indefinitely. Concrete made with poorly graded aggregate or a high water/cement ratio tends to be so much more permeable that carbonation penetrates rapidly and may reach the steel within the lifetime of the building, allowing rusting to proceed. Steel that has been given less than the minimum recommended cover will start to rust even more quickly. A high chloride content resulting from the use of excessive or unevenly dis-

Fig 9 Exudation and cracking in exterior concrete containing alkali-reactive aggregate

 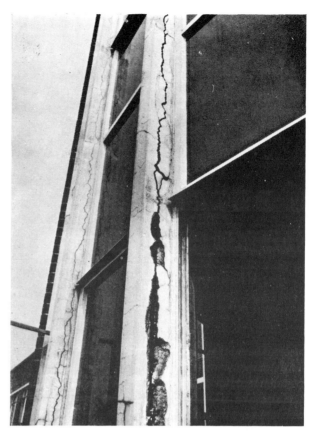

Fig 10(a) and (b) Cracking of window mullions because of rusting of reinforcement

Fig 11 Cracking of mullion following rusting of reinforcement

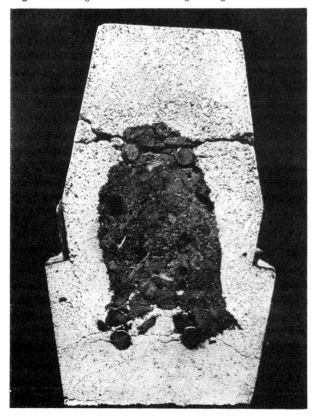

tributed amounts of calcium chloride as an accelerator can cause corrosion damage even if the alkali has not been neutralised. In both cases the corrosion products occupy more volume than the original steel, and the stresses created often lead to spalling and the appearance of rust stains (Figs 10 and 11). Fig 11 shows a section of cast stone surrounding a coarse aggregate concrete core; the permeability of the cast stone permitted early carbonation and water penetration, rusting and cracking followed.

The minimum thicknesses of cover needed to meet durability requirements in various conditions of exposure and for several grades of concrete are set out in Digest 59 *Protection against corrosion of reinforcing steel in concrete.* Where low depths of cover must be employed, the steel will need additional protection such as zinc coating (*see* Digest 109 *Zinc-coated reinforcement for concrete*).

Frost and salt crystallisation damage

Ice crystals, forming as a result of the freezing of water, and salt crystals, growing because the temperature of the solution falls or because evaporation is causing concentration, both exert forces within the pores of building materials that may cause complete disintegration. The best quality concrete will normally resist such forces, particularly if it is aerated, but the forces are very aggressive in combination and a lowering of concrete quality that would not cause trouble in most situations will be sufficient to allow damage to occur to concrete in positions such as kerb stones (Fig 12). The way in which frost attack readily follows any incipient deterioration due to other causes has been mentioned several times already.

Damage by sea-water

A similar situation obtains when concrete is exposed to sea-spray. In sea-water, crystallisation forces are supplemented by a complicated chemical attack and, with unsuitable concrete, rust stains, surface scaling, spalling and complete disintegration may all occur. The most severe condition of exposure occurs in pores in sea-water at a position just above the high tide level. Only the best concrete can survive under these conditions for any length of time. It has even been asserted that concrete cast in situ cannot be made good enough for such conditions and that only the best precast concrete should be used. Concrete containing steel reinforcement should have a 28-day strength of at least 42 MN/m² (indicating low permeability) and the steel should nowhere be nearer the surface than 50 mm (*see* Digest 59 *Protection against corrosion of reinforcing steel in concrete*).

References

1 BRS Digest 150 Concrete: materials
2 BRS Digest 13. Concrete mix proportioning and control
3 EVERETT L H and GUTT W H : Steel in concrete with blast-furnace slag aggregate. Magazine of Concrete Research Vol 19, No 59 ; June 1967 pp 83–94
4 GUTT W H , KINNIBURGH W and NEWMAN A J : Blast-furnace slag as aggregate for concrete. Magazine of Concrete Research Vol 19, No 59 ; June 1967 pp 71–82
5 RILEM : General report presented at a Symposium on 'The behaviour of concretes exposed to seawater' Palermo, May 1965
6 MORRIS D D : Concrete surfaces. Concrete Vol 2, No 6 ; June 1968 pp 263–266
7 L'HERMITE R G : Volume changes of concrete. Fourth International Symposium on the Chemistry of Cement Session 5, Paper 3 p 33. Washington DC 1960
8 LEA F M : The chemistry of cement and concrete. 2nd edition p 637. Edward Arnold & Co 1956
9 SNOWDON L C and EDWARDS A G : The moisture movement of natural aggregates and its effect on concrete. Magazine of Concrete Research Vol 14, No 41 ; July 1962 pp 109–116
10 MIDGLEY H G : The staining of concrete by pyrite. Magazine of Concrete Research Vol 10, No 29. August 1958 pp 75–78
11 EVERETT L H : The corrosion and protection of steel in concrete. Cebelcor Corrosion Week Vol 1 ; 1965 p 20

Fig 12 Frost attack on poor quality concrete kerb unit. The water stain indicates its absorptive property. The less absorptive concrete alongside has survived

Cracking in buildings

This Digest examines the causes of cracking in buildings, and shows with the help of illustrated examples how an understanding of the factors responsible is necessary, both for correct diagnosis and repair, and, more important, for minimising future trouble in new buildings by good design and workmanship.

Most buildings develop cracks in their fabric, usually soon after construction, sometimes later. Much of the early cracking is superficial, easily repaired, and unlikely to recur to any great extent. Only rarely does cracking indicate serious structural failure. But whether superficial or not, much can be done to minimise and in some cases avoid cracking by recognising that movement of building materials and components is inevitable, and must be allowed for in design.

Diagnosis of specific causes of cracking is often difficult; every building is unique, and several factors may co-operate in producing the defect. Before repairs or remedies are sought, one needs to know:

(a) the cause of cracking;
(b) its effect on the performance of the building;
(c) whether movement is complete, incomplete, or intermittent (e.g. seasonal).

The movements responsible for cracking are given in Table 1.

Extent of movement

Table 2 gives an idea of the size of movement to be expected from changes in temperature and moisture content in 3 m lengths of building materials in common use. Thermal and moisture movements apart, prediction of the extent of movements is difficult, if not impossible.

Initial drying shrinkage of Portland cement products
See Digest 35

Shrinkage increases with increasing cement and water contents, and the initial shrinkage can be 50 per cent greater than any movement caused by subsequent wetting and drying. Heavy aggregate concrete usually shows less shrinkage than lightweight aggregate concrete. Some aggregates are shrinkable themselves.

Initial moisture expansion of fired clay products
See Digests 164 and 165

The initial moisture expansion of clay products after firing can be large and for practical purposes is irreversible. Much of the expansion occurs within the first two to three days after firing, but with normal materials which are a few days old when used, expansion rarely exceeds 25 mm in 30 m.

How do cracks occur?

Cracks occur either between or within components. As an example of the first, cyclic thermal movement of block A (Fig. 1) permanently displaces block B so as to produce a crack in the structure without, necessarily, failure of either component. Due to ingress of debris into cracks, movement of B could be progressive.

Fig. 1

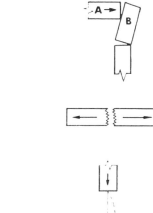

Table 1 Movements and principal causes

Cause	Effect	Duration	Examples of materials affected
1. Temperature changes	Expansion and contraction	Intermittent diurnal, seasonal	All; *see* Table 2
2. Moisture content changes			
(a) Drying	Shrinkage	Principally short-term, due to loss of initial moisture	Mortar, concrete, sandlime bricks, unseasoned timber
(b) Wetting	Expansion	Short-term, due to initial take-up of moisture	Ceramic products
(c) Drying alternating with wetting	Expansion and contraction	Seasonal	Poorly protected joinery, shrinkable clay soils
3. Other physical changes:			
(a) Loss of volatiles	Contraction	Short-term or long-term	Mastics
(b) Ice or crystalline salt formation	Expansion (in building materials); frost heave	Intermittent, dependent on weather conditions	Porous natural stones and other building materials; soils
4. Loading			
(a) On structure			
(i) Dead and imposed loading within design limits	Normally insignificant		
(ii) Structural over-loading	Excessive deflection and distortion		
(b) On ground	Settlement	Extent of settlement varies with seasons	Silts and peaty ground particularly susceptible
5. Soil movements, e.g. mining subsidence, swallow holes, landslips, soil creep, earthquakes	Settlement		
6. Vibration from traffic, machinery, sonic booms			Authenticated cases of damage are rare
7. Chemical changes:			
(a) Corrosion	Expansion	Continuous	(a) Metals
(b) Sulphate attack	Expansion	Continuous	(b) Portland cement and hydraulic lime products, e.g. concrete and mortar
(c) Carbonation	Shrinkage	Continuous	(c) Porous Portland cement products, e.g. lightweight concrete, asbestos-cement

In this case movement is largely in the direction of the forces applied. Quite frequently, it is at right-angles to them. Movement of only 0.25 mm in 6 m can produce a bulge of about 25 mm, e.g. in cladding units subjected to vertical compression.

Cracking *within* components, however, involves the strength of the material much more directly. When building components are restrained, their strength is often exceeded by stresses arising from movement in the materials, and cracking results. In practice, therefore, good design is based on an understanding of the movements involved and avoids unnecessary restraint as much as possible. Damaging stresses are then kept to a minimum.

Restraint is supplied by the component itself when *differential* movements occur in the component (e.g. as a result of drying from one face only, or to different temperatures on opposite faces). Distortion and often cracking then follow.

Diagnosis

The cause of cracking cannot always be determined with absolute certainty. Inspection may have to be repeated at intervals to establish the duration of the movements responsible. Diagnosis in a particular instance is greatly helped by a thorough knowledge of the history of the components involved and of the building since the time of construction. The likely causes should be checked for consistency with the number, width, depth, length, location and direction of cracks and the probable modifying effects of restraint.

Circumstances vary widely in practice, of course, and no list could take into account every combination of factors that might be encountered.

While the examples illustrated are fairly typical of those reported to the BRS, they are by no means exhaustive.

Table 2   Approximate unrestrained movements of a 3 m length

Material	Thermal movement (30°C change)	Moisture movement (dry to saturated)
	mm	*mm*
Steel	0·900–1·050	—
Aluminium	2·100	—
Copper	1·450	—
Glass	0·950	—
Bricks[2] (fired clay)	0·425–0·600	0·075–0·300
Bricks (sand lime)	1·200	0·300–1·500
Dense concrete, mortars[1]	0·825–1·200	0·600–1·800
Neat gypsum plaster	1·500–1·750	Negligible
Sanded plasters	1·000–1·250	Negligible
Asbestos cement	0·700	0·600–2·340
Marble, dense limestone	0·475	Negligible
Plastics	1·250–8·750 (This range excludes polythene; see Digest 69)	Usually negligible
Wood: along grain / across grain* (See PRL Tech. Note 38: 1969, for movements related to timber species)		0·025 tangential: 5%–15% radial: 3%–5%

* 3 m length not applicable

Notes

Thermal movement:
The 30°C temperature range may greatly exceeded in practice.
Colour, orientation, thermal conductivity and insulation all play a part.
Thus a black panel, insulated at the back, can reach 70°C

Moisture movements:
Two important omissions from Table 2 are:
1. Initial drying shrinkage of Portland cement products.
2. Initial moisture expansion of fired clay products.

Significance of cracking

Cracking can affect a building in a number of ways. If severe, it may result in a loss of stability, in rain penetration and air infiltration, heat loss and reduced sound insulation, all of which mean a loss in the efficiency of the building. Usually cracking is not severe but it is nearly always unsightly and unacceptable to occupants. Correct diagnosis will decide whether a satisfactory repair is possible, or, in extreme cases, economically worthwhile.

Moisture expansion of brickwork

See Digests 164 and 165

New walls are sometimes damaged by moisture expansion, particularly if they contain short returns. In this example (Figs. 2*a* and *b*), the damp-proof course, acting as a slip joint, allowed the brickwork above to expand with no significant restraint and the brick return in the wall was rotated. In general, provided that the brickwork is at least three months old, it can be assumed that the initial expansion is complete and that a satisfactory and permanent repair can be made.

Moisture expansion of new brickwork can cause trouble. Here, in conjunction with drying shrinkage of *in-situ* concrete columns, it puts the infilling brickwork under compression. The resulting stress was relieved by outward bowing of the brickwork (Figs. 3*a* and *b*). The size of the forces involved is illustrated by the way in which the intermediate nib

was pulled away. Weathertightness and stability were impaired and a satisfactory repair required rebuilding the damaged elements.

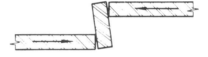

Fig. 2a

Fig. 2b

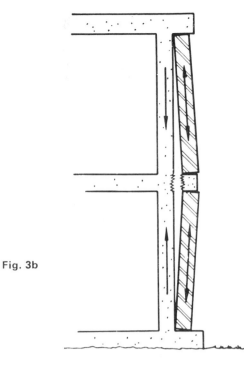

Fig. 3a   Fig. 3b

Differential settlement— unconsolidated fill or soft ground

See Digests 63, 64, 67 and 142

The dangers to the structure of building on unconsolidated fill or soft ground are obvious and there can be no certainty that settlement and cracking will not recur after repairs have been made; with settlements of this kind, movements are often large and their timing unpredictable. This bungalow (Figs. 4a and b) was built partly on made-up ground which was not properly consolidated and probably contained much unsuitable material. Steel drums, trunking, paint tins and even car bodies have been known to find their way into uncontrolled tips.

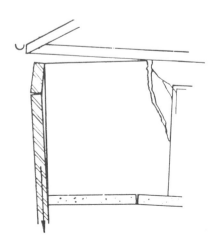

Fig. 4a

Fig. 4b

Frost damage to foundations

See Digests 63, 64 and 67

In Britain, completed and occupied buildings are rarely damaged by 'frost heave' in the soil; what damage there is is usually confined to severely exposed parts of buildings founded on predominantly chalky and fine sandy soils. In some of these there may be a build-up of ice layers which cause the foundations to lift, but even then only in exceptionally severe winters. This example (Figs. 5a and b) illustrates some fairly typical effects. The house was newly built on chalky soil, with chalk fill under the floor slabs. It was unoccupied—and therefore unheated—and the parts most affected were those most exposed.

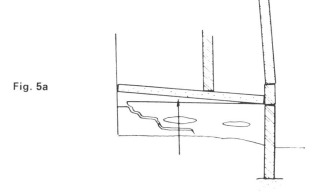

Fig. 5a

Fig. 5b

Differential settlement and uplift— shrinkable clay

See Digests 63, 64 and 67

Clay soils shrink and expand with changes in moisture content, some more than others. In Britain these changes are seasonal and under grass can extend to a depth of about 1 m; foundations shallower than this will be affected to varying extents. Where tree roots dry the ground to greater depths—3 m or so—they can, as in this example (Figs. 6a and b), cause particularly severe damage. Cracks in external brick walls are commonly of this stepped diagonal kind. The reverse action can occur where established trees are cut down or removed: clay soils may then swell and lift the foundations unevenly.

Fig. 6a

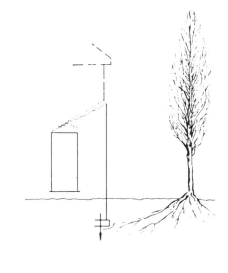

Fig. 6b

Sulphate attack—walls

See Digest 89

Sulphate attack requires the presence of soluble sulphates, Portland cement and water. The circumstances in which brickwork is attacked, particularly rendered brickwork, are dealt with fully in Digest 89. Parapet walls, free-standing external walls and retaining walls are all vulnerable, and dense renderings often give trouble, not only because they prevent evaporation of water from the wall behind, but because they frequently shrink and crack and let the water in (Figs. 7a and b). A warning is also necessary concerning the use of Keene's cement or gypsum plaster in place of lime in cement/lime/sand mortars. No more effective way could be found of inducing sulphate attack: these materials *consist* of sulphates. In the example, initially defective construction readily admitted rainwater and the dense rendering prevented it from evaporating. The cement in the mortar was attacked first, causing expansion of the bed-joints and typically horizontal cracking of the rendering. Provided that stability is not impaired, the rendering in such instances could be replaced by a weak, porous rendering based on sulphate-resisting cement.

Fig. 7a

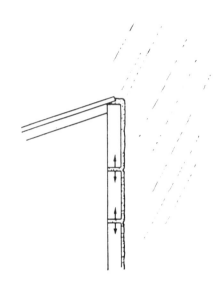

Fig. 7b

Sulphate attack—floors

See Digest 174

Hardcore or filling containing sulphate must not be used below concrete floor slabs. Gypsum products are sometimes inadvertently used in hardcore, but the most widespread reported cases of failure have involved colliery shales. These, as well as containing sulphates, may be incompletely burnt before use, with the result that they swell when wetted. In the example (Figs. 8a and b), sulphate attack of the underside of the concrete slab caused it to arch and crack, and the walls to bulge. In cases like this, if stability is unimpaired, the fill could be replaced by sulphate-free material—*not* by the broken floor slab which may be contaminated with sulphates.

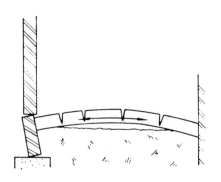

Fig. 8a

Fig. 8b

Drying shrinkage
See Digests 49 and 178

Shrinkage cracking is perhaps the commonest form of cracking encountered in buildings. It affects many building materials, e.g. sand lime bricks, lightweight concrete products, some plasters—external and renderings, and extensive details of its occurrence and avoidance are given in Digests 49 and 178. The example (Figs. 9a and b) shows a commonly

reported failure in a dense cement-sand external rendering. Such renderings are often applied with the object of excluding rainwater, yet in practice they fail to do so because they shrink and crack. The familiar 'map pattern' cracking is typical of drying shrinkage in renderings. In exposed situations the damp conditions necessary for sulphate attack may be set up. Note the difference between the map pattern and the pattern of cracking associated with sulphate attack.

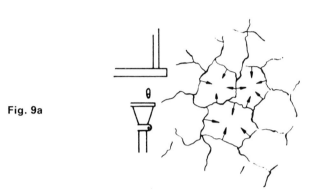

Fig. 9a

Fig. 9b

Thermal movement—flat roofs
The thermal movement of flat roofs exposed alternately to the sun and the night sky can be large—about 5 mm for every 10 m for concrete—and operates continuously. Often movement is restrained at some point, e.g. where the roof abuts another building or where a lift shaft or stair well is carried up through the roof slab. The effects of movement are then concentrated elsewhere. The example (Figs. 10a and b) shows how walls at right-angles to the long axis of the roof, and furthest from the restrained parts of the slab, are cracked by rotation of the part in contact with the underside of

the slab. In addition, the tops of walls running in the direction of the long axis exhibit shear cracking. These two types of cracking are often complicated by the tendency of the slab to bow upwards in the centre when its top surface is hotter than the underside.

Repairs are unlikely to be durable unless the roof movements are reduced. Practical considerations usually limit remedial measures to improvement of above-roof insulation and provision of reflective surface treatment. In new buildings, joints and separation of internal walls from roofs can help to prevent trouble.

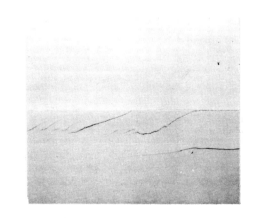

Fig. 10a

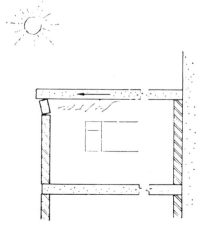

Fig. 10b

Deflection of floors

See Digest 35

Suspended reinforced concrete floor slabs deflect under their self-weight and superimposed loads, and this deflection is expected. Occasionally, however, drying shrinkage in an asymmetrically reinforced slab can contribute markedly to further deflection. In the example shown (Figs. 11a and b), shrinkage has been accentuated by the inclusion of shrinkable aggregates in the concrete. The resulting additional deflection has removed support from the foot of the partition wall above, and cracking has occurred.

It must be noted that in cases like this it is extremely difficult to say how many factors are collectively responsible for cracking (poor design and workmanship may also contribute), still less is it possible to say what each has contributed in producing the defect. The inclusion of this example is a reminder of the difficulty of clear-cut diagnosis of the causes of cracking in practice.

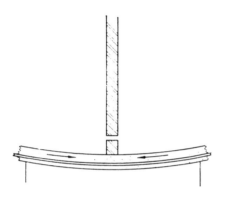

Fig. 11a

Fig. 11b

Digests referred to in the text:

 35 Shrinkage of natural aggregates in concrete
 49 Choosing specifications for plastering
 63 Soils and foundations—1
 64 Soils and foundations—2
 67 Soils and foundations—3
 89 Sulphate attack on brickwork
142 Fill and hardcore
164 Clay brickwork: Part 1
165 Clay brickwork: Part 2
174 Concrete in sulphate-bearing soils and groundwaters
178 Autoclaved aerated concrete

Other publications:
Princes Risborough Laboratory Technical Note 38 : 1969. The movement of timbers
(single copies free on application to Distribution Unit, Building Research Station)

Protection against corrosion of reinforcing steel in concrete

This Digest discusses the protection of steel in concrete. It deals with the factors responsible for unsatisfactory performance and indicates the requirements for depth and quality of concrete cover which must be met if this is to be avoided.

The main emphasis is on reinforced concrete, with particular reference to CP 114 : 1957 (amended 1967) *and* CP 116 : Part 2 : 1969, *'Structural use of precast concrete'. Some examples from* National Building Studies Special Report 33 *illustrate circumstances in which failure or unsightliness of concrete has occurred in practice.*

Reference is also made to CP 115 : 1959 *because similar precautions apply also to the protection of steel in prestressed concrete.*

Lightweight aggregate concrete is dealt with briefly.

Some dimensions in this Digest have been retained in Imperial units because they are quoted from British Standards Codes of Practice which at the time of writing have not been metricated. Figure 2 shows the actual Imperial sizes used in the example.

Functions of cover

It is common experience that iron will rust unless protected from air and moisture. Protection against corrosion is sought by specifying concrete of good quality and adequate depth of cover to the steel. Provided that the quality and depth of cover are properly selected for the intended use then trouble from corrosion is extremely unlikely, but 'intended use' must take into account not only structural requirements but conditions of exposure also. Thus the concrete cover must *protect* the steel as well as transmit external loading forces to it. The cover must also provide adequate fire resistance.

Factors favouring corrosion

These may involve the physical or chemical condition of the concrete cover itself, an unusually aggressive environment to which the concrete is exposed or a combination of these factors. They may be enumerated as follows:

1. Inadequate depth of cover.

2. Inferior quality concrete (e.g. owing to poor compaction or too high a water/cement ratio).

3. Corrosive substances present in some ground waters and in marine and industrial environments.

4. Salts, e.g. chlorides, incorporated in the concrete when mixed.

5. Poor quality aggregates, e.g. certain shrinkable aggregates, mainly of Scottish origin, whose use can lead to early failure of the cover.

6. Cracks in the cover deep enough to allow moisture, etc., to penetrate to the steel.

Effects of corrosion

If for any reason the cover is inadequate and corrosion develops, three main effects may be observed:

1. Cracking or disruption of the cover caused by the expansion which accompanies the corrosion of steel.

2. Loss of strength where the steel is reduced in cross-section.

3. Rust staining of adjacent areas.

How corrosion occurs

Corrosion is a complex electro-chemical process. It begins when galvanic cells are formed between areas where there is no corrosion (cathodes) and areas where corrosion can occur (anodes). How and to what extent the formation of these cells depends upon atmospheric and chemical conditions is not entirely clear, though it is well known that environments as described in (3), p. 29, favour corrosion.

Two types of galvanic cell are possible; one depends on local differences in concentration of oxygen in the concrete, the other upon different concentrations of anions such as carbonate, chloride or sulphate. The effect of corrosion currents is to carry iron into solution, which then forms rust scale with the oxygen present.

It is important to remember that *differences* in oxygen and/or salt concentrations may carry a significant risk of corrosion although the *actual* concentrations of dissolved gases and solids are low. (This is the reason why, as emphasised later, thorough mixing of any additives is necessary and thorough washing with clean water is required for any concrete surfaces previously treated with hydrochloric acid.)

Prevention of corrosion
Design requirements for good practice

The importance of specifying and ensuring that all steel is adequately protected by concrete of appropriate quality and depth is set out in the relevant Codes of Practice: CP's 114, 115 and 116.

CP 114: 1957—'The structural use of reinforced concrete in buildings'. Clause 307 is most relevant to this Digest. It gives the thicknesses of cover required for normal tensile, compressive, shear or other reinforcement in columns, beams and slabs, subject to the requirement that for all external work, for work against earth faces and for internal work in corrosive conditions, the cover should not be less than $1\frac{1}{2}$ in. for all steel, including stirrups, links, etc., except where the face of the concrete is adequately protected by cladding or coating. The Code does not deal with prestressed concrete or with recommendations for precast factory-made reinforced concrete units.

CP 115: 1959—'The structural use of prestressed concrete in buildings'. This Code covers both work done on site and the manufacture of precast prestressed concrete units. Clause 308 should be referred to for details of the concrete cover necessary.

CP 116: Part 2: 1969—'Structural use of precast concrete'. This Code attempts to bring together all the considerations on materials workmanship, inspection and testing, and fire resistance, which govern the standard of structural precast concrete units.

The required thickness of concrete cover has been laid down mainly in relation to exposure conditions and concrete strength, and Table 1 of this Digest (which is Table 1 of the Code) gives the grade of concrete necessary for the particular strength requirement and then specifies the cover needed for that grade in different conditions of exposure. There is not space enough here to deal with all the footnotes to the Table; reference should be made to the Code itself.

Avoidance of defects in practice
Design

This section enlarges upon the precautions in design, construction and workmanship that must be observed if the risk of corrosion arising from any of the factors dealt with on page 29 is to be minimised. The precautions are considered here under the headings 'Design', 'Materials', 'Construction and workmanship' and 'Exposure'. Reference should also be made to the Codes of Practice for a more detailed account.

The design of the member or component must take account of all factors that may adversely affect the protection given to the steel. It must be appreciated at the outset that the *effective* cover is the cover to *all steel*, including stirrups, hooping, and binding wire, and not merely that to main bars.

There is a much greater risk of attack where moisture, soot and dirt can collect on concrete surfaces and such surfaces should therefore be sloped to throw off water. Also, extra concrete cover should be provided or the top should be covered with a metal or other flashing. Beams with the top surface exposed and reinforced concrete parapet walls are particularly vulnerable. Copings and sills often do not need reinforcement and wherever possible should be designed without it. If these units are large, care must also be taken to minimise the risk of damage during handling. With heavy precast members it is necessary to position the lifting points in such a way that the handling stresses are not excessive.

The number and spacing of reinforcing bars, stirrups, etc., must be such as to permit the concrete to be

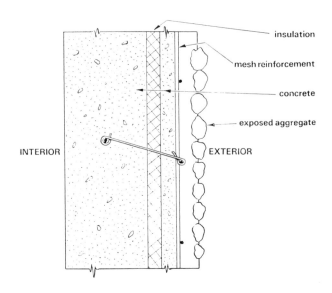

Fig. 1. Vertical cross-section through typical external wall panel

placed and consolidated without difficulty and without reliance on over-wet mixes.

Sudden changes of section or of the proportion of steel should be avoided wherever possible.

The design of precast concrete wall panels, particularly sandwich panels, needs care. Exposure may be relatively severe, as in industrial or marine atmospheres, and where the exposed area is large. The tendency to reduce thickness and so save weight must be resisted; it may be possible to restrict the reinforcement to ribs.

Walls of 'sandwich' construction are common to several large panel systems. The outer leaf of concrete may be of about 75 mm nominal thickness and lightly reinforced with steel mesh (Fig. 1). It is necessary to ensure adequate cover to this reinforcement, special care being needed if an exposed aggregate finish is used. The ties linking the outer leaf with the inner should be highly resistant to corrosion; if they are of a metal different from that of the reinforcement (silicon bronze is often used), there is a greater risk of corrosion of the steel unless direct contact between it and the ties is prevented.

NOTE: The 'designed' cover must be adequate to accommodate the tolerances in the size of each unit and in the binding and fabrication of the reinforcement; it must also allow for deformation or displacement of the reinforcement when the concrete is placed and compacted.

Table 1. Precast concrete—grades and cover to CP 116
Grades of fully compacted concrete for strength and durability purposes, using cement complying with B.S.12 or B.S.146

PART A. SELECTION OF THE GRADE OF CONCRETE NECESSARY TO MEET STRENGTH REQUIREMENTS

Age at test	Specified works cube strength, N/mm², for Grade:				
	A	B	C	D	E
28 days	21	25·5	30	40	50
7 days	14	17	20	28	37

PART B. SELECTION OF THE GRADE OF CONCRETE AND MINIMUM COVER NECESSARY TO MEET DURABILITY REQUIREMENTS

Conditions of exposure	Minimum nominal concrete cover, in mm, to all steel, for concrete made with aggregates complying with B.S.882 or B.S.1047, for Grade:				
	A	B	C	D	E
INTERNAL Non-corrosive	19	15	15	15	15
Corrosive: e.g. roof units subject to condensation	25	19	15	15	15
Severely corrosive: e.g. roof units subject to corrosive fumes	N.A.*	38	25	25	25
EXTERNAL Sheltered in non-industrial areas: e.g. in occupied buildings surrounded by other buildings	25	25	25	20	20
Sheltered in industrial areas or work against non-sulphate-bearing earth faces	40	25	25	25	20
Exposed in non-industrial areas: e.g. open farm buildings	N.A.	40	25	25	25
Exposed in industrial areas or subject to mild sulphate attack	N.A.	N.A.	40	25	25
Exposed to sea water or weak chemical attack	N.A.	N.A.	N.A.	50	50
Subject to salt used for de-icing: e.g. roadside structures	N.A.	N.A.	40	25	25

*N.A. = not allowed under the particular conditions of exposure

Materials

There is no specific mention of cements under this heading; so far as the corrosion risk is concerned, there is no great difference in the behaviour of concrete made from different kinds of cement manufactured in the United Kingdom.

1. Aggregates. Nowadays the suitability of aggregates for concrete is less open to question than formerly.

As far as is known, the shrinkable aggregates considered in Digest 35 are limited in the British Isles to Scotland. The fine 'map' cracking resulting from the use of shrinkable sand for fine aggregate can be overcome by air-entrainment within the range 2–6%. But where the coarse aggregates are shrinkable three effects are possible which increase the risk of corrosion:

(a) In large panels having a heavily reinforced rib around a lightly reinforced web, cracking may be induced at the change in sectional shape.

(b) In thin, asymmetrically-reinforced structural slabs, deflection accompanied by cracking is possible. This could be serious as regards corrosion when the underside is exposed, e.g. in balcony slabs.

(c) In multi-storey structures, some shrinkage of the whole framework may produce spalling or cracking of the framework and its infill panels when provision for movement between them is inadequate.

2. Chlorides. Salts aggressive to steel can be added to concrete by using sea water or unwashed sand or aggregate from marine sources, or by incorporating calcium chloride as an accelerating admixture. Chlorides increase the risk of corrosion; therefore the chloride content of concrete should not exceed the equivalent of $1\frac{1}{2}$% anhydrous calcium chloride by weight of cement. If chloride from any source is present, it is important to specify well-graded aggregates, low water/cement ratio, high cement ratio and thorough compaction, so that low permeability concrete is produced.

Chloride additives should be dissolved in the mixing water and not added as dry powder so as to avoid risk of uneven concentrations which can set up corrosion currents.

In some circumstances the surfaces of precast concrete units are washed with dilute hydrochloric acid. While cases of failure from this cause are rare, this practice should be closely controlled because variations in the absorption of chloride leads to increased risk of corrosion.

3. Admixtures. Air-entraining, water-reducing or set-controlling admixtures can help to produce concrete of low permeability and absorption and increased uniformity and durability.

Construction and workmanship

1. Placing and fixing reinforcement. Carelessly placed or insecurely fixed reinforcement is liable in places to be nearer the surface than originally intended. It is important that as much reinforcement as possible should be assembled as units, to jig and preferably welded to minimise displacement of bars during concreting.

2. Spacers. Concrete and plastics spacers are used to prevent contact between the reinforcement and the moulds during placing. But the force of concrete tipped from overhead skips or hoppers into moulds of considerable depth, e.g. storey-height wall panels, will readily displace the reinforcement unless this is very firmly held. In practice it is very difficult to ensure this. (Reinforcement once deformed tends to remain deformed; hence the frequent reduction of cover observed, even on the underside of slabs cast face down.) Chair-type spacers are easily displaced by the impact of wet concrete. Circular spacers with good lateral stability are preferable.

It is not yet clear whether plastics spacers will prove to be as satisfactory in use as concrete spacers; some test specimens including plastics spacers have been exposed at Garston and spalling of concrete surrounding the spacers occurred. The cause of this is not known with certainty; experience suggests that it is unwise to introduce a quite different material into the concrete when the same can be used satisfactorily. On the other hand plastics spacers are much more convenient to manufacture and handle.

3. Formwork. Undersized formwork takes up some of the space intended for cover; badly made formwork will allow water and cement to leak from the edges and the corners of the forms, leaving permeable, honeycombed concrete, particularly from an over-wet mix.

Wire ties for holding formwork in position are sometimes concreted-in and later clipped off flush with the surface. This causes rust staining, or worse, and should be forbidden.

4. Compaction. The air voids left by insufficient rodding or vibration of the mix not only weaken the concrete but reduce the effectiveness of the cover as protection for reinforcement. Well-consolidated concrete helps to preserve the corrosion-inhibiting effect of alkalinity at the surface of the steel. If the porosity is such as to allow air and moisture (containing carbon dioxide and possibly other acid gases) to penetrate the cover and reduce the alkalinity, then this protective effect is lost.

Special care should be taken with poker vibrators to avoid risk of displacing the reinforcement.

5. Construction joints. A good bond is essential at joints to avoid the risk of more than a superficial crack forming. Surface cracks seldom let in enough moisture to start corrosion, but badly made joints, perhaps honeycombed, invite trouble. Columns cast in several lifts occasionally reveal honeycombed corners; these are likely spots for corrosion to start.

Exposure

The vulnerability of copings, cills and other projections and of large plane-surfaced walls of reinforced concrete exposed to the weather is discussed in *National Building Studies Special Reports* 25 and 33. Table 1 of this Digest shows how conditions of exposure have been taken into account in the preparation of CP 116.

Precast versus in-situ work— tolerances in manufacture

It is commonly assumed that precast concrete is manufactured to finer tolerances (with regard to the positioning of reinforcement) than concrete cast *in situ*. Normally *in situ* work is subject to less effective supervision than precast and the distinction is recognised by the different recommendations of CP 114 and CP 116. Yet an investigation at BRS of the tolerance problems associated with placing reinforcement in beams and slabs, has shown how uncertain is the final position of the reinforcement, even in the most carefully controlled precast work. Some field measurements of cover of several precast elements of proprietary systems showed deviations of up to half the 'design' cover intended. This emphasises the importance of not reducing the margins of cover.

Preventing corrosion of steel in concrete floors

Reinforced concrete floors require special consideration, especially in the following circumstances:

1. Where the finish itself is unaffected by corrosive liquors but does not provide sufficient protection of the underlying structure. Examples are:

(*a*) Concrete surfaces permeable to saline wash waters which do not affect the concrete itself.

(*b*) Epoxy and polyester floorings sold for use in corrosive situations and laid up to 6 mm thick. Many liquids that do not affect these floorings may leak through them, particularly when some wear has occurred. The risk may not be recognised when they are laid by firms with little chemical engineering experience.

2. Where the finish, e.g. granolithic concrete, may disintegrate. Here the user might carry out repairs to the concrete yet not recognise that the steel below is corroding.

3. Where the floor finish can disintegrate to produce a corrosive chemical. In this category there is only magnesium oxychloride. This flooring has been responsible for at least one collapse of a reinforced concrete floor caused by the action of magnesium chloride on the reinforcement. The Code of Practice for *in situ* flooring, CP 204, points to the need for protecting the metalwork of gas, water and electrical services by 25 mm of dense concrete when this

flooring is used *even in dry conditions*. In wet conditions the flooring should never be used because the reinforcement cannot be protected by bitumen or galvanising.

4. In corrosion-resistant flooring where detailing at channels, gulleys, upstands, etc., is defective.

5. Where there is a change of use in a factory and it passes unnoticed that a corrosion-resistant floor *designed to resist other chemicals* may not be suited to the new use.

6. Where, before laying epoxy resin flooring, washing with hydrochloric acid to remove laitance is recommended. (Hydrochloric acid may also be used to make concrete floors less slippery.)

Examples of failed cover and spoiled appearace*
Precast reinforced concrete mullions

Examination of the mullions some 10 years after installation showed cracks in the concrete and some exposed rusty reinforcement where concrete had spalled. Some patching was attempted but as the $\frac{3}{8}$ in. bars had less than $\frac{1}{4}$ in. cover and the binding wire almost none at all, the depth of cover could not be increased without producing unsightly bulges in the concrete. Six years later more cracks had appeared; the slenderness of the mullions (incorporating probably more steel than was structurally necessary), the inadequate depth of cover and exposure to fairly corrosive conditions, had all combined to produce quite rapid cracking and spalling of the concrete.

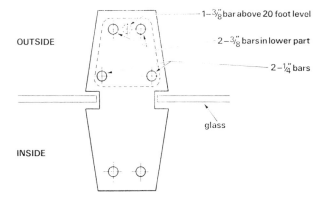

Fig. 2. Plan of concrete mullion in a high window freely exposed to the weather

In-situ reinforced concrete string courses

The supervision exercised over control of concrete mix proportions and water/cement ratio, the inspection of reinforcement in the forms before placing the concrete, also the use of spacer blocks to ensure correct cover—all these precautions had been meticulously specified and should have been taken in

*These are taken from *National Building Special Report 33*. 'A qualitative study of some buildings in the London area'.

casting the lintel in Fig. 3a, yet the cover to the stirrups could not have been more than 3 mm.

In the example in Fig. 3b, the tops of lanterns were of reinforced concrete covered with asphalt. The exposed concrete at the edge had cracked and spalled, revealing reinforcement with only about 8 mm cover.

Fig. 3a

Fig. 3b

Diagnosis and repair

Reference should be made to *National Building Studies Special Report* 25, pp. 16–23, in which a full description of *guniting* and other methods of repair is given. Repair is often difficult and, to be effective for long, the unsightliness of locally increased depth of cover has to be accepted. The appearance of the fresh concrete used for repair should approximate as closely as possible to that of the old.

Reinforced lightweight aggregate concrete

Experience has shown that when chemically inert aggregates are used in lightweight aggregate con-

crete of sufficient depth, and the same close attention is given to workability, cement content, aggregate grading and compaction as is needed to produce good quality dense concrete, there is every likelihood that the reinforcement in lightweight aggregate concrete will resist corrosion saisfactorily. Carbonation* may be faster and the carbonated surface layer somewhat deeper than in corresponding dense concretes, but with careful compaction and adequate cement content it is possible to reduce the rate of carbonation of any concrete.

For *in situ* reinforced lightweight aggregate concrete exposed to the weather, an increase of $\frac{1}{2}$ in. is advised over the cover recommended for dense concrete in CP 114 : 1957. This means that for exposed surfaces the cover should be not less than 2 in. This requirement has been embodied in the recent amendments to CP 114.

For precast lightweight aggregate concrete, Clause 356 of CP 116 : Part 2 : 1969 requires that the cover to all steel be increased by 12 mm compared with the values given in Table 1 of this Digest.

For further information reference should be made to 'Lightweight Concrete' by Short and Kinniburgh, Chapter 11.

*Carbonation is reaction with carbon dioxide in the air.

References
NATIONAL BUILDING STUDIES
Special Reports
No. 24. A note on the History of reinforced concrete in buildings
No. 25. The durability of reinforced concrete in buildings
No. 33. A qualitative study of some buildings in the London area

Research Papers
No. 30. The durability of reinforced concrete in sea water

BRS DIGESTS
No. 13. Concrete mix proportioning and control
No. 35. Shrinkage of natural aggregates in concrete
No. 109. Winc-coated reinforcement for concrete
No. 111. Lightweight aggregate concretes: structural application
No. 123. Lightweight aggregate concretes
No. 150. Concrete: materials
No. 178. Autoclaved aerated concrete
(All the above are published by H.M.S.O.)

BOOKS
Lightweight concrete, A. Short and W. Kinniburgh, London, 1963, CR Books Ltd.

Failure patterns and implications

During the period 1970–1974, the Building Research Advisory Service made detailed investigations of over 500 defective buildings. The reports have been analysed to discover the faults most likely to be encountered and to identify ways in which the incidence of building defects might be reduced.

The findings of 510 investigations of building defects are analysed in Table 1 by building type, showing also the most common defects in each. It was considered that 11 per cent of the buildings had defects that could endanger life; the functional performance of 66 per cent was impaired; the remaining 23 per cent had defects of a superficial, largely aesthetic nature.

Dampness (*see* Table 2)

Half the defects investigated were varieties of dampness; these are often related, for example, rain penetration or entrapped water in an insulating structure will increase the risk of condensation.

Condensation [110]   Surface condensation proved to be a problem mainly of housing, particularly council housing. Significant, sometimes gross, inadequacies in heating and/or ventilation could explain every instance and it may be that council tenants are less willing or less able to provide sufficient warmth and ventilation than are the owners of private houses. The construction, however, was not necessarily blameless; it could often be argued that the thermal insulation [108] provided, though meeting the requirements in force at the time of design, was too low and the thermal mass too high for the type of occupancy involved. In the private sector, surface condensation often followed double glazing [140] and efficient draught-stripping. Unwittingly, the owners had reduced the air changes to less than the acceptable limit for the form of construction and the level of heating provided.

Interstitial condensation problems were fairly evenly spread over all building types. Most could be attributed to failure in design to make adequate provision for preventing moisture vapour from reaching cold, sensitive parts of the structure. The most serious cases in roof spaces were found over swimming pools; some roofs needed complete replacement after only a few years' service and in others the corrosion of metal supporting structures will be a continuing problem. In some instances, no steps had been taken to avoid interstitial condensation and remedial measures were difficult and expensive.

Entrapped water   Dampness due to water entrapped during construction can, in some instances, take years to dry. [163] Heavy concrete roof structures, especially where the insulation was in the form of aerated concrete screeds, gave the most trouble. [8] Construction water contributed to this but the main source appeared to be rain or snow falling during the construction period so that even the so-called 'dry' insulating screeds gave some trouble. Blistering of roofing felts, [144] caused by water trapped between successive layers of felt, was also a fairly common cause of complaint.

Rising damp   Only a few cases of rising damp were reported. Its occurrence in floors was usually in new property where a satisfactory damp-proof membrane [54] had either not been specified or had been badly installed. Failure or staining of floor finishes frequently followed. Most of the walls [27, 77] investigated had a previous history of dampness and proprietary (chemical or 'electro-osmotic') damp-proof courses had been installed, apparently without success. In some instances, the proprietary system had not been properly installed; in others, it had patently failed to stop the rising damp.

Defects other than dampness (*see* Table 3)

Cracking (structural and superficial) and detachment (usually of finishes or 'veneers') comprised two-thirds of all defects other than dampness.

Cracking [75]   The few cases of cracking due to foundation movement were attributable to the presence, or recent removal, of trees close to buildings on shrinkable clay. Cracking in floors was nearly all in industrial or office buildings, due either to excessive loadings or to faults in design or execution that impaired the performance of the floors. [47, 104] Much of the cracking in walls, loadbearing or non-loadbearing, and in finishes was caused by differential moisture movement between adjacent parts of the structure. There were more complaints of cracking in private houses than in council houses but

Building type	Proportion of total sample No	%	Most common defects	Incidence in building type %
HOUSING				
Council houses	64	13	Condensation	59
			Rain penetration	13
Council flats	55	11	Rain penetration	38
			Condensation	33
Private houses	65	13	Rain penetration	33
			Cracking	20
			Condensation	18
Private flats	11	2	Rain penetration	64
NON-HOUSING				
Offices; public buildings	90	18	Floors	28
			Roofs	23
			Rain penetration	28
			Cracking	19
Factories	65	13	Cracking (mainly floors)	29
			Rain penetration (mainly roofs)	29
Schools	28	5	Roofs	39
			Floors (mainly finishes)	32
Hospitals	23	5	Floors (mainly finishes)	35
			Roofs	26
Swimming pools	13	3	Detachment of tiles	46
			Roof-space condensation	46
Universities; colleges	21	4	⎫	
Shops	18	4	⎬ No clear pattern	
Churches	10	2	⎪	
Other	47	9	⎭	

Table 1   Sample analysed by type of structure, showing also the most commonly occurring defects

this was probably due to possible effects on the value of the houses.

Detachment   Detachment of brick slips or rendering from multi-storey framed flats was the third most common complaint about council flats. Shrinkage and creep of the frame, combined often with expansion of the brick infilling, placed unintentional loads on the slips or rendering covering the edges of the floor slabs. Normally, no provision had been made in the design for this differential movement. Similarly, where tiles or mosaics became detached, movement joints had seldom been provided even though they are recommended in Codes of Practice. Tiling adhesion also gave trouble, mainly because a wrong adhesive had been specified or the correct one mishandled. Detachment of floor finishes was commonest with impervious sheet materials; dampness in the substrate affecting the adhesives [54] was the most common cause, but there were some cases of loss of plasticiser by migration into unsuitable flooring adhesives [33] or because of over-aggressive chemical cleaning agents. Detachment of paint films [106] was often traced to the use of wood primers with poor mechanical properties, particularly when damp. Many of the shop-applied primers used in recent years have been inadequate in this respect. Some of the newer non-lead primers compare unfavourably with the older lead-based (toxic) materials, but a forthcoming British Standard for wood primers should help to avoid this.

Causes of defects (see Table 4)

Faulty design   The largest single type of fault was in making the wrong choice of material or component for a particular situation, eg a wrong adhesive for floor tiles on a heated sub-floor, or the use of cavity fill outside the recommendations of its Agrément Certificate. Necessary cavity trays and flashings were sometimes absent from the design but inadequacies seemed often to stem from poor detailing of the situation where damp-proofing layers had to meet obstructions. Many designers provided only a vertical section through some part of the structure; in practice, difficulties occurred not on the line of the section but at the ends of windows and at returns, and these were seldom, if ever, illustrated adequately.

Other faults included the omission of solar-reflective treatment on flat roofs; poor detailing of special, locally made, wood windows and a tendency to support so-called lightweight partitions inadequately, often on timber floors. Some designs were so complex that they were not likely to be properly executed; these too were classed as faulty. A fault could also be in a bought-in component, such as a window unsuited to the severe exposure for which it was knowingly supplied, or in a sub-contracted service.

Faulty execution   Water entrapped during construction was the commonest cause of trouble. Water would drip from lightweight insulating screeds

Type of dampness		Detailed breakdown				Cause	
Rain penetration	136	through walls	57	of masonry	39	direct penetration of solid walls direct penetration of cavity-filled walls poor dpms, trays, etc	8 15 16
				of concrete panels (through joints) other	10 8		
		through roofs	49				
		through windows	17				
		other	13				
Condensation	90	surface	56	council housing private housing	38 10	inadequate heating or ventilation	48
				other	8		
		interstitial	34	housing factories offices hospitals other	14 4 4 2 10	inadequate vapour control in design	22
Entrapped water	29	in roof structure or insulation in floor structure other			19 4 6		
Rising damp	23	in walls in floors	18 5	dpc failure	12		
Other	4			(There was some overlap between categories)			

Table 2 Analysis of 254 'dampness' defects (=50 per cent of total sample)

for months, sometimes years, after construction. Other faults stemming from this included efflorescence on plastered brickwork and disruption of floorings from water trapped between an impervious flooring and a damp-proof membrane below a thick floor slab.

Poor execution of damp-proof membranes, flashings and cavity trays was also a frequent cause of defects; even when the design was satisfactory, a damp-proof layer might be incomplete or absent. Leaking mastic joints, mostly to windows, were an important cause of failure, usually because of careless application.

Some other examples of poor execution were misplaced thermal insulation, bridging of floating floors, wrong water/cement ratios or mix proportions for concrete, perforation of water barriers, poor preparation of concrete for subsequent renderings, misuse of tiling adhesives, omission of fixings and wall ties, displaced concrete reinforcement, inaccurate assembly of components.

Faulty materials and components These were among the less common causes of defects investigated. Hardcore was sometimes highly reactive chemically, and certain concrete blocks, intended specifically for facing work, were so readily permeable to driven rain that normal designs for damp-proof membranes and cavity trays could not always cope with the flow of water in the cavity. Failures of chemical and 'electro-osmotic' damp-proofing systems, and difficulties with paints have already been mentioned.

Unexpected user requirements Surface condensation in housing was, as noted earlier, invariably caused by inadequate heating and/or ventilation. Other instances where the expectations of the occupier worked against the design included the use of very aggressive cleaning agents on vinyl floorings and a few cases where the occupiers were perhaps over-sensitive to minor blemishes or cracking in finishes.

Table 3 Analysis of 256 defects other than dampness (=50 per cent of sample)

Type of defect		Location	
Cracking	93	due to foundation movement in floors in loadbearing walls in non-loadbearing walls in wall and floor finishes other	8 28 20 10 14 13
Detachment	75	tiles and mosaics floor finishes paints and other finishes other	27 16 9 23
Other	88		

Conclusions

The major short-coming in design appeared to be failure to make use of authoritative design guidance. This could be simply failure to appreciate the value of Codes, Standards and Agrément Certificates or it could be due to the sheer volume of guidance available; it might stem from a disdain for the 'standard solution', based on the assumption that the designer can work out everything from first principles. There was often insufficient attention to detail; most of the problems of rain penetration arose from inadequacies in the design of damp-proof membranes and cavity trays. The fact that so many buildings leak because of patent design faults should not be accepted with equanimity and yet 'the masterpiece which leaks' has been with us for many years. Greater use of standard details could bring an improvement; non-standard details must be thought out in three-dimensional form and illustrated clearly. It should not be left to the man on the site to discover the difficulties, sometimes impossibility, of executing the intended design.

In the field of execution, the pattern was more complex. More individuals are involved in the construction of a building than in its design and there are thus more opportunities for individual failings to emerge. A higher standard of supervision is necessary if the more glaring instances of poor workmanship and the omission of important details are to be avoided. Something better than the present system of spot checks may be necessary in critical areas of the construction, such as the installation of cavity trays in multi-storey construction, of wall ties in brick cladding, and the preparation of backgrounds to receive rendering and tiling. It is most important, throughout the construction period, to give better protection against the worst effects of wet weather and freezing conditions to unfixed materials and components, as well as to structures. All building is subject to some bad weather but relatively few buildings suffer seriously because of it. It seems that even quite simple protective measures during the worst conditions bring considerable benefits.

Faulty materials, etc and unexpected user requirements together accounted for less than a quarter of the defects analysed. It is unlikely that much can be done to counter the effects of changing user requirements but many of the problems with materials and

Cause of defect		Most common faults in category	
Faulty design	295	Choice of material or component	49
		Inadequate provision for movement	38
		DPMs; flashings; cavity trays, etc	29
		Inadequate control of water vapour	23
Faulty execution	176	Entrapment of water	41
		Leaking mastic joints	17
		Poor execution, omission of DPMs, flashings, cavity trays, etc	21
Faulty materials, components or proprietary systems	63	Non-conventional dpc system	12
		Paints	7
Unexpected user requirements	58	Condensation due to inadequate ventilation	48
Other	8		

(There was some overlap between categories)

Table 4 Causes of defects analysed

the like could be avoided if designers were more critical in their selection and more precise in specification. They should refuse, much more often, to accept materials, components or systems which do not offer worth while guarantees of performance measured against accepted criteria such as British Standards. In the end, poor products will only survive if designers continue to specify them.

References (BRE DIGEST numbers)

  8 Built-up felt roofs
 27 Rising damp in walls
 33 Sheet and tile flooring made from thermoplastic binders
 47 Granolithic concrete, concrete tiles and terrazzo flooring
 54 Damp-proofing solid floors
 75 Cracking in buildings
 77 Damp-proof courses
104 Floor screeds
106 Painting woodwork
108 Standardised U-values
110 Condensation
140 Double glazing and double windows
144 Asphalt and built-up felt roofings: durability
163 Drying out buildings

2 Foundations and Walls

Soils and foundations : 1

This Digest and the next show how soil conditions on site affect the design of foundations and the subsequent behaviour of buildings.

In the past the choice of foundation type has been little influenced by soil conditions but the increasing use of sites with difficult soils has more serious implications for foundation design and calls for a better appreciation of the way soil reacts to applied loads and natural forces.

This Digest therefore considers the principles of soil behaviour and examines the movements which result from the construction of foundations or which can be induced by other factors such as the weather, vegetation and subsidence.

Digest 64 deals with the choice of building sites and the investigations necessary to determine soil conditions. Digest 67 considers the types of foundation most appropriate to these conditions.

Interaction between superstructure, foundation and soil

A building, its foundation and the supporting soil interact with one another in a complex manner, the behaviour of one depending upon, and influencing, that of the others. Foundation design must therefore take into account not only the type of structure to be supported, its function and the constructional materials to be used, but also the soil conditions on site. The basic properties of soils are outlined below.

Soil properties

Soil structure

Most soils consist of solid particles of varying shapes and sizes, with water and, to a lesser extent, air filling the spaces between them. Large particles (sands) are held together mainly by their weight and when loose have very little strength. In fact, strength is related to the closeness of the packing and to the size of external forces; the influence of additional water on strength is only marginal unless it is flowing rapidly (*see* p. 45). On the other hand, the amount of water that can be held by fine particles (clays) is very much larger, the water films between the particles being responsible for the characteristic stickiness which binds them together. The strength of clays therefore depends on how much water they contain. The strength increases as the film thickness is reduced, e.g. by the drying action of tree roots.

Shrinkage and swelling

When water is removed from a soil the solid particles tend to move closer together. Such movement is very limited in sands because of the negligible amounts of water held between the particles, but in clays the proportions of solid matter and water are more nearly equal and particle movements can be appreciable. Clays therefore shrink when they are dried, the shrinkage being accompanied by an increase in strength.

Conversely, when clays absorb water the water films thicken and the clays swell and lose strength. In sands the volume changes are almost negligible. Soils of intermediate particle size, such as silts, have properties intermediate between those of sand and clay.

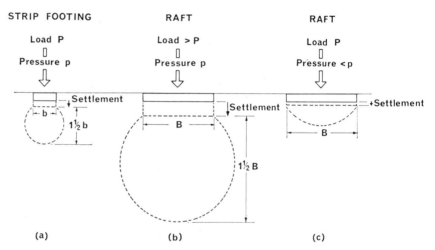

Fig. 1 Stress envelopes and settlements

Consolidation

Increased external pressure on a soil, e.g. that applied by a foundation load, increases both water and soil pressures. Water is squeezed from between the solid particles and driven to areas where the water pressure is less, while the soil particles are forced into closer contact with each other. As the ground is compressed so the foundation settles. This process of consolidation continues until the water pressure has fallen to its original value and the forces between the particles have increased by an amount equal to the newly applied load. If the soil particles and consequently the pore spaces are large, as in sands, the water movements are rapid. Foundations on sands therefore settle quickly once the load is applied and settlement after construction is completed is unlikely to be of any significance.

With clays the story is different; they offer considerable resistance to the expulsion of water and settlement caused by consolidation can continue for years after construction.

If the load on a soil is reduced, e.g. by excavation, the process just described is reversed: water tends to move towards the unloaded areas and swelling of the soil occurs.

Shrinkage (including consolidation) and swelling are thus fundamental to an understanding of soil behaviour. Often they operate simultaneously, as, for example, when the weight of clay removed by excavation approximates to the new structural load. Then long-term swelling may have settlement superimposed upon it.

Movements caused by loading

The extent to which solids deform under pressure depends on properties such as hardness, and the size of the imposed load. Soils behave similarly and a load applied through a foundation always causes settlement. However, not even uniform ground uniformly loaded settles evenly and the complex properties of soil make it difficult to assess the settlement of individual foundations or to predict the distortion of buildings as a whole.

Settlement of shallow foundations

Under normal loading shallow foundations consisting of strip and pad footings and rafts increase the pressure in a uniform soil significantly to a depth and breadth roughly equal to one-and-a-half times the breadth of the foundation. The resulting settlement depends on the increase in pressure and the soil properties in an imaginary envelope bounded by these dimensions (Fig. 1 (a)).

For the same bearing *pressure* the settlement of a broad foundation or raft will be greater than for a narrow one (Fig. 1 (b)), but the total load carried by the raft will be greater.

It the *load* is the same the pressure on the raft will of course be less than that on the narrow foundation, and the depth to which pressures in the soil are of any importance will be much less than one-and-a-half times the breadth of the foundation (Fig. 1 (c)). The settlement of a raft is thus less than that of a strip footing carrying the same load.

In practice this simple appraisal needs modification when firmer or weaker strata pass through the stressed zones as, for example, when sand overlies soft clay.

Settlement of deep foundations

Pile foundations are supported by frictional forces acting at the surface of each shaft and by bearing forces acting at the point or base. Only small movements are necessary for frictional forces to be developed and in clay soils these can be much greater than the bearing forces at the base. In sand or gravel most of the resistance to a pile is provided at its base irrespective of whether this is pointed or flat. The settlement of a single pile under working conditions is related to its breadth or diameter, and is usually very small. In fact, in stiff soils the compression of the pile itself may be comparable to the settlement necessary for the development of supporting forces.

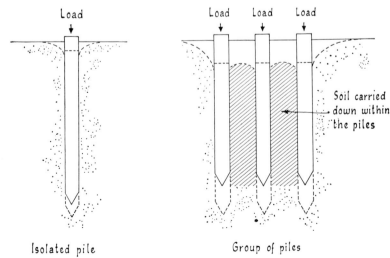

Isolated pile

Group of piles

Fig. 2 Pile settlements

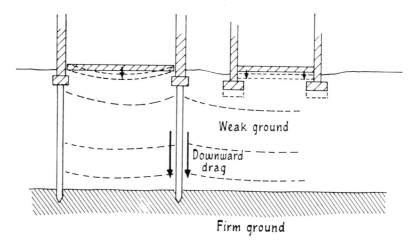

Fig. 3 Weak ground consolidating
and increasing pile load

Piles in a closely spaced group tend to carry the soil within the perimeter of the group down with them as they settle and this soil may be less effective in providing support than the soil outside the group. Thus the strength of a pile group in clay is frequently less than the sum of the strengths of the individual piles. In sand the increased compaction of the soil during pile-driving can often more than compensate for this loss. A closely spaced group behaves very much as a single foundation and the settlement at the design load is likely to be related more to the size of the whole group than to that of a single pile (Fig. 2).

Piles are frequently used to carry loads through soft soils containing a lot of water to a firm layer in which the points are founded. In these circumstances the soft soils may consolidate under the weight of floor slabs or adjacent buildings and exert a downward drag on a pile instead of supporting it; this tends to increase the load which must be carried by the point (Fig. 3).

Basements with a raft floor and retaining walls are a useful form of deep foundation which is less common now than it deserves to be. By excavating for the basement a weight of soil roughly equal to that of the building, the net increase in pressure on the soil—and hence the probable settlement—can be kept very small.

Soil movements from causes other than loading

These movements, which are not necessarily vertical or evenly distributed, are caused, for example, by seasonal weather changes, the growth or removal of vegetation, by earth flows and subsidence and, less frequently, by the particular use of the structure in question. The problems raised by these movements are usually most acute with soils composed of fine particles.

The behaviour of clay soils
Clays which shrink on drying and swell again when wetted are commonly responsible for the movement of shallow foundations. If such clays are firm enough to support buildings of a few storeys they are known as firm shrinkable clays.

(i) *Shrinkage and swelling caused by vegetation and climate.* The roots of plants penetrate soil to considerable depths and dry it when rainfall is low in summer. Beneath large trees and shrubs permanent drying has been detected in the United Kingdom at depths of 5 m or more, and shrinkage of the order of 100 mm has been measured at the ground surface. Beneath grasses shrinkage occurs to depths of about 2 m, but drying to these shallow depths is less likely to be permanent, the water transpired by the grasses in summer usually being replaced by rainfall the following winter. Even so, vertical movements of more than 25 mm have been measured at the surface between April and September. A building on shallow foundations close to vegetation is therefore liable to seasonal movements or long-term settlement, depending on the root growth. To some extent the building protects the clay beneath it from seasonal drying and wetting, and movement is more likely under the outer walls and corners. Shrinkage of clays occurs horizontally as well as vertically and so there is a tendency for walls to be drawn outwards in addition to settling and for cracks to open between the clay and the sides of the foundations. These cracks allow water to enter during the following winter and to soften the clay against or beneath the foundations (Fig. 4).

Fig. 4 also shows typical cracking of the building. During the winter these cracks partially close but, because of the relative displacement of parts of the building and the accumulation of debris within the cracks, closure is seldom complete and the cracks go on widening each dry summer.

To reduce the risk of damage as far as possible it is advisable, *as a rough guide,* not to erect buildings on shallow foundations closer to single trees than their height at maturity. The roots of groups or rows of trees competing for water over a limited area can be much more extensive, and, again *as a rough guide,* one-and-a-half times the mature height of the trees is suggested as the limiting distance. It is of course equally important that young trees should not be planted closer to buildings than these distances.

(ii) *Swelling caused by tree removal.* When trees are felled to clear a site for building, considerable time should be allowed for the clay (which was previously dried by tree roots) to regain water. Otherwise there is a serious risk that as the clay swells it will lift the building.

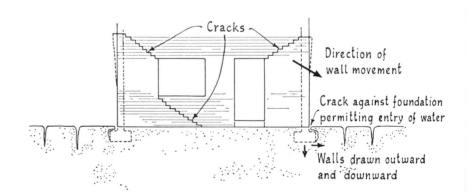

Fig. 4 Cracking associated with shallow foundations on shrinkable clay

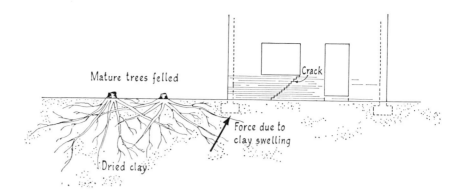

Fig. 5 Consequences of tree felling

And because the swelling is most marked close to the sites of the trees which have been removed, damage is likely from relative movements (Fig. 5). The pressures that dried clays develop when reabsorbing water are often greater than those applied by shallow foundations, and the resulting upward movements can continue for several years. For example, regular measurements made by the Building Research Station on an office block built in 1959 on a site cleared of trees a year previously show an upward movement of about 6 mm per year since construction was completed. Observations suggest that these movements may continue for up to ten years.

(iii) *Shrinkage caused by artificial drying.* Boilers and furnaces inadequately insulated from the clay beneath have been known to dry and shrink the clay, and so cause cracking of the concrete foundation slab through lack of support. Heating appliances not normally provided with adequate air ventilation or water channels between the furnace and the base should have such cooling systems installed as part of the foundation.

The behaviour of sandy soils

Water can move much faster through sands than through fine-grained soils; some foundation problems are directly attributable to this property.

(i) *Loss of ground.* Dense beds of sand are normally excellent foundation soils but occasionally water washes out the finer particles, leaving the coarser material in a less stable condition. This happens, for example, when fine sands and silts are affected by water flowing underground from high ground nearby; these exhibit a 'quick-sand' condition, particularly if an excavation is made, and much of their bearing capacity can be lost. Such situations must be dewatered or avoided completely for building purposes.

(ii) *Frost heave.* During severe winters in the United Kingdom frost may penetrate the soil to a depth of 600 mm or so. If the water table is close to the ground surface and the spaces between the soil particles are of a particular range of sizes—as they are with fine sands, silts and chalk—water can move into the frozen zone and form ice lenses of increasing thickness. As a result the ground surface is lifted in what is known as 'frost heave'. For this reason these materials should not be used as filling under floor slabs. Well-heated buildings are unlikely to be affected because of heat loss to the ground, but not so the outer walls of poorly heated houses, nor houses under construction—the concrete ground floor slabs of the latter are particularly vulnerable until glazing is complete. The slabs tend to heave more than the external walls, and service connections and wall to floor connections can be damaged. Unheated garages and outhouses, often built on concrete slabs and footings shallower than those of adjoining houses, are likely to be similarly affected.

Organic soils and made-up ground

Peats and other soils containing a lot of organic matter in the form of decaying vegetation vary greatly in volume as their water content changes. They are also very compressible and settle readily even under their own weight. Made-up ground behaves in much the same way and settles for many years unless it is good material, carefully placed, and compacted in thin layers. The bearing capacities of sites filled by end-tipping are often poor and variable; these sites should never be built upon unless deep foundations passing through the fill can be provided. Poorly compacted fill is unsuitable for foundations no matter how long it consolidates under its own weight.

Large-scale movements

Some foundation movements result from deep-seated instability in what would otherwise be good foundation soil. They can be caused by natural or geological phenomena, artificial agencies or by a combination of both.

(i) *Slopes and landslips.* Clay soils on sloping sites are likely to move downhill, albeit slowly, if the angle of slope exceeds about 1 in 10. Larger landslips occur intermittently above cliffs, river valleys and deep cuttings.

(ii) *Swallow holes.* In chalk and limestone areas cavities in the bedrock can form by the action of underground streams or water courses dissolving the rock away. If the overburden collapses into a cavity, as is common where the overburden is sandy, a 'swallow hole' is formed at the surface with consequential damage to buildings above or nearby. Because water movement is essential to swallow hole formation, soakaways should always be placed at a safe distance from buildings in these areas.

(iii) *Mining subsidence.* Large settlements must be expected in mining areas as the ground subsides over workings. Usually the ground surface 'stretches' as the front of a subsidence approaches and buildings start to tilt towards it. The tilt eventually decreases but the settlement increases as the ground beneath is affected. If structural damage is of a minor character buildings slowly return to a more or less plumb position at a lower level. To withstand the horizontal and vertical forces acting on a building during subsidence the construction should be either rigid, using a heavily reinforced concrete raft, or extremely flexible; movements can then be accommodated without serious damage to structure or finishes. Usually, small brick houses on quite thin rafts reinforced to resist the horizontal forces can survive moderate movements without undue damage.

Movement and damage

The effect of a differential vertical movement h between any two points A and B on a building depends on their distance apart. It is therefore more useful to measure differential movement as 'angular distortion', defined as h/AB (Fig. 6). Brickwork and plaster quickly show the effects of differential movement and from the limited data available the onset of cracking can be associated with an angular distortion of about $1/300$. This is equivalent to a differential movement of 10 mm over a span of 3 m. Warehouse and factory buildings of framed construction can usually tolerate larger angular distortions but at about $1/150$ structural damage may be expected unless the joints have been specially designed to tolerate movements.

Fig. 6 Angular distortion

Soils and foundations: 2

This Digest outlines the soil and other investigations necessary in assessing the suitability of sites for new buildings. Digest 63 deals with the movements resulting from interactions between soils and foundations; foundation design is discussed in Digest 67.

The need for site investigation

An investigation of the site is needed when any building work is envisaged that is likely to be affected by conditions below ground level. This applies equally to alterations and extensions of existing work and to new schemes. It is of particular importance at the present time, when the possible use of sites that have been avoided as building land in the past is being considered. This may seem to be stating the obvious, but in fact it is known that schemes have been prepared, and in some cases work actually started, before any consideration has been given to below-ground conditions at the site and whether they are suitable for the project in hand. The extent of the investigation will depend largely on the situation, size and type of the proposed work.

This Digest is intended to emphasise the need for an early appraisal of the site so that any special measures that may be required to deal with difficult conditions can be planned at the outset. Many other aspects which bear on the intended use of the site, and which will need to be considered, such as leases, wayleaves, limitations on use and so on, are outside the scope of the Digest.

Outlined below are the main stages that can be undertaken in an investigation. A comprehensive study of the procedure is contained in the British Standard Code of Practice CP 2001 : 1957, *Site investigations.*

Stage 1. Information available off site

The local authority should be regarded as a main source of information at this stage. Its intimate knowledge of the soil and general conditions in the area, particular difficulties that can arise and local building practice can be invaluable.

Older editions of the Ordnance Survey maps, ancient maps and records from other local sources can also provide useful clues to the positions of features that might cause difficulty, such as infilled ponds, ditches and streams, disused pipes, sites of old buildings and services. Current maps, plans and records that might also be studied to advantage are set out in the Appendix.

Stage 2. Site reconnaissance

Useful information can be obtained from a surface exploration of the site and its surroundings. Nearby buildings should be looked at to see if they show any signs of distress or damage, and if possible the depth and types of foundations used should be established. The information gathered in this stage can be grouped under the following headings:

Topography

In walking over the site, nearby quarries, cuttings, ditches and slopes should be examined. These should show whether the soil conditions vary. Topographical features such as a step in the line of a valley may indicate a geological fault or a zone where shattered rock has been more rapidly eroded than the surrounding rock. Broken and terraced ground on hill slopes, especially when steep, may be caused by landslips. While gentle slopes usually make good building sites because of the drainage they promote, slopes greater than about 1 in 10 should be examined for soil creep. Slowly moving clay slopes are often responsible for the tilt of walls, fences and trees. If the ground is heavily grazed, cattle terraces along the contours are indicative of downhill creep.

Low-lying flat areas in hilly country may have been the sites of lakes and suggest the possible presence of soft silty soils and peats. On the other hand, mounds and hummocks in more or less flat regions frequently indicate former glacial conditions and the possibility of boulder clay and glacial gravel overlying solid strata.

In limestone or chalk country, craters or gentle depressions usually indicate swallow holes formed by the collapse of sandy or loamy soils into the fissured rock below. Examples may be seen in the Mendips, in parts of Pembrokeshire and Monmouthshire, on the edge of

Fig 1 Damage caused by trees on clay

the London basin, and wherever chalk or limestone occur. Local farmers will be familiar with them because they are potential cattle traps—to be fenced off or kept filled in.

Unstable conditions can also occur where springs issue from fine sand and silt strata on grassy slopes. The sand frequently erodes when turf is removed for building purposes, and ground of this nature is best avoided.

Where a polygonal pattern of cracks about 25 mm wide is seen in the ground surface during a dry summer, the surface soil is shrinkable. Shallow depressions round mature trees in open ground, broken kerb-stones and frequent repairs to paved surfaces close to trees in developed areas are further indications of shrinkage due to drying (Fig. 1). Larger cracks, more or less parallel to each other, are frequently indicative of deeper-seated movements such as are caused by mining, brine pumping, or landslips.

Flooding

Sites along river valleys and coasts may be liable to flooding from time to time, and the highest recorded flood levels should be established. Dry inland valleys may also be flooded as a result of heavy rain or melting snow, particularly when the soil beneath the snow is frozen.

Groundwater

The water levels in nearby ponds, streams and rivers noted in a site reconnaissance may not be a good guide to the level of the water in the adjoining country; near coasts and estuaries the groundwater level may fluctuate with the tide. The groundwater conditions in each of the underlying strata should be determined, as excavation below water level, particularly in fine sands, is difficult and costly. A layer of clay at foundation level may also confine a lower bed of sand with a high water pressure and cause uplift during excavation.

Because of constructional difficulties, foundations on sands and gravel should, where possible, be kept above the groundwater level. Where basements are to be constructed, precautions should be taken to ensure that they do not 'float' if the water level rises during construction. For purposes of basement design it should be assumed that the water level in clay soils extends to the ground surface.

Some soils contain sulphates; under certain conditions these may cause corrosion of buried concrete, iron and steel. If the presence of sulphates is suspected, the groundwater should be analysed, care being taken to avoid contamination of the samples by surface water.

Vegetation

The kinds of vegetation growing on a site can provide further useful pointers to the level of the water table in the ground for at least part of the year. For example, naturally occurring reeds, rushes, cotton-grass, poplars and willows indicate a high water table, whereas bracken and gorse usually indicate a well drained soil. The presence of stunted specimens of heather and gorse often means that the water table is occasionally too high for the good health of these plants. However, many plants tolerate a wide range of soil types and climatic conditions, so that the conclusions drawn from such inspections should preferably be checked with other evidence.

A change in the vegetation over quite a small area may indicate an important change in the subsoil or rock formation, and show where more detailed soil investigations should be made. Unless it cannot be avoided, individual buildings should not be founded in varying soils because of the probability of differential settlements.

The existence of peats and swamps will usually be obvious. Such sites should be avoided unless deep and extensive foundations are justified. The shrinkage of clays caused by plant roots is discussed in Digest 63. Most of the damage is caused by large trees and, in the London area, poplars have been particularly troublesome because they grow rapidly and are often planted closely spaced to form screens. If trouble from this source is anticipated, buildings close to the site and particularly near trees should be examined carefully.

The absence of vegetation typical in surrounding areas may suggest made-up ground, and a fairly superficial examination may reveal brick, wood, rubble and other kinds of mineral or chemical matter.

Stage 3. Site history

Previous uses of a site may suggest acceptable types of foundation for the proposed new works or in extreme cases make it clear that the site is unsuitable for new building. In areas where there have been underground workings, such as worked-out ballast pits, quarries, old brickworks, coal mines, mineral workings and brine pumping, enquiries should be made to establish their exact location. Reports of damage to structures, services and drainage systems should be investigated.

Sites previously cleared of orchards or woodland may be of dried clay and this must be allowed to re-absorb moisture and swell before construction is started—unless specially designed deep foundations are to be provided.

A good deal of site history will of course be apparent from site reconnaissance and the study of maps and local records. The latter should be searched for evidence of landslips, floods, bomb craters, disused drainage systems and so on. In urban areas, the positions of sewers, drains and services should be verified to avoid risk of damage by new foundations later.

Stage 4. Soil investigations

The previous Digest showed that foundation movements are of two kinds: those caused by the foundation load acting on the soil, and those caused by soil movements generated by other factors. The objects of soil investigations are to determine the strength and deformation characteristics of the soil under load and to identify the conditions in which soils are otherwise susceptible to movement. Some guidance on both will have been obtained by visual examination of the exposed surface of the site, while other simple tests, not involving detailed measurement, can yield useful results.

Scope of the investigations

In plan
For buildings of up to four storeys, sufficient inspection pits should be dug near the boundaries of the site to establish the soil profile. On a sloping site, or one with rock near the surface, other pits may have to be dug nearer the centre so that any variations in profile may be noted.

In depth
In the last Digest the depths were given to which soils are stressed by different types of foundation. Soil investigations should therefore be made to these depths at least.

If the inspection pits or the information obtained from other sources mentioned above suggest that piled foundations will be necessary then the investigation must be made to greater depths and a specialist firm should be consulted. In investigations for raft and piled founda-

Table 1 Soil identification

Soil type	Field identification	Field assessment of structure and strength	Possible foundation difficulties
Gravels	Retained on No. 7 BS sieve and up to 76·2 mm Some dry strength indicates presence of clay	Loose—easily removed by shovel 50 mm stakes can be driven well in	Loss of fine particles in water-bearing ground
Sands	Pass No. 7 and retained on No. 200 BS sieve Clean sands break down completely when dry. Individual particles visible to the naked eye and gritty to fingers	Compact—requires pick for excavation. Stakes will penetrate only a little way	Frost heave, especially on fine sands Excavation below water table causes runs and local collapse, especially in fine sands
Silts	Pass No. 200 BS sieve. Particles not normally distinguishable with naked eye Slightly gritty; moist lumps can be moulded with the fingers but not rolled into threads Shaking a small moist lump in the hand brings water to the surface Silts dry rapidly; fairly easily powdered	Soft—easily moulded with the fingers Firm—can be moulded with strong finger pressure	As for fine sands
Clays	Smooth, plastic to the touch. Sticky when moist. Hold together when dry. Wet lumps immersed in water soften without disintegrating Soft clays either uniform or show horizontal laminations Harder clays frequently fissured, the fissures opening slightly when the overburden is removed or a vertical surface is revealed by a trial pit	Very soft—exudes between fingers when squeezed Soft—easily moulded with the fingers Firm—can be moulded with strong finger pressure Stiff—cannot be moulded with fingers Hard—brittle or tough	Shrinkage and swelling caused by vegetation Long-term settlement by consolidation Sulphate-bearing clays may attack concrete and corrode pipes Poor drainage Movement down slopes; most soft clays lose strength when disturbed
Peat	Fibrous, black or brown Often smelly Very compressible and water retentive	Soft—very compressible and spongy Firm—compact	Very low bearing capacity; large settlement caused by high compressibility Shrinkage and swelling—foundations should be on firm strata below
Chalk	White—readily identified	Plastic—shattered, damp and slightly compressible or crumbly Solid—needing a pick for removal	Frost heave Floor slabs on chalk fill particularly vulnerable during construction in cold weather Swallow holes
Fill	Miscellaneous material, e.g. rubble, mineral, waste, decaying wood		To be avoided unless carefully compacted in thin layers and well consolidated May ignite or contain injurious chemicals

tions, samples for soil testing should normally be obtained from boreholes; these are a more economic and practical proposition than deep inspection pits. Shrinkage of clays is to be expected to depths of about 2 m and they should invariably be examined to these depths. Where trees are growing on clays, boreholes to about 5 m are needed.

Information required

Information is required on the following soil characteristics and the depths at which they are observed:

    soil type
    soil uniformity
    whether deformable or breakable in the fingers
    whether gritty, smooth, plastic, sticky
    whether homogeneous, fissured or shattered
    presence of organic or foreign matter
    colour, smell
    depth of water table.

Soil identification

In this Digest it is possible only to discuss the qualitative aspects of soil identification. Table 1 classifies soil types as they are identifiable in the field and indicates their suitability for various foundations.

Quantitative tests in the field and the laboratory will, however, be necessary where a comprehensive account of soil conditions is required, and reference should be made to CP 2001:1957 and BS 1377:1967, *Methods of testing soils for civil engineering purposes.*

Sampling

Equipment for sampling depends on whether inspection pits or boreholes are taken out and this, as suggested above, depends upon the depth of investigation necessary. For boreholes the simplest tool is the post-hole auger; with this two men can easily reach 7–8 m in soft or firm clays. It is important that the samples are extracted in as undisturbed a form as possible and that they are immediately protected from drying, because otherwise wrong conclusions may be drawn about the soil conditions. Inspection pits are of course more accessible than boreholes and allow removal of clay from the walls with a spade or knife. In sands and gravels, casing tubes prevent collapse of the borehole and percussive tools are necessary, and the services of specialist firms should be used.

Appendix—Sources of information
British Ordnance Survey Maps

The most useful are likely to be the large and medium scale maps and plans, ranging from 1/1250 to 1/25 000. Six-inch (1/10 000) maps cover the whole of Great Britain and 25-in. plans (1/2500) cover all areas except waste and mountainous districts. These maps and plans may be purchased from the Main Agents:

Cook, Hammond & Kell Ltd
22-24 Caxton Street   } for England and Wales
London SW1

Thomas Nelson & Sons Ltd
18 Dalkeith Road   } for Scotland
Edinburgh EH16 5BS

Further information is available from The Director General, Ordnance Survey, PO Box 32, Romsey Road, Maybush, Southampton SO9 7BR

Air photographs

Air photographs covering England and Wales at scales of 1/10000 and 1/20000, and enlargements of these, can be obtained from the Air Photographs Officer, Department of the Environment, 2 Marsham Street, London SW1. In Scotland enquiries should be addressed to the Department of the Environment, Directorate of Scottish Services, Argylle House, 3 Lady Lawson Street, Edinburgh EH3 9SD. Details of the area and grid references should be quoted.

Geological Survey Maps

The geology of much of Great Britain has been recorded on 1 in. (1/50000) scale maps and that of many coal-mining areas and the County of London on 6 in. (1/10000) maps. Manuscript 6 in. (1/10000) maps of other areas may be inspected at the Institute of Geological Sciences Library in London, and at the appropriate Geological Survey Offices in Leeds, Edinburgh and Belfast. Much additional information is available as memoirs, reports and handbooks. Requests for lists of maps, currently available, and other enquiries should be addressed to The Director, Institute of Geological Sciences, Exhibition Road, South Kensington, London, S.W.7.

Meteorological Office publications

These are available as daily, monthly and annual records of the climate in Britain and are generally obtainable from H M Stationery Office. Enquiries should be addressed to the appropriate office of the Meteorological Office.*

Admiralty charts and publications

The charts show high and low water marks for Home waters and the levels of the sea and river beds with reference to a low-water datum. The Authority for chart information is the Hydrographer of the Navy, Ministry of Defence, Old War Office Building, Whitehall, London S.W.1.

Mining records

In coal-mining areas the Divisional Offices of the National Coal Board should be consulted for details of active and prospective workings and for records of abandoned workings. Records of abandoned mines of other than coal and oil-shale are held by the Department of Trade and Industry.

---

*Advisory offices of the Meteorological Office:

Meteorological Office	Meteorological Office	Meteorological Office
Met O.3	Tyrone House	26 Palmerston Place
London Road	Ormeau Avenue	Edinburgh
Bracknell	Belfast	EH12 5AN
RG12 2SZ	BT2 8HH	

References

British Standard Code of Practice, CP 2001 (1957), 'Site investigations'.

British Standard BS 1377: 1967, 'Methods of testing soils for civil engineering purposes'.

Digest 63   Soils and foundations: 1

Digest 67   Soils and foundations: 3

Digest 95   Choosing a type of pile.

Digest 174   Concrete in sulphate-bearing soils and groundwaters.

Soils and foundations: 3

This Digest considers the factors governing the choice of foundations for buildings and shows in what circumstances the choice is dependent upon soil conditions and other site characteristics such as vegetation and nearby buildings. The Digest should be read in conjunction with Digests 63 and 64, which deal with soil and foundation behaviour and site investigations.

Construction types

Both the type of construction and the subsequent use of the building are important determinants of foundation design. Strip footings are usually chosen for buildings in which the load is carried mainly on walls. Pad footings, piles or pile groups are more appropriate when the structural loads are carried by columns. If differential settlements must be controlled to within fine limits, shallow strip or pad footings (except on rock or dense sand) will probably be inadequate and surface rafts may have to be considered as an alternative.

Foundation loading

The forces carried at ground level by each load-bearing wall or column of a building should be calculated, taking account of how roofs and floors are supported. Superimposed loadings are specified in the Building Regulations 1972, and BS CP 3, Chapter V; Part 1 : 1967, *Dead and imposed loads,* and BS 648 : 1964, *Schedule of weights of building materials,* enables calculation of dead load forces.

A typical two-storey semi-detached house of about 85 m² area, in cavity brickwork, with lightweight concrete or clay block partitions, timber floors and a tiled roof, has a mass of 100 tonnes (approx. 1000 kN) excluding the weight of the foundations. The loads at ground level are, in kN/m, approximately : party wall 50, gable end wall 40, front and back walls 25 and internal partitions less than 15. While the use of modern materials tends to reduce the *total* loads, some forms of construction, e.g. the cross-walled type, may exert higher foundation loads on *individual* walls than is the case with more traditional forms.

When the foundations have been designed, their weight must be added to the loadings already calculated so as to obtain the total bearing pressures on the soil beneath.

Soil data

Inspection pits, samples from boreholes and simple field tests suggested in Table 1 of *Digest 64* should provide data enabling near-surface soils to be identified and their strengths estimated. Geological maps and local records will often indicate whether the soils beneath pits and boreholes are likely to influence foundation design.

Adjacent buildings

New construction must not put the stability of existing properties at risk. If new foundations are placed close to those of an existing building, the envelopes of stressed soil will overlap and the loads on the soil will increase. As a result, clays may consolidate further and cause cracking of both buildings by differential settlement.

When an excavation is made, the stability of adjacent buildings may be threatened unless the excavation is adequately supported. This is particularly important with sands and gravels which derive their support from lateral restraint. Water draining towards excavations below the water table can also disturb the ground beneath adjacent buildings by increasing the effective weight of the soil and by carrying fine particles away.

When piles are to be driven the effects of vibration on surrounding soils must be considered.

Vegetation

Clays which have supported mature trees for many years will be in a dried state and likely to swell when the trees are felled (*see Digest 63*). Buildings erected before swelling is completed will therefore be subject to uplift. Unless the resulting differential movements can be accommodated by the structure or eliminated by the foundations, it will be necessary to defer

Table 1. Choice of foundation

Soil type and site condition	Foundation	Details	Remarks
Rock, solid chalk, sands and gravels or sands and gravels with only small proportions of clay, dense silty sands	Shallow strip or pad footings as appropriate to the load-bearing members of the building	Breadth of strip footings to be related to soil density and loading (*see* Table 2). Pad footings should be designed for bearing pressures tabled in CP 101 : 1972. For higher pressures the depth should be increased and CP 2004 : 1972 'Foundations' consulted	Keep above water wherever possible. Slopes on sand liable to erosion. Foundations 0·5 m deep should be adequate on ground susceptible to frost heave although in cold areas or in unheated buildings the depth may have to be increased. Beware of swallow holes in chalk
Uniform, firm and stiff clays: (1) Where vegetation is insignificant	Bored piles and ground beams, or strip foundations at least 1 m deep	Deep strip footings of the narrow widths shown in Table 2 can conveniently be formed of concrete up to the ground surface	
(2) Where trees and shrubs are growing or to be planted close to the site	Bored piles and ground beams	Bored piles dimensions as in Table 3	Downhill creep may occur on slopes greater than 1 in 10. Unreinforced piles have been broken by slowly moving slopes
(3) Where trees are felled to clear the site and construction is due to start soon afterward	Reinforced bored piles of sufficient length with the top 3 m sleeved from the surrounding ground and with suspended floors, or thin reinforced rafts supporting flexible buildings, or basement rafts		
Soft clays, soft silty clays	Strip footings up to 1 m wide if bearing capacity is sufficient, or rafts	*See* Table 2 and CP 101 : 1972	Settlement of strips or rafts must be expected. Services entering building must be sufficiently flexible. In soft soils of variable thickness it is better to pile to firmer strata (*See* Peat and Fill below)
Peat, fill	Bored piles with temporary steel lining or precast or *in situ* piles driven to firm strata below	Design with large safety factor on end resistance of piles only as peat or fill consolidating may cause a downward load on pile (*see* Digest 63) Field tests for bearing capacity of deep strata or pile loading tests will be required	If fill is sound, carefully placed and compacted in thin layers, strip footings are adequate. Fills containing combustible or chemical wastes should be avoided
Mining and other subsidence areas	Thin reinforced rafts for individual houses with load-bearing walls and for flexible buildings	Rafts must be designed to resist tensile forces as the ground surface stretches in front of a subsidence. A layer of granular material should be placed between the ground surface and the raft to permit relative horizontal movement	Building dimensions at right angles to the front of long-wall mining should be as small as possible

construction until swelling is complete, which can mean a delay of many years.

To avoid this delay the following alternative methods should be considered :

(i) Anchoring the building by reinforced bored piles sleeved from the ground over their top 3 m, and providing suspended floors. Beams spanning between the piles must be well clear of the ground surface.

(ii) Using flexible framed construction without brickwork or plastering.

(iii) Making the building rigid by either constructing a basement or reinforcing the foundations and brickwork.

Buildings erected close to standing trees should be supported on piles of sufficient depth, and for small structures bored piles are likely to be the most economical. Where nearby vegetation is insignificant, strip footings 1 m deep are usually adequate.

Choice of foundation type

Subject to the factors already considered, Table 1 gives the most appropriate foundations for buildings of not more than four storeys for a variety of typical soil conditions.

Economic and constructional factors

The availability of builders' plant can influence the relative costs of foundation types, particularly for small works. Large works may require specialist equipment; if so, the foundation design chosen should make the fullest use of it.

Experience has shown that, in shrinkable clay areas, short piles bored with mechanical augers are competitive in cost with traditional strip footings of the required depth, even for quite small contracts. For single house contracts bored piles are usually slightly more costly than strip footings, but the extra cost is justified by the additional safety obtained.

In any case, simple costing on a labour-plus-materials basis may be misleading. Construction of bored piles can often continue through the winter months when the trenches for strip foundations would be waterlogged or damaged by exposure to frost. On large sites, once all vegetation has been cleared, piles can sometimes be placed in one operation in summer, leaving above-ground construction to continue through the following winter. In addition to use on clay sites, bored-pile foundations with pre-cast ground beams should be useful for low-rise industrialized systems; in cross-wall house construction more than 10 piles are rarely necessary.

Constructional problems must also be considered. Elimination of water from excavations other than by pumping from drainage sumps can be expensive. Foundations on sands and gravels should be kept above the water-table whenever possible; if not, water should be drained or pumped away from the excavation rather than towards it so as to reduce the risk of erosion at its face. If the sides of excavations in coarse-grained soils are not sufficiently shallow to prevent collapse, support by timbers or sheet piles is necessary. Cuts in firm clay and chalk normally stand unsupported for short periods at steeper slopes than in granular soils, although some very soft clays lose much of their strength when disturbed. Clay and chalk surfaces deteriorate when exposed to water and frost and should be protected by concreting. Ground which has softened must be removed. Filling often has to be placed within the foundations of a building to bring the ground level up to that necessary for pouring concrete floor slabs. This cannot be compacted with mechanical plant, particularly if the fill level is higher than that of the ground outside, without risk of damaging the brickwork. The fill should therefore be chosen for its ability to bed well under light compaction. Alternatively, the fill should be placed and compacted before the foundations are laid.

Table 2. Minimum width for strip foundations

Soil type	Field assessment of structure and strength	Minimum width (mm) for total load (kN/m) of not more than:						
		16	24	32	40	48	56	64
Gravels and sands	Loose	300	450	600				
	Compact	225	225	300	375	450	525	600
Silts	Soft	450	675	900	Silts are frequently combined with sands or clays. Values for composite types are given in the Building Regulations			
	Firm	300	450.	600				
Clays	Very soft	450	675	900				
	Soft	360	525	675				
	Firm	260	325	375	450	560	675	750
	Stiff or hard	225	225	300	375	450	525	600
Peat	Soft	Footings should be in firm ground beneath the peat. Rarely does investigation show that the peat itself will support foundations						
	Firm							
Chalk	Plastic	Assess as clay above						
	Solid	Equal to the width of the wall						
Fill		To be determined after investigation						

Table 3. Load-carrying capacity of bored piles (in kN)

Strength classification	Diameter of pile (mm)	Length of pile (m)				
		2·5	3	3·5	4	4·5
Stiff	250	40	48	56	64	72
(Unconfined shear strength	300	50	60	70	80	90
more than 70 kN/m²)	350	65	77	90	102	115
Hard	250	55	65	75	85	95
(Unconfined shear strength	300	70	82	94	106	118
more than 140 kN/m²)	350	95	108	120	132	145

Note: The figures are for clay which increases in strength with depth to the 'stiff' and 'hard' classifications near the bottom of the piles. The figures should not be applied to piles in other situations.

Design
Strip footings
The recommendations for strip footings in Table 2 are in SI units which correspond approximately to the provisions of the Building Regulations (1972) and BS CP 101 : 1972, *Foundations and substructures for non-industrial buildings of not more than four storeys*. The table gives minimum values for the width of strip foundations in soil types identified in Table 1 of *Digest 64*.

Pad footing and rafts
Pad footings and surface rafts should be designed using the bearing capacities tabled in CP 101 : 1972. They should be proportioned wherever possible so that the centre of area of the foundation is vertically beneath the centre of pressure of the imposed loads, and the thickness and reinforcement should be calculated to resist all shear and bending forces. An angle of spread of load of 45° to the vertical may be assumed.

The bearing pressure on soil beneath deep rafts or basements is reduced because of the amount of soil excavated. Further, because of the associated walls, deep rafts possess considerable rigidity. These two advantages may be somewhat offset, however, by the greater expense of deep rafts compared with piles and ground beams.

Note: The design of raft foundations requires considerable knowledge and care, and expert advice should be taken.

Short bored piles
Table 3 gives load-carrying capacities for bored piles in shrinkable clay soils. A simple method of design not requiring laboratory measurements of clay strength is referenced (Ward and Green) below. It is most important that an adequate thickness of compressible material such as loose ash is placed between the ground beams and the clay surface to allow for relative movement. Concrete floor slabs, if used, should be isolated from the beams and main walls. Suspended floors are preferable when swelling is expected.

Other foundations
Except for major works, when expert advice must be taken, the foundations of all extensions, garages and bay windows should be of the same form and at the same depth as the foundations of the main building.

Further reading
Digests
63 Soils and foundations : 1
64 Soils and foundations : 2
142 Fill and hardcore

Papers
Green H Building on shrinkable clays—some applications of short concrete piles *JRIBA* 1952, **59** (April) pp. 212–213

Green H Long-term loading of short-bored piles. *Geotech.*, 1961, **11** (1) (March) pp. 47–53.

Lacey W D and Swain H T Construction theory : design for mining subsidence *Archit. J.*, 1957, **126** (October 10), pp. 557–570.

Ward W H House foundations, *JRIBA*. 1947, **54** (February), pp. 226–235

Ward W H and Green H House foundations : the short-bored pile. Public Works and Municipal Services Congress 1952

Concrete in sulphate-bearing soils and groundwaters

Withdrawn see Digest Nº 250 June 1981

This Digest discusses the factors responsible for sulphate attack on concrete below ground level, and recommends what can be done, by suitable selection of cement type and concrete quality, to resist attack by naturally-occurring sulphates.

Digest 90 is now withdrawn.

Factors influencing attack

Aqueous solutions of sulphates attack the set cement in concrete, the chemical reactions occurring depending upon the kind of sulphate present and the nature of the cement. The rate of attack depends greatly on the permeability of the concrete. The factors influencing attack are:

(1) the amount and nature of the sulphate present;
(2) the level of the water table and its seasonal variation;
(3) the form of construction;
(4) the type and quality of the concrete.

If sulphate conditions cannot be prevented from reaching the structure, the only defence against attack lies in the control of the fourth factor; it cannot be too strongly emphasised that fully compacted concrete of low permeability must be used.

Occurrence of sulphates Sulphates occur mainly in strata of London Clay, Lower Lias, Oxford Clay, Kimmeridge Clay and Keuper Marl. The most abundant salts are:

  calcium sulphate (gypsum or selenite)
  magnesium sulphate (Epsom salt)
  sodium sulphate (Glauber's salt).

Sulphuric acid and sulphates in acid solution occur much less often, for example, near colliery tips, in marshy country and where pyrite in the soil is being slowly oxidized.

Sulphates are sometimes present in materials such as colliery shale used as fill beneath solid concrete ground floors. Moisture from the ground carries the salts to the underside of the concrete, which they attack, leading to expansion and cracking of the floor and the surrounding structure.

Brick rubble, particularly with adhering plaster, ashes and some industrial wastes, are potential sources of damage by sulphate attack.

The solubilities of the salts mentioned—expressed as grams of sulphur trioxide (SO_3) per litre of solution —vary considerably. That of calcium sulphate is only $1 \cdot 2$ g (SO_3) per litre, compared with about 150 and 200 times this value for magnesium and sodium sulphates respectively. The SO_3 content of groundwaters therefore gives an indication that one or both of the latter sulphates may be present.

Movement of groundwater Sulphates can only continue to reach concrete by movement of their solutions in water. Thus concrete which is wholly and permanently above the water table is unlikely to be attacked, even though capillarity in the subsoil may cause some migration of salts to zones above the water table. Below the table, however, movement of water may replenish the sulphates removed by reaction with concrete, thereby maintaining the attack. Movements may be vertical or horizontal, depending on seasonal variations in rainfall and on the geology of the site and its environs. A low sulphate content in the soil does not eliminate the possibility of sulphate attack, since groundwater may flow from adjacent areas, particularly if the soil has been disturbed, e.g. by laying pipes.

Form of construction Given the same concrete quality and corrosive conditions, massive forms of construction will, as expected, deteriorate less quickly than thin sections. Special considerations apply to piles, since if the surface skin of concrete is attacked there could be changes in the friction on the pile shaft. Precast piles have advantages over those cast *in situ;* concrete quality—in particular compaction—is more easily controlled, since placing is less difficult (*see* Digest 95).

In basement structures, retaining walls, or culverts, for example, the concrete may have to resist strong lateral water pressure on one side only. This favours both water penetration and concentration of salts on the other side if evaporation of water from that side can occur. Similarly, partly buried concrete may draw up sulphates in solution from beneath by a combination of capillarity and evaporation at the exposed surfaces.

At first sight precast concrete pipes may appear rather more vulnerable to attack than other forms of concrete; they are thin in section and may be subjected to water pressure from one side only. Against this, however, is the fact that the concrete quality is usually high, to satisfy BS 556, and, providing the appropriate cement is used, this is the best safeguard against attack. (The internal corrosion of concrete pipes by sulphate salts in the effluent is discussed in Note No. 6: 1959 by the Water Pollution Research Laboratory).

Type and quality of concrete Concrete of low permeability is essential to resist sulphate attack; hence the concrete must be fully compacted. The mix must be so designed that it has sufficient workability to allow full compaction and yet has a free water/cement ratio no greater than that specified for the particular soil conditions. 'Free' water is the total weight of water in the concrete less that absorbed by the aggregate. (A method of measuring water absorption of aggregates is given in BS 812, Section 4).

Where sulphates are present, the mix should be designed to have a cement content not less than, and a free water/cement ratio not greater than, the values specified in Table 1 as appropriate to the severity of the conditions and the type of cement. For a particular situation, the cement content may have to be greater than the minimum specified in the table, so as to achieve the required workability within the limits of the maximum free water/cement ratio. This is particularly so for *in situ* concrete piles where the overriding consideration is to ensure complete compaction and therefore structural integrity of the pile; in this case, the mix must be designed to produce a highly workable but cohesive concrete. Admixtures for concrete such as air-entraining or water-reducing agents may give some limited improvement in sulphate resistance. Admixtures containing workability aids improve compaction and

allow the use of lower water/cement ratios, but those containing calcium chloride are not recommended. All precast units and any type of concrete using supersulphated cement require particular care during the initial curing period, so as to ensure minimum permeability and a hard surface.

Types of cement

In concrete prepared from ordinary or rapid-hardening **Portland cement** (BS 12) one reaction which occurs in sulphate solutions is with the hydrates formed from any tricalcium aluminate in the cement. Another involves the calcium hydroxide released during hydration. These reactions lead to a considerable expansion in the cement, finally resulting in the breakdown of the concrete. A considerable resistance to sulphate attack is obtained when the tricalcium aluminate content of the cement is kept low. Portland cements complying with BS 12 usually contain a significant proportion of tricalcium aluminate, but in **sulphate-resisting Portland cement** complying with BS 4027 the amount is limited to 3·5 per cent.

The resistance of concrete made with **supersulphated cement** (BS 4248) to attack by sulphates over the range of concentrations commonly encountered in groundwaters is similar to that of sulphate-resisting Portland cement. This cement is not currently produced in the UK but it has been found that good quality concrete made with it has an acceptable life in mildly acid conditions. Laboratory tests indicate that when immersed in strong magnesium sulphate solution (up to 3·5 per cent SO_3) concrete samples prepared from supersulphated cement lose strength more quickly than those prepared from sulphate-resisting Portland cement. In strong sodium sulphate solution, the current evidence is divided but, on balance, the relative resistances appear to be reversed.

The sulphate resistance of cements based on mixtures of granulated blastfurnace slag and Portland cement clinker increases with the proportion of slag. In addition to factory-produced cements, ground granulated blastfurnace slag is available for introduction at the mixer. BS 146 for **Portland-blastfurnace cement** does not set a minimum level for slag content and this cement is therefore classified with ordinary Portland cement. BS 4246 for **low heat Portland-blastfurnace cement** specifies a minimum slag content of 50 per cent which is probably less than is required for any substantial improvement in sulphate resistance over ordinary Portland cement but until the result of long-term tests are available there is little UK data on which to base precise recommendations.

The inclusion of pozzolanas improves the sulphate resistance of ordinary Portland cement concretes. Selected and classified pulverised-fuel ashes with good pozzolanic properties are available in the UK but here again the results of long-term tests are awaited.

Table 1 Requirements for concrete exposed to sulphate attack

	Concentration of sulphates expressed as SO$_3$				Requirements for dense, fully compacted concrete made with aggregates meeting the requirements of BS 882 or BS 1047			
	In soil		In ground-water	Type of cement	Minimum cement content			Maximum free water/cement ratio
	Total SO$_3$	SO$_3$ in 2:1 water:soil extract			Nominal maximum size of aggregate			
Class					40 mm	20 mm	10 mm	
	%	g/litre	parts per 100 000		kg/m^3	kg/m^3	kg/m^3	
1	less than 0·2	—	less than 30	Ordinary Portland or Portland-blastfurnace	240	280	330	0·55
2	0·2–0·5	—	30–120	Ordinary Portland or Portland-blastfurnace	290	330	380	0·50
				Sulphate-resisting Portland	240	280	330	0·55
				Supersulphated	270	310	360	0·50
3	0·5–1·0	1·9–3·1	120–250	Sulphate-resisting Portland or supersulphated	290	330	380	0·50
4	1·0–2·0	3·1–5·6	250–500	Sulphate-resisting Portland or supersulphated	330	370	420	0·45
5	over 2	over 5·6	over 500	As for Class 4, but with the addition of adequate protective coatings of inert material such as asphalt or bituminous emulsions reinforced with fibreglass membranes				

Notes

This table applies only to concrete made with aggregates complying with the requirements of BS 882 or BS 1047 placed in near-neutral groundwaters of pH 6 to pH 9, containing naturally occurring sulphates but not contaminants such as ammonium salts. Concrete prepared from ordinary Portland cement would not be recommended in acidic conditions (pH 6 or less); sulphate-resisting Portland cement is slightly more acid-resistant but no experience of large-scale use in these conditions is currently available. Supersulphated cement has given an acceptable life, provided that the concrete is dense and prepared with a free water/cement ratio of 0·40 or less, in mineral acids down to pH 3·5.

The cement contents given in Class 2 are the minima recommended by the manufacturers. For SO$_3$ contents near the upper limit of Class 2, cement contents above these minima are advised.

For severe conditions, eg thin sections, sections under hydrostatic pressure on one side only and sections partly immersed, consideration should be given to a further reduction of water/cement ratio and, if necessary, an increase in cement content to ensure the degree of workability needed for full compaction and thus minimum permeability.

Classification of sites and recommendations for concrete

For classification purposes sites have been divided into five categories of increasing severity, based on the sulphate contents of the soil and groundwater. The recommended type of cement and the minimum cement content for each of these classes are given in Table 1. It must be remembered that the divisions between the classes are somewhat arbitrarily drawn and that the recommendations are judgments based on present knowledge.

Sampling and analysis of soils and groundwaters

All reliable information about the site should be examined in assessing the need for extensive analysis of the soil. The information should include an estimate of the sulphate content of any groundwater samples obtained during site investigation. The main danger in classifying sites on the basis of groundwater analysis alone lies in the difficulty in obtaining samples that are not diluted with surface water.

Suitable soil samples may be obtained from the test boreholes made for engineering purposes. They should be taken at every 1–2 m and wherever an obvious change in stratum occurs. Economic considerations will govern the number of soil samples analysed. When the cost of analysis is low compared with the preparation and bulking of the sample it is preferable to analyse the samples separately. If, to save costs, samples are combined, this should only be done for samples from the same depth in different boreholes when the type of stratum is the same.

Sulphate contents of the groundwater can be determined by any suitable analytical method. Concentrations in the fourth column of Table 1 are customarily expressed as parts SO_3, per 100 000 parts of water, so that analytical figures expressed in grams of SO_3 per litre must be multiplied by 100. The total sulphate content of the soil may be obtained by extraction with hot dilute hydrochloric acid, and is expressed as the percentage of SO_3 per dry weight of soil. If the sulphate present in the soil is predominantly the calcium salt, its low solubility may result in the total sulphate content giving too severe a classification for the site. In cases where the total sulphate exceeds 0·5 per cent it is suggested that the water-soluble sulphate should be determined. The soluble sulphate salts can usually be extracted from the soil using twice the weight of water and expressed as grams of SO_3 per litre of water extract. Classification on this basis is given in column 3 of Table 1.

The detailed analytical procedures for these determinations are published in a BRE Current Paper*, together with the methods for the quantitative determination of the metallic ions present.

Interpretation of analytical results The results of all the individual chemical analyses should be available to the engineer to assist him in deciding on the precautions necessary. If classification is based solely on the analysis of groundwaters, it should correspond to the highest sulphate concentration recorded. If classification is based on the analysis of only a small number of soil samples and the results vary widely, it may be worth while to take further samples for analysis. When a larger number of results are available it is suggested that the site classification should be based on the mean of the highest 20 per cent of the results. When the soil samples have been combined before analysis the selection should be more stringent, and the mean of the highest 10 per cent of results is suggested.

**British Standards
referred to in the text**

BS 12   *Portland cement (ordinary and rapid-hardening)*
        Part 2 : 1971 Metric units

BS 146 : 1958 *Portland blastfurnace cement*

BS 556   *Concrete cylindrical pipes and fittings including manholes, inspection chambers and street gullies*
        Part 2 : 1972 Metric units

BS 812 : 1967 *Methods of sampling and testing of mineral aggregates, sands and fillers*

BS 4027 *Sulphate-resisting Portland cement*
        Part 2 : 1972 Metric units

BS 4246 *Low heat Portland-blastfurnace cement*
        Part 2 : 1974 Metric units

BS 4248 : 1968 *Supersulphated cement*

---

*CP3/68 *Analysis of sulphate-bearing soils in which concrete is to be placed.* S. R. Bowden.

Clay brickwork: 1

This digest comments on the selection of clay bricks and mortars for use with them in a wide range of building elements. It relates the behaviour of brickwork in differing conditions of exposure and use to the properties of the bricks. The second part, No. 165, will be published next month.

Together these will supersede Nos. 65 and 66 which are now withdrawn.

Varieties, qualities and types

Clay bricks are classified in BS 3921 : Part 2 : 1969 *Bricks and blocks of fired earth, clay or shale* as follows :

Varieties: *common*—suitable for general building work

facing—made or selected for appearance

engineering—a dense, strong brick conforming to defined limits of absorption and strength

Qualities: *internal*—suitable only for internal use

ordinary—normally durable in the external face of a building

special—durable in conditions of extreme exposure to water and freezing

Types: *solid*—small* holes not exceeding 25 per cent of the volume of the brick are permitted; alternatively, frogs not exceeding 20 per cent of the total volume are permitted

perforated—small* holes may exceed 25 per cent of the total volume of the brick

hollow—the total of holes, which need not be small, may exceed 25 per cent of the volume of the brick.

cellular—holes closed at one end exceed 20 per cent of the volume.

The widening of the definition 'solid' to include bricks with frogs or small holes is not consistent in all sources of information. For example, BS 743 : 1970 *Materials for damp-courses* calls for bricks with no holes, as does Table 5 of CP 121 : Part 1 : 1973 *Notional fire resistance of walls*, although Building Regulations 1972, in Schedule 8 *Notional periods of fire resistance* refers to solid bricks but allows 25 per cent perforation. Furthermore, three hand-holes,

each up to 3250 mm² cross-section (equivalent to 64 mm diameter), are allowed by the Standard within the 25 per cent and these are over half the width of the brick.

'Special' refers to a defined quality of brick, although bricks of shapes other than rectangular prisms are referred to as 'standard specials' and BS 4729 : 1971 gives dimensions for a range of these special shaped bricks in relation to the Imperial size of brick given in BS 3921 Part 1 and the co-ordinated metric size of brick given in BS 3921 : Part 2. Note that the two sets of dimensions, although very similar, are not straight Imperial to metric conversions and the bricks are not truly interchangeable.

Sizes

Work sizes and co-ordinating sizes of bricks to BS 3921 are illustrated in Fig 1.

The tolerances on the sizes of bricks are fixed by giving maximum and minimum dimensions, not on individual bricks, but on batches of 24 bricks chosen at random, as in Table 1.

It follows statistically from this method of measurement that batches are unlikely to contain more than 1 per cent of bricks outside the limit for length of ± 6 to 7 mm. Nevertheless, for critical work the bricklayer may need to recognise a much longer or shorter brick if it occurs and not to use it, thus avoiding complaints about the variation of perpends.

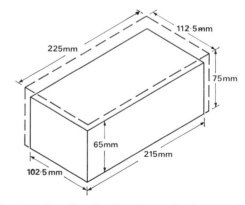

Fig 1 Work sizes (firm lines) and co-ordinating sizes (broken lines) of bricks to BS 3921

---

* 'small' holes are less than 20 mm wide or less than 500 mm² in cross-section

Table 1 Overall measurements of 24 bricks

	maximum	minimum
	mm	mm
length	5235	5085
width	2505	2415
height	1620	1530

Table 2 Proposed sizes for metric modular bricks

Designation	work size		
	length	width	height
mm	mm	mm	mm
300 × 100 × 100	288	90	90
200 × 100 × 100	190	90	90
300 × 100 × 75	288	90	65
200 × 100 × 75	190	90	65

Table 3 Proposed size limits for metric modular bricks

Work sizes		limits of size (24 bricks)	
		maximum	minimum
	mm	mm	mm
length	288	7012	6812
	190	4626	4494
width	90	2205	2115
height	90	2205	2115
	65	1605	1515

The brick sizes in BS 3921 are as yet only co-ordinated metric sizes. Proposals for the designation and work sizes of metric modular bricks have been made in the BS Draft for development 'Clay Bricks with Modular Dimensions' and are quoted in Table 2. Some or all of these brick sizes may already be available in some areas.

The proposed limits on the dimensions of these bricks, measured over a random sample of 24 bricks, are given in Table 3.

Weight

Clay brickwork weighs from about 2 tonnes/m³ (2 kg/m² per mm thickness) for typical common bricks to 2·4 tonnes/m³ for bricks of high density (eg engineering bricks).

Appearance

Where colour and texture are important, these should be agreed on the basis of samples representative of the production range. Occasionally there may occur bricks of attractive colour such as salmon pink which might indicate comparative underfiring of the bricks. Such bricks may lack durability and, whilst a few of these may be acceptable in work subjected to normal exposure, it might prove unwise to use bricks all of this kind, selected on grounds of colour, in conditions of more severe exposure.

Table 4 Minimum qualities of bricks and recommended mortar groups (i–v of Table 5)

Constructional element	Early frost hazard [a]			
	no		yes	
	brick	mortar	brick	mortar
Internal walls and inner leaf of cavity walls	internal	v	ordinary	iii or plasticised iv
Backing to external solid walls	internal	iv	ordinary	iii or plasticised iv
External walls; outer leaf of cavity walls:				
—above damp-proof course	ordinary	iv[c]	ordinary	iii[c]
—below damp-proof course	ordinary	iii[d, g]	ordinary	iii[b, d, g]
Parapet walls; free-standing walls; domestic chimneys:				
—rendered [e]	ordinary	iii[f]	ordinary	iii[f]
—not rendered	special preferred or ordinary	ii iii	special	ii
Sills and copings; earth-retaining walls backfilled with free-draining material	special	i	special	i

Notes

(a) During construction, before mortar has hardened (say 7 days after laying) or before the wall is protected against the entry of rain at the top.

(b) If the bricks are to be laid wet, see 'Cold weather brick-laying', Digest 160.

(c) If to be rendered, lay in mortar not weaker than group iii, preferably with sulphate-resisting cement.

(d) If sulphates are present in the groundwater and ordinary quality bricks are used, use sulphate-resisting cement in the mortar.

(e) Parapet walls of clay bricks should not be rendered on both sides; if this is unavoidable, select mortar as though not rendered.

(f) If the presence of sulphates in the bricks is suspected, group iii mortar made with sulphate-resisting cement is preferred.

(g) CP 121 considers the zone of brickwork more than 150 mm above ground level and below damp-proof course to be at greater risk and suggests the use of 'special' quality bricks.

Table 5 Mortar mixes (proportions by volume)

	Mortar group	Cement : lime : sand *	Masonry-cement : sand	Cement : sand, with plasticiser
Increasing strength but decreasing ability to accommodate movements caused by settlement, shrinkage, etc	i	1 : 0–¼ : 3	—	—
	ii	1 : ½ : 4–4½	1 : 2½–3½	1 : 3–4
	iii	1 : 1 : 5–6	1 : 4–5	1 : 5–6
	iv	1 : 2 : 8–9	1 : 5½–6½	1 : 7–8
	v	1 : 3 : 10–12	1 : 6½–7	1 : 8

Direction of changes in properties

equivalent strengths within each group ←→

increasing frost resistance →

improving bond and resistance to rain penetration ←

Where a range of sand contents is given, the larger quantity should be used for sand that is well graded and the smaller for coarse or uniformly fine sand.

Because damp sands bulk, the volume of damp sand used may need to be increased. For cement : lime : sand mixes, the error due to bulking is reduced if the mortar is prepared from lime : sand coarse stuff and cement in appropriate proportions; in these mixes 'lime' refers to non-hydraulic or semi-hydraulic lime and the proportions given are for lime putty. If hydrated lime is batched dry, the volume may be increased by up to 50 per cent to get adequate workability.

* The addition of an air-entraining agent might improve the frost-resistance of cement : lime : sand mortars

Ordinary quality bricks are required by BS 3921 to be reasonably free from deep or extensive cracks, from damage to edges and corners and from pebbles. A more exacting standard is set for special quality bricks. For many purposes, slight cracking will have little effect on strength or resistance to rain and the main criterion is aesthetic but in highly stressed brickwork only a very minor amount of cracks should be allowed.

The standard also calls for the bricks to be free from expansive particles of lime. This is to avoid the cracking which might occur when the lime hydrates after the bricks have been built in. Experience has shown, however, that when lime particles smaller than 3 mm diameter hydrate they produce only a small 'pock mark' which, provided that there are not many of them, can usually be ignored. Particles larger than this might, if present in any quantity, cause unsightly blemishes or even severe cracking.

A cut (not broken) surface of a brick should show a reasonably uniform texture but this does not imply that the particles should be of uniform size.

The standard for internal quality bricks is less severe and they may not be suitable for fair-faced work; if required for this purpose, this should be specified.

Quality of bricks for elements of brickwork

Table 4 shows the minimum qualities of bricks and the recommended mortars for durability, whilst Table 5 gives the proportions by volume of the mixes recommended in Table 4. These recommendations are illustrated in Fig 2.

Characteristics

Compressive strength

BS 3921 specifies a minimum strength of $5 \cdot 2$ MN/m^2 for bricks; this is sufficient for the loadings in low-rise housing and similar buildings and ensures that the bricks are strong enough to be handled. Higher strength should be specified only when it is going to be used. Table 6 classifies bricks in terms of strength. At the lower end of the range, where the strengths are only about 7 MN/m^2 apart, normal variations will give a wide overlap of strength of individual specimens from different classes. Strength is not necessarily an index of durability. Bricks of Class 7 and upwards are usually durable, but there are bricks approaching this strength which decay rapidly if exposed to freezing in wet conditions and others, very much weaker, which are durable.

Designation	Class	Average compressive strength MN/m^2 not less than	Average absorption (boiling or vacuum) per cent weight, not greater than
Engineering brick	A	69·0	4·5
	B	48·5	7·0
Load-bearing brick	15	103·5	No specific requirements
	10	69·0	
	7	48·5	
	5	34·5	
	4	27·5	
	3	20·5	
	2	14·0	
	1	7·0	

Table 6 Strength and absorption

Fig 2 Minimum qualities of clay brick for various positions

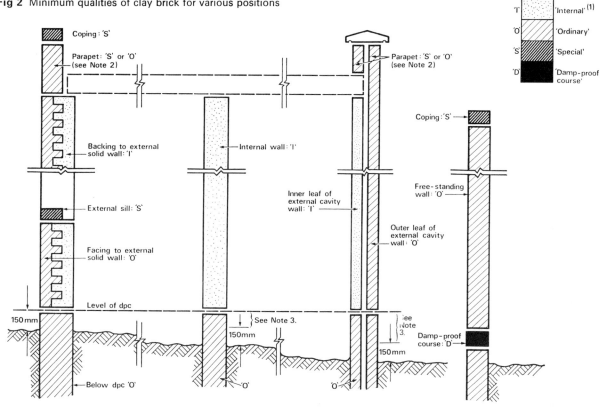

Notes

1 If there is early frost risk, use 'ordinary' quality

2 Parapets: rendered on one side only, 'ordinary'
not rendered, 'special' preferred and necessary
with early frost risk

rendered on both sides, not desirable but if unavoidable use 'special'

3 CP 121 considers this zone to be at greater risk and
suggests the use of 'special' quality bricks

Fire resistance

Schedule 8 of the Building Regulations 1972 groups together clay, concrete and calcium silicate brickwork as having the same order of fire resistance, but there are some differences between Schedule 8 and CP 121 : Part 1 : 1973 for the minimum thickness of unplastered and plastered brick walls. Thus, Schedule 8 provisions will meet the mandatory requirements but CP 121 is also useful because it recommends thicknesses of walls built with bricks in which the perforations exceed the 25 per cent volume limit assumed in Schedule 8.

Absorption

Water absorption does not necessarily indicate the behaviour of a brick in weathering. There are no specific requirements in BS 3921 for the absorption of clay bricks other than engineering bricks (*see* Table 6) and bricks for use as damp-proof courses.

Low absorption, ie less than 7 per cent by weight, usually indicates a high resistance to damage by freezing, although some types of bricks of much higher absorption may also be frost resistant. No simple correlation can be offered—with some types of bricks a range of absorption from 8–12 per cent by weight will cover the range from resistant to non-resistant to frost damage; on the other hand another type of brick with a range of absorptions from 12–18 per cent might still be frost-resistant even at the higher absorption.

Clay brickwork: 2

This digest concludes the comments of the previous issue on the selection of clay bricks and mortars for use with them.

Digests 65 and 66 should now be withdrawn.

Characteristics (continued)

Thermal and moisture movements

Thermal expansion The coefficient of linear thermal expansion of clay brickwork has been taken as 5×10^{-6} per °C; it is, however, difficult to predict accurately the likely movement of a wall because of the restraint due to internal friction or internal restriction. Further, because the two surfaces of a wall are often heated unequally, there may be a tendency to differential movement within the wall thickness. Although thermal movement is, in theory, reversible, this may not be wholly true of brickwork in practice because of friction and other effects.

Moisture expansion As clay bricks cool after firing in the kiln they start to take up atmospheric moisture and expand, at a high rate initially but thereafter decreasing, though the movement may continue at a slow and diminishing rate indefinitely. Measurements made at BRS have shown that a typical brick would be expected to expand by about 0·8 mm per metre in the first eight years, of which about half occurs in the first week. There is considerable variation in behaviour between bricks of different origins; thus, some engineering bricks, if only moderately fired, can have larger expansions of up to, say, 1·6 mm per metre, though if well fired to a low absorption the same bricks will usually give very low expansions.

Recent work suggests that the ratio of brickwork expansion to brick expansion is about 0·6, provided no other source of expansion (such as sulphate expansion of the mortar) is also present, and this is considered later under 'Design'. Superimposed on this moisture movement is a small reversible wetting and drying movement which is not likely to exceed 0·02 per cent. There is no evidence that this reversible expansion lessens with time.

The long-term moisture expansion of bricks and brickwork is not accelerated by dipping the bricks in water and is not reversed when they dry out.

Efflorescence

Very small amounts of salts, usually sulphates, which may be present in the bricks and alkalis from the cement used in the mortar are sufficient to produce an efflorescence during the period when a building is drying out. This is likely to be unsightly rather than harmful and should eventually disappear although sulphate efflorescences may recur in spring and autumn for some years.

Efflorescence is destructive only in exceptional instances where the soluble salts crystallise just below the brick surface which, if weak, may then crumble.

If bricks become saturated before the work is completed, the probability of subsequent efflorescence is increased. Brick stacks should, therefore, be protected from rain at all times; during laying, the bricks should be moistened only to the extent that is found absolutely essential to obtain adequate bond between bricks and mortar; newly built work should be protected from rain. The risk of efflorescence may be reduced by using bricks of low soluble salts content but a more useful indication of behaviour can be obtained by making the efflorescence test described in BS 3921.

The most common places for efflorescence to occur are where brickwork may get wet, for example, parapets and earth-retaining walls, and where deficiencies in design may allow excessive water to get into the brickwork.

Efflorescence should always be dry brushed away before rendering or plastering a wall; wetting it will carry the salts back into the wall to reappear later.

Staining

Some bricks may produce rust stains after building in; the cause is the presence of ferrous salts, often but not necessarily associated with dark-coring. The staining may show on the bricks but is more noticeable on light-coloured mortar joints. The risk of staining is accentuated by saturation during storage or during construction. If staining is likely from the reputation of the bricks, the best safeguard is to keep the bricks as dry as possible. In critical work, it might pay to leave the joints raked back for 6–8 weeks after construction to allow the stain to develop on the raked-back mortar, and subsequently point, wetting the joints as little as possible. With time, the solubility of the iron in the bricks diminishes and further risk of staining is negligible.

Sulphate attack

Sulphate attack on brickwork is the result of the reaction of tricalcium aluminate, present in all ordinary Portland cements, with sulphates in solution. Its effect is an overall expansion of the brickwork due to expansion of the mortar joints, followed in more extreme cases by progressive disintegration of the mortar joints. A vertical expansion of up to 0·2 per cent may occur in facing brickwork and as much as 2 per cent in rendered work; horizontal expansion is rather less but may be more obvious. Serious attack is rarely noticeable in less than two years and can thus usually be distinguished from moisture expansion which becomes apparent, if at all, in the first few months after building.

BS 3921 limits the amount of soluble sulphates only in 'special' quality bricks and it must be assumed, unless the manufacturer can produce reliable evidence to the contrary, that all other quality bricks contribute to sulphate attack.

The effect of sulphate attack on mortars can be minimised by specifying the richer mixes, for example, $1 : 0-\frac{1}{4} : 3$ or $1 : \frac{1}{2} : 4-4\frac{1}{2}$, or (better still) $1 : 5-6$ with plasticiser instead of lime, and by using sulphate-resisting Portland cement, which is low in tricalcium aluminate, supersulphated or, in certain instances, high alumina* cement.

Construction water is not normally sufficient to cause sulphate attack but repeated wetting and drying over a period of years is closely correlated with it. Parapets and free-standing walls are most likely to be affected but in regions exposed to driving rain (*see* Digest 127) all external brickwork is potentially at risk if the other necessary factors are present.

Sulphate attack on brickwork is dealt with in more detail in Digest 89.

Frost resistance

BS 3921 gives only partial guidance on the behaviour of bricks in freezing conditions. Bricks for internal walls are not required to resist frost and may, therefore, need protection if stacked on site during the winter. Bricks of ordinary quality are suitable for exposure in external walls between roof and ground-level damp-proof course and should resist frost for one winter whilst stacked on a building

* Lime must not be added to high alumina cement.

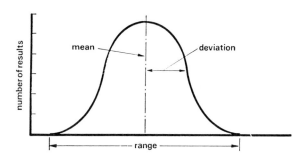

Fig 3 Normal distribution curve

site; it is assumed that in service they are unlikely to be wet enough to be damaged by freezing. Bricks of special quality are suitable for situations where they may become and remain very wet, and may be frozen in that condition.

There is no frost test in BS 3921 but bricks of special quality are deemed to be frost-resistant if they satisfy one of the following requirements:

(*a*) The manufacturer shall provide evidence that bricks of the quality offered have given satisfactory service in conditions at least as severe as those proposed for not less than three years in the locality for which their use is being considered.

(*b*) In the absence of such evidence, sample panels should be built in an exposed position under independent supervision. Bricks that behave satisfactorily for not less than three years can be regarded as frost-resistant.

(*c*) Where neither of the foregoing is possible, a brick that is of engineering classification either as regards strength or water absorption shall be deemed to be frost-resistant.

Over most of the British Isles, frost damage is rare in external walls between damp-proof course and eaves, though it is not uncommon in parapets, free-standing walls and retaining walls where care has not been taken in selecting the bricks. In areas of severe exposure, frost damage can occur between damp-proof course and eaves, and even in window reveals; local experience is often the best guide to the suitability of particular bricks in such areas.

Testing and control

Soluble salts content If a single characteristic such as the soluble salts content of all the bricks in a load were to be determined, the results would give a distribution curve of the form shown in Fig 3; but testing on this scale is clearly impracticable. The result for a single brick might lie anywhere within this range and would therefore be meaningless but BS 3921 reduces to an acceptable level the chances of unrepresentative sampling by requiring the sample for soluble salts analysis to be prepared

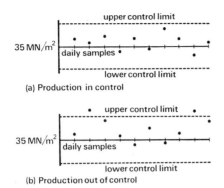

Fig 4 Control charts for strength

from ten bricks, representing a delivery of 2 000 to 10 000 bricks.

Strength In the same way, ten bricks are taken for the compressive strength test. Although it may be found that an individual brick varies by 20 per cent or more from the average, the permissible stresses allowed by CP 111 : Part 2 : 1970 *Structural recommendations for loadbearing walls* take account of this, being based on the average strength of ten bricks. It is, therefore, both unnecessary and uneconomic to insist that every brick is above a certain strength. The quality control charts of a manufacturer (*see* Fig 4) can yield strong evidence as to the consistency of production.

Dimensions Attempts to design in multiples of brick sizes, to avoid cutting, do not always work out on site. Bricks below the intended size, but within the permitted tolerances, may require unsightly thick joints. Bricks above the intended size can be even more troublesome. The Standard suggests that 'where for special reasons closer tolerances are required . . . this can best be done by agreement between the user and the manufacturer and a useful basis of decision will be the routine control charts of brick dimensions'.

Design

Dampness Bricks differ in their tolerance of wet conditions but wet brickwork introduces risks of sulphate attack on mortar, efflorescence and frost damage. Brickwork should, therefore, be designed so that it does not remain excessively wet. This calls for correctly located and effective damp-proof courses, copings, flashings etc (*see* Digest 77).

For brickwork that is liable to be extremely wet for long periods, for example, parapets, free-standing and retaining walls, and chimney stacks, bricks of special quality are preferred. Parapets are seldom trouble-free and, if used, will often dictate the choice of brick for the whole of the external walling, as it will not usually be acceptable architecturally to use one facing up to roof level and a different one for the parapets.

Movement Thermal and moisture movements are discussed on page 66. The moisture expansion of brickwork is, on present evidence, about three-fifths that of the brick; the difference is probably due to restraint, as well as to mortar creep and shrinkage. BS 3921 does not provide a test for moisture expansion. Some manufacturers can provide useful data, but in the absence of this it is suggested that movement joints should provide for a *movement* of 10 mm in a 12 m length of walling. This will accommodate some movement due to sulphate attack but not all of the movement caused by severe sulphate attack. If the brickwork is effectively enclosed within a concrete or reinforced concrete frame, the combined effects of brickwork expansion and frame shrinkage and creep should be considered and appropriate compressible joints should be incorporated at tops, and in some cases at the ends, of the walls or infill panels. Short returns, under 600 mm long, of half-brick thickness are specially vulnerable to cracking as a result of expansion (*see* Digest 75) and should be avoided.

Sulphate attack The risk of sulphate attack can be minimised by providing a generous overhang at eaves and verges, together with flashings and damp-proof courses at sills and elsewhere to prevent the ingress of water from above.

Parapets and free-standing walls should be avoided if possible; if not, these should be built to the recommendations of CP 121 Clause 3.5.3.6, taking the following precautions:

—design copings with generous overhang and adequate drip, with damp-proof course under.

—provide a continuous damp-proof course at roof level in parapets and at the base of free-standing walls, above the expected soil level. To develop bond so as to resist overturning, the latter could be of damp-proof course bricks set in 1 : 3 cement and sand mortar.

—provide movement joints not more than 12 m apart.

—use low-sulphate bricks

—specify mortar mixes according to the previous recommendations, preferably using sulphate-resisting cement.

Earth-retaining walls are most vulnerable to attack and should be built in clay brickwork only if the bricks meet the requirements of BS 3921 for 'special' quality; sulphate-resisting mortar should be used. If, however, cavity construction is adopted, 'ordinary' quality bricks may be acceptable for the outer leaf (*see* Digest 89). Adequate copings and expansion joints should be provided. Drainage holes should be formed through the base of the wall; these must be lined if necessary to avoid conducting water into any cavity present.

Weathering

Natural weathering will usually enhance the appearance of good brickwork but some of the effects of poor detailing and design on appearance are discussed and illustrated in Digest 46.

Cleaning and maintenance

Routine maintenance and cleaning of brickwork is not normally required but if after prolonged exposure to a heavily polluted atmosphere cleaning becomes necessary, the methods described in Digest 113 can be used. The control of lichens, moulds and similar growths is discussed in Digest 139.

Some measures to be taken in the renovation of buildings damaged by floodwater are described in Digest 152.

Should repointing become necessary, the old mortar should be raked out to a depth of at least 20 mm and the mortar used for repointing should not be appreciably stronger than the original bedding mortar.

Ordering

When ordering, bricks should be identified by:

    variety—common, facing
    quality—internal, ordinary, special, engineering*,
    damp-proof course
    type—solid, perforated, hollow, cellular
    size—*see* Fig 1 and Table 2†

If 'internal' quality bricks are required for fair-faced work, this should be stated.

If appropriate, the strength class (*see* Table 5†) should be stated; this is essential for calculated load-bearing brickwork.

If required for facings, the colour and texture should be stated (usually by reference to agreed samples).

* Although defined in BS 3921 as a 'variety' this might more properly be considered as a 'quality'.
† Of Digest 164.

Advisory and technical services

Building Research Advisory Service:

    Building Research Station
    Garston, Watford WD2 7JR
    Telephone: Garston (Herts) 76612
    Telex: 923220

    Birmingham Engineering and Building Centre
    Broad Street, Birmingham B1 2DB
    Telephone: 021-643 8961

    Scottish Laboratory, Kelvin Road
    East Kilbride, Glasgow G75 0RZ
    Telephone: East Kilbride 33941

The Brick Development Association:

    19 Grafton Street, London W1X 3LE
    Telephone: 01-409 1021

Further reading

BRE Digests

46 Design and appearance: 2
61 Strength of brickwork, blockwork and concrete walls
75 Cracking in buildings
77 Damp-proof courses
89 Sulphate attack on brickwork
113 Cleaning external surfaces of buildings
127 An index of exposure to driving rain
139 Control of lichens, moulds and similar growths
160 Mortars for bricklaying

British Standards and Codes of Practice

BS 12 : Pt 2 : 1971 Portland cement (ordinary and rapid-hardening)
BS 476 Fire tests on building materials and structures: Pt 8 : 1972 Test methods and criteria for the fire-resistance of elements of building construction
BS 743 : 1970 Materials for damp-proof courses
BS 890 : 1972 Building lime
BS 915 : Pt 2 : 1972 High alumina cement
BS 1198–1200 : 1955 Building sands from natural sources
BS 3921 : Pt 2 : 1969 Bricks and blocks of fired earth, clay or shale
BS 4027 : Pt 2 : 1972 Sulphate-resisting Portland cement
BS 4248 : 1968 Supersulphated cement
BS 4729 : 1971 Shapes and dimensions of special bricks
CP 111 : Pt 2 : 1970 Structural recommendations for load-bearing walls
CP 121 : Pt 1 : 1973 Brick and block masonry

Calcium silicate (sandlime, flintlime) brickwork

This digest gives guidance on selection of the appropriate classes of calcium silicate bricks and mortars for use in a wide range of conditions of loading, dampness and freezing, internally and externally, above and below ground level. The disposition and methods of forming movement joints, and of making junctions with other materials, are described.

Identification

Generic name

Calcium silicate bricks consist of a uniform mixture of sand, or uncrushed siliceous gravel, or crushed siliceous gravel or rock, or a combination of these, with a lesser proportion of lime, mechanically pressed and the materials chemically bonded by the action of steam under pressure. Suitable pigments may also be included.

Sandlime describes bricks in which only natural sand is used with the lime.

Flintlime bricks contain a substantial proportion of crushed flint.

Classes

BS 187 : Part 2 specifies classes of calcium silicate bricks according to their compressive strength and drying shrinkage (*see* Table 1). The class numbers are a legacy of the values for compressive strength previously quoted in imperial units, viz compressive strength = class number $\times$ 1000 lbf/in^2 (approx).

Uses and limitations

Subject to selection of the appropriate class of brick and mortar, these bricks can give satisfactory service in a wide range of conditions of loading, dampness and freezing, internally and externally, above and below ground (*see* Fig 1 and Table 1). Most manufacturers offer sandlime and flintlime bricks in many colours in each of several classes.

All calcium silicate bricks, except those of Class 1 (which should not be used in wet conditions), are resistant to attack by most sulphate salts in soil and groundwater but where these are present the vulnerability of the mortar to attack must be considered. The bricks may be attacked by high concentrations of magnesium sulphate or of ammonium sulphate sometimes present in industrial wastes used for filling sites. If contaminated by chlorides, eg calcium chloride, common salt or seawater, all classes are liable to suffer if attacked by severe frost.

The drying shrinkage of calcium silicate bricks calls for care in design, in storage and during building—unless they are to be used in permanently damp conditions.

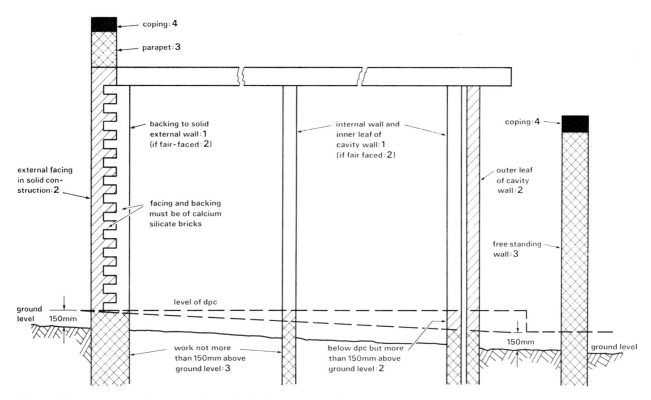

Fig 1 Minimum classes of calcium silicate bricks for various positions

Description

Constituents

Sand and flint aggregates are the major constituents and their suitability depends on the grading, the nature of the surface of the grains and any coatings on them, and the amounts of impurities present. The properties of the aggregates have an important influence on the quality of the bricks.

Either quicklime or hydrated lime is used but hydration must be complete before the bricks are pressed, to avoid expansion during subsequent steam treatment.

Suitable pigments can be incorporated in the mix and a high proportion of the bricks now made in this country are coloured in this way.

Manufacture

Mixing processes vary according to whether ground quicklime or hydrated lime is used. In the *silo or reactor process* ground quicklime and sand are mixed, usually in a screw or pan mixer, with an excess of water beyond that required to hydrate the lime; the mix is then stored in the silo for 3 to 24 hours to hydrate before being remixed and passed to the press. In the *drum hydration* process, ground quicklime and sand are mixed with a small excess of water over that required for hydration of the lime in a

large revolving drum, in the presence of low-pressure steam which increases the temperature and so accelerates hydration. A pan mixer, or a rod mill, is then used to complete the mixing and to incorporate the remaining water necessary for pressing. In processes using dry hydrated lime, the sand and lime are mixed directly in the mixer or mill with the necessary water for pressing.

The bricks are then shaped under high mechanical pressure and put into hardening chambers (autoclaves) into which steam is slowly admitted until the required pressure is attained. The steam pressure is maintained for 4 to 15 hours according to the steam pressure used.

Associated materials

Mortar mixes for use with all classes of brick in various situations are set out in Table 2 (*see also* Digest 160).

Calcium silicate bricks do not impose any restrictions on the selection of materials to be used for damp-proof courses, flashings, ties, metal fastenings etc with which they might be in contact.

Shape and size

Accurate shape and size and square arrises are normal with this type of brick.

Table 1

CLASS	BS 187 : Pt 2 requirements		Suggested uses (it is permissible to use a stronger class of brick than is indicated)		Preferred mortar group for class of brick	
	Average compressive wet strength MN/m²	Maximum drying shrinkage % of original wet length			Frost risk during construction	
					none	present
1	7·0	Not specified	Internal walls	Not available in facing quality	v or iv	iv (air-entrained) or iii
			Inner leaf of cavity walls			iii
			Backing to solid external walls		iv	
2	14·0	2A 0·025 2B*0·035	External walls, outer leaf of cavity walls and facing to solid walls : work below dpc but only if more than 150 mm above ground level		iv	iii
3	20·5	3A 0·025 3B*0·035	Parapet walls, rendered	Brickwork liable to be continuously saturated with water (but not chloride solutions, *see* text) or to be subjected to freezing when saturated	iv iii	iii
			Parapet walls not rendered; external freestanding walls and work below 150 mm above ground level			
4	27·5	0·025	Sills and copings; earth-retaining walls back filled with free-draining material	Unprotected brickwork below ground—but if sulphates are present sulphate-resisting mortar is required	ii	ii
5	34·5	0·025	Calculated load-bearing brickwork wherever these high strengths are essential		to be specified by designer	
7	48·5	0·025				

*Not to be used where the high drying shrinkage would increase the risk of crack formation. Suitable therefore for piers, unrestrained or partially restrained infill panels of short length and short internal walls not restrained at both ends. Not to be used with mortars stronger than group iv—except that group iii may be used when there is risk of freezing.

Table 2 Mortar mixes (proportions by volume)

	Mortar group	Cement : lime : sand	Masonry-cement : sand	Cement : sand, with plasticiser
Increasing strength but decreasing ability to accommodate movements caused by settlement, shrinkage, etc	i	1 : 0–¼ : 3	—	—
	ii	1 : ½ : 4–4½	1 : 2½–3½	1 : 3–4
	iii	1 : 1 : 5–6	1 : 4–5	1 : 5–6
	iv	1 : 2 : 8–9	1 : 5½–6½	1 : 7–8
	v	1 : 3 : 10–12	1 : 6½–7	1 : 8

Direction of changes in properties:

← equivalent strengths → within each group

increasing frost resistance →

← improving bond and resistance to rain penetration

Where a range of sand contents is given, the larger quantity should be used for sand that is well graded and the smaller for coarse or uniformly fine sand.

Because damp sands bulk, the volume of damp sand used may need to be increased. For cement : lime : sand mixes, the error due to bulking is reduced if the mortar is prepared from lime : sand coarse stuff and cement in appropriate proportions; in these mixes 'lime' refers to non-hydraulic or semi-hydraulic lime and the proportions given are for lime putty. If hydrated lime is batched dry, the volume may be increased by up to 50 per cent to get adequate workability.

The work sizes and co-ordinating sizes (ie inclusive of mortar joint) of bricks to BS 187 : Part 2 are shown in Fig 2. The Standard specifies the following limits of manufacturing sizes:

	maximum mm	minimum mm
length	217	212
width	105	101
height	67	63

Bricks of co-ordinating sizes are available from some manufacturers. The sizes are likely to follow the recommendations of DD . . . *Clay bricks with modular dimensions* (in course of preparation) viz:

Designation	Work sizes length	width	height
mm	*mm*	*mm*	*mm*
300×100×100	290	90	90
200×100×100	190	90	90
300×100×75	290	90	65
200×100×75	190	90	65

Weight

Calcium silicate brickwork as laid weighs about 2 tonnes per cubic metre ($= 2$ kg/m^2 per mm thickness).

Appearance

The basic colours are white, off-white, cream or pale pink but facings are available in various pastel shades and darker hues. The white bricks in particular provide moderately good light reflectance when laid flush as facings to internal surfaces or to light wells and enclosed courts, without further applied decoration. All the colours deepen considerably when wet.

The surfaces of sandlime bricks are usually smoother than clay bricks but textured facings are available from some makers.

All bricks except those of Class 1 are required by the Standard to be free from visible cracks and noticeable balls of clay, loam and lime.

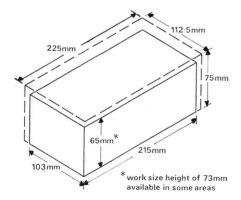

Fig 2 Work sizes (firm lines) and co-ordinating sizes (broken lines) of bricks to BS 187 : Part 2

Characteristics

Strength

The strengths given in Table 1 are average compressive strengths when wet; the strength of dry calcium silicate bricks is 30–50 per cent higher than when saturated.

Fire resistance

Schedule 8 of the Building Regulations 1972 groups together clay, concrete and calcium silicate brickwork as having the same order of fire resistance.

Gases

The only gases normally present in the atmosphere which affect calcium silicate bricks are sulphur dioxide and carbon dioxide. Prolonged exposure to moist air containing sulphur dioxide decomposes the hydrated calcium silicate cementing agent and forms finally a skin of calcium sulphate (gypsum) and hydrated silica. Above ground, atmospheric carbonation, which occurs in depth slowly with age, slightly increases the strength but causes slight shrinkage.

Liquids

Absorption The total water absorption is usually 7–16 per cent (by weight), similar to some clay, other than engineering, bricks.

Moisture movements The drying shrinkage of bricks to BS 187 : Part 2 should not exceed 0·025 per cent of the original wet length, except for bricks of classes 2B and 3B for which the limit is 0·035 per cent and class 1 for which no limit is specified (*see* Table 1). Subsequent expansion on wetting is likely to be about the same.

Thermal

Thermal conductivity The thermal conductivity (k value) of masonry of density 2000 kg/m^3 (from IHVE Guide) is:

at 1% moisture content* (= 'protected' situations):

0·92 W/m °C

at 5% moisture content* (= 'exposed' situations):

1·24 W/m °C

*moisture content by volume

Thermal expansion The coefficient of linear expansion is about 8 to 14×10^{-6} per °C, which is about one-and-a-half times that of fired clay bricks. This value is for the material in the unrestrained condition and for an area of walling it will be rather less.

Durability

The resistance of calcium silicate bricks to frost action is related mainly to their mechanical strength and this has been taken into account in making the recommendations set out in Table 1 and Fig 1.

They normally contain no soluble salts such as produce efflorescence on some clay bricks.

Exposure to salt spray causes some erosion of the surface, probably as a result of the repeated crystallisation of the salt with which they become impregnated, with alternate wetting and drying. They are not recommended for use where liable to exposure to sea-spray.

Working characteristics
The bricks can be cut readily to form closers etc but purpose-made bricks to BS 4729 : 1971 can be obtained for many special purposes and, when available, should be used particularly in facing work.

The bricks do not take nails or screws directly, but they are easily drilled to receive plugs for these; they will quickly take the edge off masonry drills unless the detritus is cleared regularly from around the drill point.

Design

Movement joints
Below damp-proof course Brickwork below damp-proof course usually remains fairly wet; moisture movement, if any, is very slight and movement joints are not normally required.

External walls Vertical movement joints should be provided above damp-proof course at intervals of 7·5–9 m, subject to the shape of the panel and the disposition of any openings. The lines at which changes in height or thickness occur are lines of potential cracking; the higher the proportion of the length of a panel to its height, the greater is the risk of cracks developing in it.

Permanent movement joints, to remain in place throughout the life of the building, are formed by butting the bricks against a suitable separator, eg a 10 or 13 mm thick strip of joint filler, or bituminous felt, polythene sheeting or building paper, and pointing with a suitable mastic or sealant of matching or contrasting colour. They are always visible since, unless they have been constructed in toothed form, they break the bond but it is sometimes possible to locate them so that they are to some extent masked by an architectural feature. Where the use of non-setting mastic is undesirable, for example where it might be subject to deliberate damage, the joint may be pointed with mortar but this should be done as late as possible in the construction of the building. Alternatively, a self-curing sealant may be used but this may be more expensive; if so, its use is likely to be confined to the lowest one or two metres of walling.

An alternative method of forming a straight vertical joint is to leave a 10 mm gap severing the wall. A convenient way of doing this is to build in three thicknesses of 3 mm plywood or hardboard, the middle strip being wider and left projecting to allow for easy removal and release of the other two. The gap is then sealed with a preformed strip mastic or with pre-compressed foamed plastics.

Probably the least conspicuous method is to incorporate a continuous strip of clear polythene sheeting, say of 250 gauge, and of the same width as the thickness of the brick leaf or wall, following the mortar joints in toothed fashion.

Temporary movement joints may be left during construction, until the initial 'settling down and drying out' period is over. The joints are toothed to follow the bond or lap of the brickwork and formed with a mortar of low strength, eg a 1 : 3 to 1 : 4½ mix (by volume) of non-hydraulic lime and sand. After drying and settling down, the lime–sand mortar joints are deeply raked out and repointed with the same mortar as used in the rest of the work.

Permanent joints are preferred if the brickwork is to be pointed as the work proceeds.

Internal walls Internal walls built in mortar mix v (Table 2) do not require movement joints provided that they can be allowed to dry out before plastering. If, however, they must be plastered before the brickwork has dried out, or if they are built in a stronger mortar, movement joints should be provided.

Stability Care should be taken to ensure the stability of walls, especially those straight on plan, both during and after construction. Where necessary, sleeved dowels of constant cross-section, or other suitable fixings, may be used to span the movement joints, giving lateral support without restraining movement in the plane of the wall.

Junctions with other walling materials
Where calcium silicate bricks are to be used for one face of a solid wall, the bricks used for backing and for the other face should also be of calcium silicate or other material of comparable drying shrinkage and not clay bricks.

Where clay bricks are to be used in conjunction with calcium silicate facings, it is necessary to cater for differential movement between the two materials by constructing the wall in two leaves. These may be tied together with the normal complement of butterfly type wall ties but they must be separated, including all edges, with, for example, polythene sheeting or a cavity. If the cavity is to be narrower than 50 mm, special measures should be taken to avoid filling it with mortar. A separating membrane should be provided around all openings. The vertical damp-proof course of bituminous felt or polythene normally used in these positions in cavity external walls will generally perform this function but it is necessary to separate the two walling materials even where a vertical damp-proof course is not otherwise required. Cavity construction has a number of advantages for external walls, including better resistance to the weather; irrespective of the type of brick used, even a one-and-a-half brick thick solid wall, unless it is rendered externally or clad, will not be sufficiently resistant to rain penetration except in sheltered conditions.

All internal walls of calcium silicate brickwork, even those on upper floors, should be bedded on a damp-proof course or a strip of polythene sheeting. At all levels where clay bricks are bedded on calcium silicate brickwork, a similar measure should be taken so as to allow small longitudinal sliding movements to occur without undue restraint.

New brickwork should not generally be toothed and bonded to existing; a straight vertical movement joint, as previously described, should be interposed. This will allow the normal differential movement between the old work and the new to occur without adverse effect.

Junctions with concrete

Concrete-encased or reinforced concrete beams, lintels or slabs should not be bedded or cast directly on to calcium silicate brickwork, particularly facing brickwork, since the restraint afforded by the concrete may encourage the brickwork to crack, or differential movement between the concrete and the brickwork may cause a ragged horizontal crack at the junction. The two materials should be separated by, for example, two thicknesses of polythene sheeting; the special polythene sheeting made to give a low coefficient of friction is particularly suitable for this. For the slip plane to be fully effective, the top of the wall should be flushed up with mortar, trowelled smooth and allowed to harden, before the slip plane and concrete are placed. In external walls, a waterproof membrane at this level will also reduce or eliminate temporary darkening of the brickwork by wetting and any staining by lime or other substances that may be leached out of the concrete by the weather. A further precaution against these effects is to place a projecting drip of a stiff material (which may extend to the full width of the wall or leaf to act as the slip plane) at the junction; this will also help to prevent grout runs when casting in situ concrete. If considerations of lateral stability so dictate, the slip plane may be pierced at intervals and bridged vertically by butterfly type wire wall ties.

It is not advisable to place, or cast in situ, concrete encased or reinforced concrete columns directly against calcium silicate brickwork, or even to 'butter'

the brickwork against the columns with mortar. The two materials should be separated by a slip plane, as described above.

When building up to the underside of beams or slabs, bituminous felt or some similar material should be interposed. If necessary for lateral stability, the sheeting may be pierced at intervals and bridged by wire ties, or some other suitable measures taken. For example, to assist with lateral restraint at the tops of walls, channels a little wider than the thickness of the wall can be formed in the concrete soffits and the brickwork built into them. Alternatively, dovetailed masonry fixings, consisting of proprietary slots and anchors, could be used. The metal slots should be cast into the concrete, so as to allow movement in the direction of the wall length, and the anchors placed at about 600 mm (maximum) centres. The anchors can be inserted in the slots as bricklaying proceeds, taken through the slip plane and bedded in the vertical joints of the brickwork.

Copings

If a brick-on-edge coping is to be used at the top of an external wall, a continuous damp-proof course of stiff material should be bedded immediately under the coping and should project to form a drip 25 mm or more beyond each face of the wall. A concrete coping (as BS 3798), preferably wide enough to oversail each face of the brickwork by about 50 mm and drip throated, used in conjunction with a damp-proof course, will give better protection than a brick-on-edge coping.

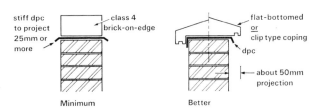

Fig 3 Copings

Applied finishes

Tiling, plastering and rendering should not be carried over permanent movement joints, or across any junction with a different material where relative movement is to be expected. At these points each coat of plastering or rendering should either be severed by a straight cut, before the work hardens, or worked up to each side of a batten, temporarily or permanently secured at the edge of the joint. The joints can be covered by battens and strips (fastened to one side only of the joint) or by patent coverings, or filled with a sealant or mastic. Similar measures should be taken with wall tiling.

Sitework

Storage

To minimise drying shrinkage, the bricks should be reasonably dry when laid. Where manufacturers take steps to ensure delivery in such a condition, the benefit will be largely lost if the bricks are allowed to become wet on the site. They should, therefore, be stacked under cover or protected from rain by covering with polythene sheeting or other waterproof material.

Laying

Individual makes and classes of brick vary in their suction and absorption characteristics and the craftsman must adjust his technique accordingly. Bricks of high suction may need to be dampened before laying, particularly during hot weather, to prevent too much water being removed from the mortar; or, better, the consistency of the mortar should be adjusted to suit the suction of the units, if necessary by using water-retaining admixtures, rather than wetting the units to suit the mortar.

Protection after laying

Partly completed work, left overnight or longer, should be protected from rain.

Cleaning and maintenance

Grease, oil and general dirt can be removed with a scrubbing brush and warm water containing detergent.

Ordering

When ordering, the purchaser should specify:

class
size
whether required for facing
colour
texture
if certification to BS 187 : Part 2 is required

Further information

British Standards Institution

BS 187 Part 2 : 1970 (Metric units) *Calcium silicate (sand-lime and flintlime) bricks*

CP 121 Walling : Part 1 *Brick and block masonry*

PD ... (in course of preparation) *Guide to specifying the quality of building mortars*

BRE Digests

49	*Choosing specifications for plastering*
61	*Strength of brickwork, blockwork and concrete walls*
75	*Cracking in buildings*
108	*Standardised U-values*
113	*Cleaning external surfaces of buildings*
139	*Control of lichens, moulds and similar growths*
160	*Mortars for bricklaying*
197—8	*Painting walls*

Other HMSO publications

Advisory Leaflet No 27 *Rendering outside walls* (DOE)
Winter building (DOE)

Sulphate attack on brickwork

This digest shows how to recognise sulphate attack on brickwork, and indicates ways in which it can be remedied in existing construction and prevented in new work.

The tricalcium aluminate constituent in ordinary Portland cements can react with sulphates in solution to form a compound called calcium sulphoaluminate or 'Ettringite', the reaction being accompanied by expansion. When it occurs in brickwork mortars, the effect is first an overall expansion of the brickwork, which can be followed later in more extreme cases by progressive disintegration of the mortar joints. Except for the special case of earth-retaining walls in brickwork, where the attacking sulphates could be derived from the groundwater, the source of sulphates is usually the soluble salts present to varying extents in most types of clay brick. The sulphates can only be transferred from the bricks to the mortar joints by percolating water—usually incident rain-water—so that sulphate attack is normally confined to external brickwork. Renderings based on Portland cement may also be affected by sulphates, though their failure when used on high-sulphate bricks is more frequently due to attack and expansion of the backing brickwork. This expansion is usually a secondary effect following the entry of water into the brickwork through defects or shrinkage cracks in the rendering.

Facing brickwork

Initially, the only evidence of sulphate attack may be horizontal cracking on the inner face of the wall, due to this being put in tension by the expansion of the outer leaf. At this stage, the mortar of the outer leaf shows little sign of damage, and may even have hardened slightly. In normal cavity work with metal ties the horizontal cracking is usually concentrated near the roof but in solid brickwork with brick ties cracking may also occur lower down (Fig 1). Sometimes differential movement can occur between the faces of brickwork; the consequent bowing of walls is a means of relieving the compression. In long stretches of brickwork some oversailing of the damp-proof course usually occurs since in practice sulphate expansion is usually less below the dpc, possibly due to restraint from the foundations (Fig 2). (This oversailing can usually be distinguished from a similar effect due to moisture expansion of the bricks by considering the time factor, discussed later.) As sulphate attack proceeds, the mortar joints take on a whitish appearance, and a narrow crack may appear in the middle of the joints (Fig 3). Later

Fig 1

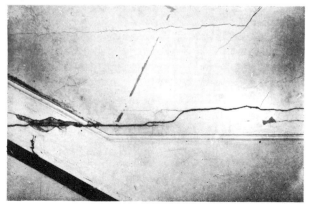

Fig 2

Fig 3

Fig 4

still, the surface of the joint spalls off, and the mortar is reduced to the strength and consistency of a very weak lime mortar. Spalling of facing bricks occasionally accompanies the advanced stages of attack, where comparatively friable bricks have been involved; this is usually a secondary effect due to transfer of excessive load on to the outer leaf of brickwork, which in turn is concentrated on the outer faces of the bricks where the mortar joints have expanded most (Fig 4).

Chimney stacks

In the past many cases have been reported of sulphate attack on unlined chimney stacks serving slow-burning appliances. The provision of liners considerably reduces the risk of attack which is caused mainly by condensation from flue gases (*see* Digest 60).

Rendered brickwork

Except in positions where very high rainfall is combined with little opportunity for drying out, properly designed and executed renderings (to BS CP 221 : 1960) will prevent the penetration of rain into the underlying brickwork. However, if rain can penetrate the rendering through cracks or poor detailing, it may become trapped and saturate the brickwork

Fig 5

for long periods. Sulphate attack may result causing expansion of the brickwork (Fig 5), and extensive areas of rendering may become detached. Sulphate crystals may be found adhering to the back faces of pieces of detached rendering. Usually, the rendering itself remains comparatively unaffected chemically; it is the expansion of the backing brickwork which has caused it to become detached. The fine map cracking due to drying shrinkage of a rendering is easily distinguishable from the horizontal and vertical cracking associated with expansion of mortar joints from sulphate attack.

The time factor

Only in exceptional circumstances is sulphate expansion seriously in evidence in under two years. Hence the oversailing at damp-proof course level due to sulphate attack can usually be distinguished from that caused by moisture expansion of bricks, since the latter is only likely to occur in the first few months after a building is erected.

Amount of expansion

A vertical expansion of up to 0.2 per cent is commonly found with sulphation of the mortar in facing brickwork; although in rare circumstances with rendered work, as much as 2 per cent has been seen.

Conditions necessary for sulphate attack

For sulphate attack to occur, three materials must be present simultaneously: tricalcium aluminate, soluble sulphates and water.

Tricalcium aluminate—This is present in ordinary Portland cement in amounts from under 8 per cent to over 13 per cent. Since, in general, the greater the amount of tricalcium aluminate in a cement the lower will be its resistance to sulphate attack, the susceptibility of ordinary Portland cement is somewhat variable; some varieties have quite high resistance. There is, however, no easy way whereby the user can estimate susceptibility (the brand-name is no guide), so that it must be assumed that all ordinary Portland cements are capable of being attacked. Sulphate-resisting Portland cements, on the other hand, have a very low tricalcium aluminate content and give a positive guarantee of resistance. Supersulphated and high alumina cements also have high resistance to sulphates.

It cannot be assumed that the greater the amount of reactive cement in a mortar mix the more liable it will be to attack; in practice a rich mix such as $1 : \frac{1}{2} : 4\frac{1}{2}$ is much more resistant than the weaker, more porous $1 : 1 : 6$ mix. The reason for this is not fully understood, though the porosity probably has an important effect.

Soluble sulphates. These are present in almost all fired clay bricks, although the amount may vary widely between different types and even between individual bricks of the same type. BS 3921 limits the amount which can be present in bricks of 'special quality' but does not specify maximum permissible amounts of sulphate for bricks of ' ordinary quality'. In all but the most abnormal conditions of design and exposure 'special quality' bricks should never promote sulphate attack. Most bricks, however, cannot meet the sulphate limitations of the 'special quality' classification, and unless the brick manu-facturer can produce evidence, in the form of control charts of sulphate content, that his bricks con-sistently satisfy the British Standard limits in this respect, it must be assumed that they may contribute to sulphate attack. (BS 3921 is discussed in greater detail in Digests 164 and 165).

Water. This is always present in brickwork during construction, but although often taking considerable time to dry out it appears insufficient by itself to cause sulphate attack. It is good practice to avoid saturation of brickwork during construction in order to limit troubles due to efflorescence. Repeated wetting and drying over a period of years is closely correlated with sulphate attack, the severity of which depends on the exposure to wet weather. Parapets and free-standing walls, which tend to get wet more often than normally protected walls between eaves and foundations, are more likely to be affected. Exceptionally, in regions exposed to driving rain, all brickwork is subject to considerable wetting; some guidance to the worst areas of driving rain can be found in Digest 127.

The most vulnerable form of brickwork is the earth-retaining wall, where water is sometimes allowed to pass continuously through the brickwork from the earth fill. Evidently the amount of water movement through brickwork is an important factor determining the susceptibility to attack. It should be noted that garden walls commonly retain some earth and so are frequently attacked.

Preventing sulphate attack in new work

Ideally, low sulphate content bricks that satisfy the provisions of BS 3921 for soluble salts should be used, but this is a perfection that may either not be justified or possible. In general terms extra pre-cautions should be taken either to increase the resistance of the mortars and renderings to sulphate attack or to limit the extent to which the brickwork becomes and remains wet, eg by improved design, as discussed later; in cases of exceptional risk (for example, in areas of excessive driving rain) both methods should be applied.

Sulphate-resisting mortars and renderings

The sulphate resistance of mortars can be increased in two ways: (1) by specifying the richer mixes, for example: $1 : 0-\frac{1}{4} : 3$ or $1 : \frac{1}{2} : 4-4\frac{1}{2}$, or (better still) $1 : 5-6$ with plasticiser in place of lime, and (2) by using sulphate-resisting Portland, supersulphated or high alumina* cements.

The sulphate resistance of renderings can be improved by the use of sulphate-resisting Portland cement. It is of greater importance, however, to avoid the penetration of moisture to the backing brickwork and to allow any that does penetrate to evaporate. Renderings based on strong mixes, particularly if given a trowelled finish, are prone to shrinkage cracking and reduce the drying rate of the brick-work. Aerated renderings may allow rain penetration into the brickwork, especially if used on absorptive bricks.

Improved design

In most areas, undue wetting of the structure can be avoided by attention to design details. For facing brickwork, accepted (though by no means univer-sally employed) measures are:
1 To provide generous overhang at eaves and verges;
2 To provide flashings and damp-proof courses at cills and elsewhere so as to prevent ingress of water from above;
3 To avoid parapets and free-standing walls unless special precautions are taken. These are:
  (a) To use low-sulphate bricks;
  (b) To design copings with generous overhang and adequate drip, with damp-proof courses under;
  (c) To provide damp-proof courses at bases of free-standing walls, i.e. above expected soil levels, and at roof level in parapets;

---

* High alumina cements should not be used with lime addi-tions, though ground limestone may be used.

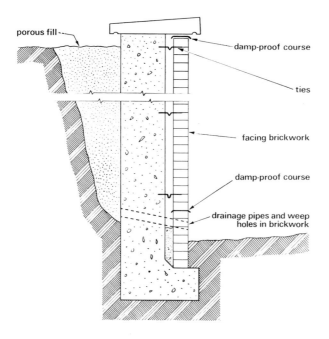

porous fill

damp-proof course

ties

facing brickwork

damp-proof course

drainage pipes and weep holes in brickwork

Fig 6

(d) To provide expansion joints not more than 12 m apart;

(e) To specify mortar mixes in accordance with the previous section.

Earth-retaining walls should be built only in fired clay brickwork if bricks wholly conforming to the 'special quality' of BS 3921 are used in conjunction with sulphate-resisting mortar mixes (eg 1 : $\frac{1}{2}$: $4\frac{1}{2}$ or stronger, and preferably containing a sulphate-resisting cement). If bricks containing appreciable amounts of sulphates must be used, as for example where it is necessary to match the remainder of a building scheme, the retaining wall can be built of *in situ* concrete, without a batter, with the facing brick layer separated from it by a cavity (Fig 6). Adequate copings and expansion joints should be provided as for parapet walls, and weep holes should be incorporated at the base of the cavity,

taking care to ensure that any drainage also provided for the retained earth does not vent into the cavity.

Remedying existing sulphate attack

Where brickwork has already been affected by sulphates the remedies to be applied depend on the extent of the damage, but all are based on the need to allow the work to dry out and thereafter to exclude moisture as far as possible. In all cases obviously poor design features must be remedied by taking the precautions outlined for new work.

Where expansion affects only particularly vulnerable details such as parapets it may be sufficient merely to correct the detailing and to cut one or two expansion joints in appropriate places.

Where attack is slightly more severe, but has taken some years to develop, and shows only as an expansion of the exterior walling without visible damage to the mortar, an experimental application of surface waterproofer may be tried, applying this to the brickwork when it is reasonably dry. Similar applications have been successful in minimising further expansion, though there is a slight risk of soft-fired bricks spalling because of crystallisation of sulphates behind the face. The waterproofer will have to be renewed at intervals of a few years in accordance with the manufacturer's recommendations (*see* Digest 125).

Where the sulphate attack is advanced and, in addition to brickwork expansion, the mortar is already showing severe damage, some form of cladding should be applied. Weather-boarding or tile hanging are suitable. Similar action should be taken where renderings have failed extensively; it is not sufficient merely to replace the rendering, which is likely to fail again due to the continued expansion of the backing brickwork. Wherever it is necessary to rebuild features completely, every effort should be made to use materials which are more suitable to the conditions.

Decay and conservation of stone masonry

The durability of a stone is influenced mainly by its internal structure, though the nature of the cementing material that binds together the particles of sedimentary rocks, limestones and sandstones, also affects their performance. The most common cause of decay of stone in the UK is the crystallisation of salts within the pores; frost damage and other forms of attack also occur.

The mechanism of various forms of decay is discussed briefly in this digest, together with some methods of maintenance, stain removal, preservation and restoration.

Types of stone

Natural building stones may be obtained from igneous, sedimentary or metamorphic rocks. Igneous rock was formed by the cooling and solidification of molten material known as magma. The igneous stone that is most commonly used for building in Britain is granite; this is, technically, a coarse-grained, crystalline rock with more than 66 per cent silica in its chemical composition. In mineral composition, granites consist mainly of quartz, mica and felspars. Their porosity is usually very low and this, together with their mineral composition, accounts for their high resistance to weathering. In the building industry, the term granite is also applied to igneous rocks containing lower proportions of silica and sometimes to very hard rocks of quite different composition.

Sedimentary rocks provide the main British building stones, ie the limestones and sandstones. The original deposits from which they were formed consisted of loose, uncemented particles produced, for example, by the weathering of earlier rock, by accumulation of animal skeletons or by chemical deposition in lakes or seas. In the course of time, the sediments became cemented together to form porous, coherent masses. Although the nature of the cementing material has a strong bearing on the durability of some types, the internal structure of the stone is generally of greater importance. Limestones consist mainly of calcium carbonate; sandstones of quartz.

Metamorphic rocks were produced from sedimentary deposits by the action of heat and pressure within the earth's crust. Slate and marble are the only metamorphic stones that are commonly used for building in Britain. Slates were formed from clay deposits and marbles were formed by the crystallisation of limestones. There are only two true marbles in the British Isles, but some dense limestones will take a polish and, in the building industry, these are often referred to as marbles.

Causes of decay

Crystallisation of salts When salts crystallise within the pores of a stone, stresses may be generated that are sufficiently large to cause local fragmentation of the stone. This process is the major cause of stone decay in the British Isles. The salts may get into the stone in a number of ways, one of the more important being the ultimate production of calcium sulphate by the reaction of limestones with sulphur dioxide dissolved in rainwater. This can lead to two types of decay. In the features of a limestone building that are frequently wetted by rain, the repeated crystallisation of the calcium sulphate dislodges particles of stone which are subsequently washed off, together with the calcium sulphate, during very heavy rainfall. The surface of the stone therefore erodes gradually. In more sheltered parts, the calcium sulphate remains in position to form a hard and often dirty skin. With certain types of stone, this skin eventually blisters to reveal an underlying layer of crumbling debris.

The calcium sulphate that is washed out of limestones may cause crystallisation damage to other building materials that can absorb the contaminated rain-washings. Damage may also be caused by washings containing magnesium sulphate, formed by reaction of sulphur dioxide with magnesian limestones. For this reason, limestone should not be used in association with sandstone or brickwork in such a way that sulphates from the limestone may be picked up by these materials.

Other common sources of salts include groundwater, sea spray and unsuitable cleaning materials. Crystallisation damage caused by freely soluble salts such as sodium chloride, sodium sulphate or sodium hydroxide normally consists of a powdering and crumbling of the entire surface of the contaminated stones. When magnesian limestone is attacked by magnesium sulphate, deep cavities may be formed.

Some stones are virtually immune to crystallisation damage whereas others are liable to quite rapid decay; resistance is strongly dependent on the internal structure of the stone and decreases as the proportion of fine pores increases.

In this country, the mechanical removal of stone by wind-borne particles occurs only in exceptional circumstances, if at all, and most instances of decay that are attributed to wind erosion are probably due to crystallisation of salts. Any increase in the rate of decay in areas that are severely exposed to wind is usually due to the increased rate of evaporation which leads to an accumulation of salts and a higher frequency of crystallisation cycles.

Chemical attack Although chemical attack on stone can lead to the formation of salts, and thus contribute to crystallisation damage, chemical attack on its own is a major cause of decay only in special instances. One such, is the decay of calcareous sandstones, which consist of grains of silica bound solely by calcium carbonate. Sulphur dioxide and carbon dioxide dissolved in rainwater react with the calcium carbonate and the loss of a very small amount of carbonate results in the loss of a large number of silica grains.

Contour scaling Air pollution of a different kind is believed to be responsible for the 'contour scaling' of sandstones. A surface crust, following the contours of the surface rather than the bedding planes of the stone, breaks away at a depth of 5–20 mm. The crust is always found to have its pores blocked with calcium sulphate, even when the stone contains no calcium carbonate. This is believed to be the result of direct pollution with calcium sulphate, the fracture being caused by shear stresses arising from differences in the moisture movement or in the thermal expansion of the choked skin and the underlying stone.

Frost Frost damage occurs only in those features of a building that are frequently frozen whilst very wet and, in the British Isles, rarely occurs between damp-proof course and eaves. Frost may provide the 'last straw' that dislodges pieces of stone that have already been loosened by some other means, but this is readily distinguished from the spectacular cracking that occurs when frost is the sole cause of the damage. As with salt crystallisation damage, the susceptibility of a stone to frost damage is governed by its pore structure. This is partly because the pore structure governs the natural degree of saturation and

partly because it governs the magnitude of the stresses that can be generated upon freezing. Most sandstones are immune to frost damage in this country.

Organic growths There is no evidence that bacteria or other micro-organisms play more than a small part in most instances of stone decay, but higher organisms such as lichens and plants can contribute to decay in some circumstances. For example, the acidic metabolic products of lichens can etch limestones, mosses can cause damage by forming reservoirs and the aerial roots of ivy can dislodge mortar from joints. However, the effects of lichens and algae are rarely serious and their presence is usually considered to enhance the appearance of stonework.

Other factors contributing to decay Sedimentary rocks have a natural bed and blocks of stone should usually be laid so that the bed is normal to the load. Face bedding, in which the bed lies parallel to the face of the wall, can lead to an increased rate of decay although it is not actually a cause of decay. The bedding planes constitute planes of weakness and the stone is more susceptible to crystallisation damage and other types of decay if the bedding layers are not restrained by the surrounding stonework.

A dense pointing mortar can also cause increased crystallisation damage by restricting the movement of water through it so that little evaporation can take place at the joints. Moisture in the wall must then evaporate from the stone itself and any salts will accumulate in the stone. Increased crystallisation damage will therefore occur. Since it is normally cheaper to repoint than to replace decayed stone, it is advisable to use a slightly permeable mortar which will deteriorate in preference to the stone. Suitable mixes are considered below.

The corrosion of steel or cast iron fixings can cause spalling of stonework. Dowels and fixings should, therefore, be made of non-ferrous metal or stainless steel as recommended in CP 121:Part 2.[1]

Conservation techniques

Cleaning The cleaning of exterior stonework is the subject of Digest 113.[2] Although unsuitable cleaning techniques or unskilled execution may damage stonework, there is no evidence that proper cleaning is harmful. On the contrary, by removing some of the soluble salts which cause decay it may prolong the life of the stone.

Stain removal Stains may be removed either by extracting the staining material with a suitable solvent, or by bleaching. In either case, it may be beneficial to apply the treatment as a poultice in an inert powder such as whiting or talc. The poultice serves to absorb the staining material or to prolong contact of the bleach with the stone. It will usually be necessary to experiment on an inconspicuous area until an effective treatment is found. More than one application might be needed.

Oil stains may be removed by using solvents such as carbon tetrachloride, dichloromethane, white spirit or proprietary dry cleaning agents. Precautions against fire or inhalation should be taken as necessary.

Copper stains can sometimes be removed by treatment with ammonia solution. Several applications may be needed and the stains are liable to reappear. The stone should be wetted with water before the ammonia is applied and should be washed down thoroughly afterwards.

Iron stains on granite or sandstone may be removed by the application of orthophosphoric acid. This cannot be used, however, on limestones, marbles or calcareous sandstones, which would be attacked by the acid, but it may be possible to bleach the stains on these stones with a solution of sodium hydrosulphite. However, it should be emphasised that this treatment may leave salts in the stone that could subsequently cause severe crystallisation damage. It is, therefore, essential to saturate the stone with water before applying the hydrosulphite solution, and to wash down thoroughly afterwards.

Stains caused by organic materials can sometimes be bleached with a solution of hydrogen peroxide. This is preferable to household bleach for this purpose as it does not leave any harmful residue in the stone.

The removal of graffiti written in paint or with a felt-tipped pen can be particularly difficult. Solvent systems may be successful, particularly when combined with the use of a high-pressure water jet or poulticing, but there is a considerable risk that the paint or ink will be absorbed more deeply into a porous stone. Mechanical cleaning is probably more reliable. Both techniques are liable to leave a conspicuous clean patch, but this can sometimes be toned down by rubbing in a fine masonry dust of the appropriate colour.

Organic growths Removal of biological growths, lichens, moulds and similar, is discussed in Digest 139.[4] The following procedure has been found to be particularly effective for removing and inhibiting growths on exterior masonry:

   apply a 1 per cent aqueous solution of a quaternary ammonium compound, preferably during the spring or autumn growing season. Moss and lichen should be saturated with the solution;

   leave for two weeks;

   remove dead growth with a stiff nylon brush and clean running water. A high-pressure water jet may be used where practicable;

after a drying period, apply an inhibitory treatment of tributyl tin oxide and a quaternary ammonium compound.

Stone preservation

Removal of soluble salts

The repeated crystallisation of salts is the most common cause of stone decay in the UK and the removal of these salts is one of several approaches to preservation. Washing with water may remove some of the salts but a proportion will be driven into the stone only to reappear at the surface as the stone dries out. A more thorough technique involves wetting the stone thoroughly and then applying a poultice of wet powdered clay. Attapulgus has been found to be more suitable for this purpose than sepiolite. As the stone subsequently dries, the salts are drawn into the poultice which is eventually removed. The operation is lengthy and may need to be repeated several times; it is only worth while if the source of the salts can be eliminated and this should always be done if possible.

Colourless preservative treatments

Water-repellent surface treatments are discussed in Digest 125.[3] Since water is involved in almost every type of stone decay, such treatments might appear to be promising preservatives. However, neither they nor any other colourless shallow treatments have been found to have any long-term preservative effect in most circumstances.[5] On the contrary, they may even accelerate decay. There are two main reasons for this. First, water will invariably get behind the treated layer, either by passing through it in the vapour phase or by absorption of rain or groundwater at some unprotected point. The water evaporates from behind the treated layer and any salts in solution crystallise there. This may lead to spalling of the treated surface. Secondly, the thermal and moisture movements of the thin surface layer may be sufficiently different from those of the underlying stone to generate shear stresses that eventually cause failure.

A more promising approach to preservation is the deep impregnation of stonework with suitable resins. A deeply penetrating treatment would secure the decaying surface to the underlying sound stone and would overcome the problems encountered with shallow treatments. In addition to consolidating the stone, a treatment of this type might be expected to prevent further crystallisation damage, either by making the salts inaccessible to water or by modifying the properties of the stone to make it more resistant. The minimum thickness of the treated layer is not known and will vary from one type of stone to another, but a thickness of at least 25 mm will probably be required in most circumstances.

The Station is currently assessing the effectiveness of various deep impregnation treatments and it is not yet possible to make any specific recommendations. The most promising materials fall into three main categories:

alkoxysilanes These materials react with water to give a silicone polymer, curing being dependent on the loss of alcohol by evaporation.

solutions of epoxy resins Common epoxy resins are rather viscous and must, therefore, be dissolved in solvent in order to achieve penetration.

With both of these classes of materials, solvents must evaporate from the surface of the stonework. This means that it is not possible to achieve complete pore filling and the treated stone remains permeable to water vapour.

waxes These are discussed in Digest 125. The stonework must be heated in order to melt the wax and in many circumstances this will not be practicable.

Deep impregnation treatments naturally require large quantities of material and the costs are such that it may be unrealistic to contemplate the preservation of anything other than valuable detail. In many circumstances it will therefore be necessary to use one of the traditional maintenance and restoration techniques.

Maintenance and restoration

The work to be undertaken will often be governed by financial considerations. The following procedures are listed in order of increasing cost.

1 Knock off any loose stone and repoint where necessary. Suitable pointing mixes are 1:2:9 cement:lime:sand (by volume) and 1:8 cement:sand with a vinsol resin plasticiser.

2 Redress the stonework until a sound face is exposed and repoint. In many cases this may be all that is necessary to give satisfactory service for a good number of years. However, it may not be practicable where there are elaborate architectural details.

3 Redress until a sound face is exposed and then restore the stonework to its original line by setting in a facing of artificial or natural stone, or by building up with a suitable mortar. The selection of durable stone will be the subject of a future digest; the principles to be observed when building up with mortar are as follows:

The exact composition of the mix should be determined by experiment, to match the colour of the surrounding stonework. Suitable mixes may be based on Portland cement, using graded sand or crushed stone aggregate, or a mixture of these. Lime may be added to increase workability, but this may also be achieved by the addition of an air-entraining agent. Accelerators, such as calcium chloride, should not be used. Any pigments that are added should comply with BS 1014 and should not exceed 10 per cent by weight of the cement. The mix should be as dry as is compatible with the retention of workability. A number of organic binders for use with crushed stone or sand have been proposed, but the Station has relatively little experience of their durability.

The thickness of the repair should normally not be less than about 20 mm at any point, although this may not be practicable in all circumstances, particularly on carved work; feather-edging should always be avoided. Non-ferrous wire or dowels should be used where necessary to improve the key. Each block should be built up individually, the joints between adjacent blocks being left open and pointed at a later date. The alternative of building up large areas and striking in artificial joints should be avoided because of the risk of crazing. Large repairs should be built up gradually, step by step, each layer being allowed to set before proceeding with the next. Repairs should not be finished with a steel trowel but with a board or rough wooden float. Laitance may be removed by applying a wet brush before the repair has set or by brushing the freshly set mortar with a stiff dry brush. To obtain the best results, the repair may be built up until it stands proud of the surrounding stonework. It is then tooled back to the required level after setting.

References and further reading

1 CP 121: *Walling:* Part 2: *Stone masonry* British Standards Institution, London

2 BRE Digest 113 *Cleaning external surfaces of buildings*

3 BRE Digest 125 *Colourless treatments for masonry*

4 BRE Digest 139 *Control of lichens, moulds and similar growths*

5 B L Clarke and J Ashurst *Stone preservation experiments* BRE: 1972 (£1·25)

6 R J Schaffer *The weathering of natural building stones* BRE: 1932, reprinted 1972 (£2)

Rising Damp in Walls

Withdrawn See Nº 245 *January 1981*

This Digest examines the circumstances in which rising damp is likely to occur and suggests possible remedies. The measures considered include providing a complete moisture barrier by inserting a damp-proof course, reducing the amount of water in the wall by drainage and evaporation, and concealing the dampness by an impermeable wall lining. Some recent developments in the technique of damp-proof course insertion are described. The treatment of rising dampness in floors is not considered here, as it is the subject of Digest 54.

Rising damp

Building materials are porous and therefore have the capacity to soak up water in much the same way as a wick. If ground water is allowed to reach the foot of the wall it will tend to rise and, unless stopped by a barrier such as a damp-proof course, will reach a height depending on a variety of factors, such as the supply of water, the pore structure of the wall materials, and the rate of evaporation from the wall surfaces. The picture is further complicated by the fact that ground water almost invariably contains dissolved salts which tend to concentrate at the wall surfaces where the water evaporates (Fig. 1). Precisely how these salts affect the ultimate height of water in the wall, or its rate of rise, is at present not clear, but their presence in the wall surface means that, even if the further rise of water is prevented, the decorations are still likely to be spoiled. This is because some of the salts originally drawn up into the wall are hygroscopic, that is, they can absorb moisture from the air, so that the surface tends to become damp whenever the air in the building is humid. Ways of dealing with plasterwork affected by such salts are described later in this Digest. It should

not be thought that the provision of a damp-proof course is likely by itself to be a complete remedy. Replacement of salt-contaminated plasterwork is nearly always necessary as well.

Identification and occurrence

Apart from water used for construction purposes, which causes only temporary inconvenience whilst drying out, dampness can result from rain penetration and condensation, in addition to rising damp. The typical effect of rising damp is to produce a roughly horizontal 'tide-mark' on the wall, above which there is no damage but below which the plaster may be disrupted and the decoration destroyed by efflorescence, or bleached or caused to lift and peel under the damp conditions (Fig. 2).

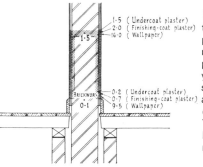

Fig. 1. Concentration of salts in a party wall in which rising damp has persisted for 80 years; the figures show the percentages, by weight of chloride plus nitrate. The shaded area is heavily contaminated.

1·5 (Undercoat plaster)
2·0 (Finishing-coat plaster)
16·0 (Wallpaper)
1·5
0·2 (Undercoat plaster)
0·7 (Finishing-coat plaster)
9·5 (Wallpaper)
BRICKWORK
0·1

Fig. 2. A wall affected by rising damp.

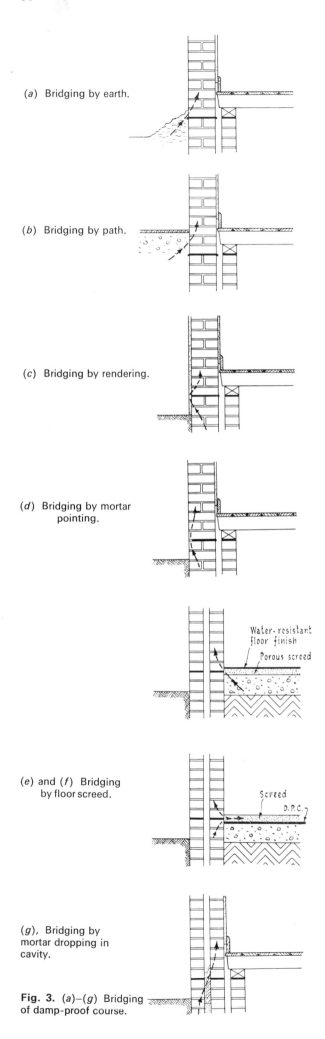

(a) Bridging by earth.

(b) Bridging by path.

(c) Bridging by rendering.

(d) Bridging by mortar pointing.

(e) and (f) Bridging by floor screed.

Water-resistant floor finish

Porous screed

Screed

D.P.C.

(g), Bridging by mortar dropping in cavity.

Fig. 3. (a)–(g) Bridging of damp-proof course.

Where hygroscopic salts have accumulated the surface appears damp and mould growth may be present; it is liable to occur on any persistently damp surfaces. Pictures and furniture placed against the wall, and clothes in wall closets, may suffer from the damp and become mouldy.

Rising damp commonly affects old houses having no damp-proof courses or ones which are faulty; it was not until the Public Health Act of 1875 that the incorporation of a dpc became compulsory. Since then, damp-proof courses in many old houses have given trouble because they were either inefficient when laid or have since become so with age. BS 743 specifies materials acceptable for damp-proof courses, including asphalt, bitumen sheet, lead, copper, slate, dense burnt clay brick and polythene. During the next few years the use of other plastics materials may be permitted. There is a good case also for including dense quality-controlled concrete, provided that means are found for ensuring the high standard that is needed.

The use of these materials in buildings constructed nowadays can easily prevent rising dampness, but, unfortunately, it is still seen in many modern houses; this is because the dpc has been bridged in some way, thus providing an alternative path along which moisture can rise up the wall. Bridging can occur in a number of ways, for instance, by solid fuel or garden earth being piled against the wall (Fig. 3a), or a path raised above dpc level (Fig. 3b). It is not at all uncommon, with buildings butting on the street, for pavements to be placed above the level of damp-proof courses—and they are likely to be bedded in ash or clinker containing soluble salts. Co-operation between architects and local authorities is needed to ensure that the pavement is below dpc level. Bridging of the dpc can also be caused by a porous rendering (Fig. 3c), by covering the exposed edge of the dpc with pointing mortar (Fig. 3d), or by mortar that has been allowed to drop between the two leaves of a cavity wall (Fig. 3g).

A common form of bridging that is not easily recognized is that caused by a porous floor screed. Although building regulations require the inclusion of a dpc in walls, there is no such regulation for solid floors. Some solid floors incorporate a damp-proof membrane beneath the floor screed, others rely on the floor finish to serve as a moisture barrier. Unless care is taken, it may be possible for the screed, which is usually porous, to transmit moisture from the wall below dpc level to that above (Figs. 3e and f). With this form of construction the position of the moisture barrier must be carefully planned and a vertical dpc may be needed to join the wall dpc to the membrane in or on the floor.

Remedial measures

No hard and fast rules can be laid down for the treatment of rising damp; the measures decided on will depend on the cost and estimated effectiveness of the treatment, as seen against the value, condition and probable life of the property. Some of the causes of rising dampness described above can be dealt with fairly simply—for instance, earth or paths above dpc level, or rendering or pointing bridging the dpc—but where there is no damp-proof course, or where it is defective, more radical measures are necessary. There are three possible approaches to the problem.

First, a complete moisture barrier may be provided, by inserting a dpc; this should lead to a permanent cure. There are also various proprietary methods that aim to produce a dpc by the injection of water-repellent substances; these are probably more appropriate for walls too thick or too unstable for a conventional dpc to be inserted. Secondly, it may be possible to reduce the amount of moisture in the wall, by hindering the access of water to it and by increasing evaporation from it. With any of these measures, it will also be necessary to replace any decayed plaster and remove accumulated salts.

Thirdly, many of the methods available for dealing with walls heavily contaminated with salts can be used alone to *conceal* the rising damp. These involve battening out or lining the inside of the wall, or using various barrier layers which prevent the damp and salts affecting the decorations. The rising damp is not stopped by such measures, and will often be driven higher; but where it is causing no structural damage such steps are useful where the property has a limited life or more drastic treatments are too costly. It may, of course, be appropriate to use measures of the second category—reducing the moisture content of the wall—in conjunction with such a lining treatment.

Methods to prevent rising damp

Inserting damp-proof courses

The traditional method of inserting a damp-proof course is to cut out a course of bricks, a short length at a time, and replace it by a course of dense engineering bricks or slates. A much less costly method is by cutting or grinding a narrow slot through a bed-joint. New tools have now been developed for this work and new materials have become available; this Digest brings the description of the newer method up to date.

Method of work

The cut may be made either by a hand-saw or by one of several types of power-driven saw*; these are described below. The cut is started in the selected course at a jamb or corner, preferably the latter as this avoids knocking out a brick to start the cut; once the cut reaches the inside it is more convenient to continue the work from inside the building. With a new chain saw developed at the Station it is possible to mortice into a joint and so work entirely from one side of a wall.

The cycle of cutting the slot and inserting the membrane may then proceed without interruption along the wall. The membrane must be inserted immediately the cut is made, generally in lengths of about 0.5m; in heavily loaded sections of the wall, e.g. at jambs and junctions, work must proceed in shorter lengths.

The sheets forming the membrane should be wide enough to project about 5mm on each side of the wall. The membrane may be of any impermeable and durable sheet material; the choice will depend in part on the width of the slot, and this in turn depends on the type of mortar and on the saw that is used. A narrow slot is produced in a wet and sticky mortar by the thin blade of a handsaw or reciprocating saw; in this case a thin rigid sheet must be driven into the slot. More usually, in a dry and crumbly mortar, a wider slot will be cut; and the new chain saw cuts a slot about 7mm wide in any mortar. This will require two layers of a thicker material to fill the slot; alternatively, a thin sheet may be used and the joint packed, by spreading a bed of mortar on the membrane before inserting it

* Since this Digest was first issued, a new method has been evolved using a combined cutting disc and dust extractor, details of which are given on p. 91.

Fig. 4. Damp-proof course insertion: mortar spread on the membrane to pack the joint.

Fig. 5. Driving a metal sheet into a narrow slot with the help of a guide frame.

and wedging slips of slate into the joint at intervals of about 0.3m (Fig. 4).

Even when the membrane is a close fit into the slot there is a slight settlement as the cut advances; measurements on a test house have indicated that 1.5mm may be expected. With a joint packed as described above, about half this settlement will occur. As a rigid sheet material, for driving into a narrow slot, half-hard copper may be used or, for a limited subsequent life of, say, 10–15 years, sheet zinc will give sufficient protection at lower cost. A guide frame may be used for driving in the sheets (Fig. 5), but this is often unnecessary.

With a wide slot, two layers of bitumen felt, each of 0.6m lengths butted together, may be inserted; they should be placed so that the joints are staggered, with at least a 75mm interval between the joints in the two layers. Copper or polythene sheet may be used and the joint packed. Soft copper sheeting can be inserted into the wide slot without fear of damage, and this is available more cheaply than the half-hard sheet required for driving into a narrow slot. High- or low-density polythene sheet, 0·02 in. (0.5mm) thick, is a cheaper alternative; high-density sheet is the more easily inserted. The polythene should be filled with carbon black, to retard deterioration where it is exposed to sunlight.

The rate of progress depends much more on the state of the wall than on the type of saw used. In regularly coursed brickwork, with a dry crumbly mortar, it may exceed 3m per hour in a 220mm wall. Where courses are irregular or obstacles have to be negotiated, the rate may be only 0.6m per hour, but corners and junctions are usually simple to negotiate. The average rate in brick walls of the type generally met with in old houses is about 1.3m per hour in 220mm walls, and 2m per hour in 105mm walls. These estimates cover the time spent in preparation, inserting the membrane and in overcoming obstacles, but not making good the plastering or repointing the brickwork externally.

Saws

The saws* available for cutting the slot include handsaws, which are operated by two men (Fig. 6),

* The names of suppliers of the saws and the proprietary treatments described in this Digest may be obtained from any Building Centre.

power-operated reciprocating saws, a circular saw, and the new chain saw.

The reciprocating saws, hand and power-operated, are of mild steel, with teeth tipped with tungsten carbide or stellite. The handsaw has a 42-in. (1066mm) blade; the 3-in. 75mm width is preferable to the 4-in. (100mm) wide blade normally supplied. Sawing so near the ground is exhausting but for short periods the work can be done as quickly as with a power saw. For a single job, the handsaw provides a cheap and practical method of cutting the slot; in any case, a handsaw is a most useful adjunct to a power saw.

Two types of power-operated reciprocating saws have been used: a light pneumatic model, weighing 2.5kg and designed to be held by the operator, and a more powerful type which requires a supporting frame for more continuous work. Other forms of saw may well be suitable; larger and more powerful tools are used by specialist contractors, and one has developed a circular saw claimed to be highly efficient.

A disadvantage of reciprocating saws is that the swarf from the slot is not removed as the cut advances, and after a time this slows down the rate of working. With a chain saw (as well as with the handsaws and circular saws), the swarf is removed by the sweep of the blade, but the chain saws ordinarily used for cutting and dressing stone cut a slot that is too wide for dpc insertion—at least 12mm wide, that is, wider than a mortar joint.

Fig. 6. Handsaw.

A new chain saw blade has been developed at the Station for use with a lightweight petrol-driven chain saw. In the modified chain (Fig. 7), the blade tips, have been replaced by tungsten carbide cutting blocks brazed into the links and supported by mild-steel buttresses; the chain is $\frac{1}{4}$ in. (6.35mm) wide and it cuts a slot only slightly wider. The saw (Fig. 8), which

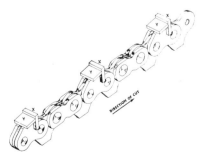

Fig. 7. The modified saw chain, with tungsten carbide cutting tips (X) supported by horizontal buttresses (Y).

Fig. 8. Chain saw.

weighs 3kg, is fitted with a guide bar 14 in. (355mm) long and will satisfactorily cut a 220mm solid wall. It is driven through a flexible shaft by a lightweight 1.675kw air-cooled petrol engine. This unit can be carried and operated by one man. The expected life of a chain and guide bar (which must have a hardened nose) is about 50m of 220mm wall.

This new development has overcome several earlier limitations of the method of dpc insertion. The chain saw is convenient to use, the rate of work is faster than with other power saws, and, when commencing a cut, it is possible to mortice into a joint—this avoids knocking out a header brick. The possibility of working entirely on one side of a wall brings with it several other advantages which are discussed below.

Practical details

The level at which the cut is made must be decided after careful inspection of the site, taking account of ground and floor levels.

For solid floors, the cut should be made in the first bed joint in which it is possible to work, above the level of the slab and at least 150mm above the outside ground level. If an impermeable flooring such as pitchmastic is to be laid over the concrete base, it must be linked with the new dpc. If a permeable flooring that is not sensitive to moisture is used, the finished level of the floor should preferably be at the same level as the dpc or, if this is not practicable and the floor level is below the new dpc, the brickwork between the dpc and the top of the floor should be treated with two coats of bitumen paint and the skirting should be protected against rot. If a moisture-sensitive floor, for instance of timber, is to be laid on the concrete, a damp-proof membrane should be provided and linked up with the new dpc; the protection of timber floors is dealt with in Digest 18.

For suspended timber floors, for proper protection the dpc should be inserted below plate level. Provided that the outside ground level permits it, this can be done with the chain saw working from the outside only, without the need to take up and relay the floor. Where this is not practicable, inserting a dpc in the first bed joint above floor level is very much a second-best solution; if it is adopted, it would be prudent to ensure that the wooden skirting will not be affected by damp and to increase the ventilation in the under-floor space.

An effective barrier against rising damp will be afforded only when the damp-proof course is taken around all internal and external walls, including chimney breasts if possible. With the chain saw, chimney breasts can be cut without removing the firebacks, except where fireplaces are back-to-back; in that case, or if other tools are used, it is possible to insert narrow widths of membrane around the chimney breast with the fireback in position, and this protection combined with the heat from the fire may suffice to keep the chimney breast fairly dry. The technique of inserting damp-proof courses has

been applied both by contractors and by the Building Research Station to a wide variety of dwellings, some of which were in poor repair. It has been shown that if care and common sense are exercised, the method is safe to employ providing:

    (i) Vertical joints are filled with mortar; otherwise, the brickwork may not bridge the slot.

    (ii) Walls are reasonably plumb and are stiffened by returns or by partitions; this implies that a damp-proof course should not be inserted in, for example, long parapet walls which sometimes occur in buildings such as factories.

Of course all brickwork should be inspected before the work begins, especially as many old walls were built in two leaves, with the outer leaf much more carefully laid than the backing and with a broken bed joint. When the brickwork is in a very decayed condition, or there is little mortar in the vertical joints, many bricks in the course immediately above the saw may become loose and drop as the saw passes under them. Sometimes one or more courses of bricks must be completely removed in sections as the cut advances and, after the membrane is inserted, replaced as headers bedded in mortar and wedged with slate. Despite the very poor conditions, settlements after inserting damp-proof courses in such walls did not exceed 0.8mm. It is convenient for the bricklayers to have several sandbags filled with dry cement-sand mix which can be prepared quickly to meet emergencies.

A problem that may be encountered in this work is that of removing cement mortar. Frequently old brickwork has been repaired—quite mistakenly—by raking out the joints and repointing with a cement-sand mortar; elsewhere cement-sand plinths have been added in an attempt to combat rising damp. In both instances the cement mortar must be removed before cutting a slot, otherwise progress is slow and the saw blades are quickly damaged. Usually this is done with a cold-chisel, a slow process which often damages the brickwork. Both jobs may be tackled more easily with a grinding disc, either fitted in an angle grinder or as a separate unit driven by the portable engine, which would in any case be required to drive the chain saw (Fig. 9). A batten

Fig. 9. Grinding disc for removing cement mortar.

aligned with the bed joint provides a convenient method of supporting and guiding the tool; a neat cut without ragged edges, about 7mm wide, is produced when two carborundum-faced grinding discs are clamped to the same spindle. Slots up to 40mm deep are cut at a rate of about 0.3m per min. When a wall prepared in this way is subsequently cut, the slot is cut more rapidly and the cost of making good the plinth or rendering is avoided.

Injecting damp-proof courses

There are several proprietary techniques which are claimed to produce a moisture barrier in a wall. These generally involve injecting water-repellent substances into holes drilled at regular intervals along the base of the wall. The wall to be treated is almost certainly damp and may be nearly saturated. Consequently, it is difficult to form a continuous barrier by injection of water-repellent substances. The most successful techniques appear to be those employing a siliconate solution in water or a siliconate/latex mixture. These materials are miscible with water at the time of injection but change, after injection, to form a water-repellent band within the wall. The siliconate solution is allowed to permeate the wall under the influence of gravity; the siliconate/latex mixture is forced into the wall under high pressure.

The success of either technique depends on the care taken by the operatives to ensure continuity in the silicone barrier.

Electro-osmosis

Several systems are in use in this country and on the Continent which aim to prevent the rise of water above a certain position in a wall (or reduce it to an insignificant amount) by electrical means. In one system, electrodes of similar metal are placed in the wall and in the ground and connected together. In another system an electrical potential from an external source is applied between such electrodes. A related system has both sets of electrodes in the wall, one on the outside and the other at a higher level inside. Yet another system has electrodes of one type of metal in the wall connected to those of another type in the ground, the dissimilar metals producing an electrical potential by galvanic action. It has been reported that some of the systems employing dissimilar metals become inoperative after a few years because of electro-chemical corrosion of the electrodes. It would be expected that similar corrosion would occur when metal electrodes are used in systems employing an external electrical potential.

The scientific basis for these systems is a subject of controversy and the Station is investigating the efficacy of the system widely used in this country.

Drainage and drying

There are some types of walling where it may be impracticable to insert or inject a dpc, for instance natural stone walls having a rubble core. Or, in other cases, the provision of a new dpc may not be feasible economically. In these cases there are several measures which can be taken to reduce the amount of ground water reaching the wall or to increase evaporation from it. These may be effective alone or they may be decided on as preliminaries to a lining treatment.

One such measure is to lower the ground water level near the wall by site drainage; another is to expose an area of wall below ground or floor level so as to encourage evaporation there, for example, by laying corrugated asbestos cement sheeting against the wall. A different approach is to provide a moisture barrier, for instance, by providing impermeable surrounds such as a pathway, draining away from the wall.

Increased heating in the building will, of course, help to dry out a wall but its effectiveness greatly depends on how bad the rising damp is and what air circulation is available in the rooms affected by it. Neither heating nor ventilation is likely to be adequate where the decorative finish is impermeable, e.g. a gloss painted surface, and restricts the evaporation of water from the inner surface of the wall. Whatever form of heating is used needs to be maintained if the effects of rising damp are to be avoided permanently, and this measure will therefore involve a fairly high and continuing expense.

According to a proprietary system designed to increase evaporation, porous tubes are inserted into the wall to encourage evaporation at the outer surface. Removing some bricks from the wall may have a similar effect, though in both these methods it is difficult to see how the increase in evaporation is sufficient to be of real benefit. Better ventilation of the external wall surface will also increase evaporation, and clearing the nearby trees and shrubs may assist in some cases.

Methods to conceal rising damp

Wall linings

Various treatments are available that will ensure that the decorations are kept out of contact with the moisture and salts in a damp wall. None of these does anything to lessen the dampness in the wall and as already mentioned they may, if they impede evaporation from the wall, actually drive it higher. It is therefore recommended that the wall surface up to 0.5m above the highest affected parts should be treated, and suitable precautions must be taken if there is any risk of the dampness reaching the first floor timbers. To limit this rise it is best to use porous decorations, such as wallpaper, distemper or emulsion paint.

The cheapest and in some ways the best method, which also provides a measure of thermal insulation, is to line with plasterboard on timber battens. To prevent rotting, the battens should have been

Fig. 10. Combined grinding disc and dust extractor in use.

pressure-impregnated with a non-staining inodorous preservative. To prevent mould growth in the cavity, the wall surface and back of the lining board should be treated with a fungicide.

Two other methods introduce an impervious layer between the wall and the new plaster and decoration. They both involve stripping off the old plaster first. One uses a backing of corrugated pitch or bitumen lathing which is mechanically fixed to the wall and plastered over. This is an effective method, provided that the fastenings are made efficiently. In the other method the wall is coated with a rubber/tar or bitumen preparation. The old plaster is first stripped, and the wall is coated with the preparation. This also is an effective treatment but the preparation may lose adhesion after about ten years. In both these cases plastering with an undercoat that does not shrink on drying is necessary; a mixture of one part browning plaster to one-and-a-half parts clean sand is usually recommended.

As a temporary expedient only, a cheaper alternative exists where the old surface is fairly sound; it may be possible to fix a barrier layer on the old plaster and to decorate over that. Suitable layers are pitch paper fixed with bitumen, lead foil fixed with a mixture of red lead and gold size, or with old fat varnish, or aluminium foil backed with a heat-sensitive adhesive which can be ironed on to the old surface.

Plastering

Apart from the proprietary treatments described above that provide an impervious backing to the new plaster and decoration, there are several plastering methods that may effectively impede damp penetration.

Where a dpc has been inserted in a wall, dampness, as already mentioned, will persist as long as hygroscopic salts remain in the wall surface; replastering will therefore be necessary to a height of, say, 0.5m above the affected area. This, however, should be delayed as long as possible to allow soluble salts to move from the masonry into the plaster.

Replastering may also be effective, for a while, where no dpc has been inserted, in preventing the dampness from reaching the wall surface. For this purpose the old plaster is stripped, the wall surface is keyed by raking out the mortar joints squarely to a depth of 10mm and an undercoat of 1 : 3 cement/sand, possibly with an integral water-proofer, or an undercoat of aerated 1 : 6 cement/sand, is applied, followed by a plaster finish coat. As a further precaution, decorations should be porous as mentioned above.

Many old walls of soft brick or porous stone are not sufficiently strong to restrain the shrinkage of a dense 1 : 3 cement/sand rendering, and in these circumstances the use of a weaker mix of 1 : 6 cement/sand plasticized by means of an airentraining agent is preferred to a cement/lime/sand undercoat of similar strength. The aerated mix is likely to be the more effective in impeding the passage of moisture and salts.

Insertion of damp-proof courses

Since this Digest was first published, there has been a further development in slot cutting technique prior to dpc insertion, resulting in increased speed and economy. A patent has been applied for.

In this method the wall is cut with a grinding disc, driven by a portable motor via a flexible drive. The glass-fibre discs impregnated with carborundum are up to 24 in. (0.6m) in diameter and are provided with a shield connected to a vacuum extractor (Fig. 10). Because almost complete extraction of dust is ensured operatives can work without masks and in confined spaces. The machine is hand-held and the rate of cut is about 0.3m per minute for a 105mm wall and about half this rate for a 220mm wall. The method has been shown to be satisfactory both with irregularly coursed brickwork and with brickwork set in cement mortar.

Further details of contractors using this method may be had on application to any Building Centre.

3 Floors, Roofs and Joinery

Damp-proofing solid floors

This digest discusses briefly site drainage and the principles of damp-proofing solid floors. Tables show the effects of ground moisture on floor finishes and the protection afforded by various damp-proof membranes.

Principles of damp-proofing

Oversite concrete and floor screeds do not keep back all ground moisture. This rises towards the surface, where it either evaporates or accumulates under a less pervious material.

The tolerance of some common floor finishes to moisture is classified in Groups **A**–**D** (*see* Table 1), which range from finishes which combine the functions of flooring and damp-proofing to those for which reliable protection against damp is always needed.

For the intermediate groups, in particular Group **C**, some judgement must be exercised in deciding whether or not to provide a membrane. Similarly, a choice must be made between hot-applied and cold-applied membranes for use under the more moisture-sensitive floorings. Consideration of the following factors will help to assess the degree of risk.

Figs. 1-3. Some typical effects of rising dampness and adhesion failure.

Table 1 Effects of rising moisture on floor finishes

Group	Material	Properties
A Finish and damp-proof membrane combined	Pitch mastic flooring Mastic asphalt flooring	Resist rising damp without dimensional or material failure
B Finishes that can be used without extra protection against damp	Concrete Terrazzo Clay tiles	Transmit rising damp without dimensional, material or adhesion failure
	Cement/rubber latex Cement/bitumen Composition blocks (laid in cement mortar)	Transmit rising damp slowly without dimensional or material failure and usually without adhesion failure
	Wood blocks (dipped and laid in hot pitch or bitumen)	Transmit rising damp slowly without material failure and usually without dimensional or adhesion failure. Only in exceptional conditions of site dampness is there risk of dimensional instability
C Finishes that are not necessarily trouble-free but are often laid without protection against damp	Thermoplastic flooring tiles PVC (vinyl) asbestos tiles Acrylic resin emulsion/cement Epoxy resin flooring	Under severe conditions dimensional and adhesion failure may occur. Thermoplastic flooring tiles may be attacked by dissolved salts
D Reliable protection against damp needed	Magnesium oxychloride	Softens and disintegrates in wet conditions
	PVA emulsion/cement	Dimensionally sensitive to moisture; softens in wet conditions
	Polyester resin flooring Polyurethane resin flooring Rubber Flexible PVC flooring Linoleum Cork carpet Cork tile	Lose adhesion and may expand under damp conditions
	Textile flooring	Dimensional and material failure, and usually adhesion failure occur in moist conditions
	Wood block laid in cold adhesives Wood strip and board flooring Chipboard	Acutely sensitive to moisture with dimensional or material failure

Wetness of site

This is influenced by the nature of the soil, the presence or absence of hardcore beneath the site concrete, and the slope of the ground. On some sloping sites, foundations can interfere with natural drainage, with consequent build-up of water pressure on the underside of the floor. In these cases, a ditch dug along the upper sides of the building, draining to a lower level, will help. The ditch may be filled, if it has a land drain in the bottom, with coarse material up to top-soil level.

Solid floors should not be subjected to water pressure unless specifically designed to withstand it; the problem then becomes one of tanking, and reference should be made to British Standard Code of Practice CP 102.

Temperature to be maintained in the building

The effect of a temperature gradient is to concentrate moisture in the cooler part and to lower the moisture content of the warmer part. Thus, if the floor surface is colder than the ground below it, moisture will tend to rise and collect near the surface;

protection against dampness is then advisable. In a permanently heated building, the risk is less, though with floor warming, a sandwich damp-proof membrane is necessary whatever the finish.

Sea-salt contamination of concrete aggregate and fill

Sea salt has two undesirable effects: it tends to keep the floor damp and it reacts with lime from the cement, liberating caustic alkali, which can contribute to an attack on floorings and their adhesives. Where sea salt is present, a damp-proof membrane is necessary.

Position of membrane

Surface membranes permit floor laying to follow completion (including cooling or hardening) of the membrane with no delay for drying time. They do not interfere with the bond between screed and base concrete; a screed can, therefore, be laid monolithically to a thickness of only 12–25 mm, or in separate construction to a minimum thickness of 40 mm (*see* Digest 104). The thicker surface membranes may also serve as a levelling compound on a well-finished concrete slab without screed or on a slightly irregular screed. Surface membranes are, however, susceptible to damage by subsequent trades; with mastic asphalt or pitchmastic membranes there is a risk of indentation under heavy loads. They should therefore be laid only just in advance of the floor finish.

If sulphates are present in hardcore under the floor or in the ground water, a surface membrane will give no protection against sulphate attack of the base concrete or screed and the risk of sulpho-aluminate expansion will be high.

Sandwich membranes located between concrete base and screed should be protected against damage by subsequent trades by laying the screed as soon as possible after completion. Hot-applied membranes can be covered by a screed as soon as they have cooled; cold-applied solutions or emulsions are likely to require several days to apply and harden. The membrane effectively eliminates any bond between screed and base; a screed laid on a sandwich membrane should therefore be at least 50 mm thick.

Any of the sheet materials recommended for use as sandwich membranes can be used below the site concrete but the base on which they are to be laid must be structurally sound, to avoid fracture of the membrane, and the surface should be sufficiently smooth to avoid puncturing the membrane. A blinding layer of weak concrete or sand, on a consolidated bed of hardcore, provides a suitable base. A membrane in this position protects the site concrete and screed against attack by any sulphates present in hardcore or ground water and permits bonding of screed to concrete base. It has, however, the disadvantage that both the concrete base and screed must be allowed time to dry before a moisture-sensitive finish can be laid.

Table 2   Materials for membranes

Material	Standard or grade	Comment
Hot-applied Mastic asphalt	BS 1410: Mastic asphalt for flooring (natural rock asphalt aggregate) BS 1076: Mastic asphalt for flooring (limestone aggregate) BS 1451: Coloured mastic asphalt for flooring (limestone aggregate)	May be used as a floor finish (*see* BS CP 204); if used as an underlay to a floor finish, the thickness should be not less than 12 mm. A compressible underlay is not recommended but glass-fibre may be used. All are suitable for surface membranes.
	BS 1097 (limestone aggregate) BS 1418 (natural rock asphalt aggregate)	When loaded, can withstand hydrostatic pressure; suitable only for sandwich membranes.
Pitch mastic	BS 1450: Black pitch mastic flooring BS 3672: Coloured pitch mastic flooring	Normally used as a floor finish but may form a surface membrane to protect other finishes. Its indentation characteristics make it less suitable than mastic asphalt.
Pitch	BS 1310: Coal tar pitches for building purposes (Grade R & B 40)	Should be laid on a primed surface to give an average thickness of 3 mm (3 kg/m^2); suitable only for sandwich membranes.
Bitumen	Should have a softening point of 50–55°C; this corresponds to a penetration number of 40–50 at 25°C	
Cold-applied Bitumen solutions, coal tar pitch/rubber emulsion, or bitumen/rubber emulsion	Not defined by any BS Specification or Code	BS CP 102 recommends 0·6 mm minimum thickness but this is for broad guidance only. The solids content will usually have been adjusted to give adequate coverage by two or three coats; the material should not be thinned by dilution or spread in thinner coats than recommended by the manufacturer. Suitable only for sandwich membranes.
Pitch/epoxy resin		Although applied in thin layers, the material is strong enough and its adhesion to concrete is usually sufficient to make it a satisfactory base for a variety of floor finishes. It cannot tolerate any cracking in the surface to which it is applied. Generally used as a surface membrane.
Sheet material Polythene film	0·12 mm thick (500 gauge)	Suitable for sandwich membranes. Joints must be properly sealed; the welting method normally used appears satisfactory. Where there is risk of damage by subsequent screed-laying operations, material about twice as thick (1000 gauge) may be used with confidence.
Composite	Polythene and bitumen, self-adhesive; thickness is in excess of 1·5 mm	Adhesion simplifies joint treatment and reduces risk of tearing.
Bitumen sheet	Bitumen sheet to BS 743	Suitable for sandwich membranes. Joints must be properly sealed.

Properties required of damp-proof layers

A damp-proof membrane must be impervious to *liquid* water; it must also have at least as high a resistance to the passage of water *vapour* as the flooring it is designed to protect.

Hot-applied membranes are considered to have the higher vapour resistance. Cold membranes of adequate thickness also have a high vapour resistance, but in practice they may have thin spots.

An integral waterproofer incorporated in the concrete or screed is not a satisfactory alternative to a damp-proof layer.

Suitable damp-proofing materials are listed in Table 2. Site experience shows that not all are equally effective but if the materials are laid to the recommended minimum thicknesses, dampness troubles are more likely to arise from poor workmanship and bad detailing than from any deficiencies in the membrane materials. If flooring laid over a membrane shows early trouble, the cause is unlikely to be a defective membrane; the latter will usually require several months to show in the form of a flooring failure.

Drying

A long delay before laying the finish is unavoidable for all sandwich membranes, because the screed has to be left to dry out. Even under favourable conditions this may take as long as one month per 25 mm thickness. Thus, a 50 mm thick screed would take at least two months to dry. Where a membrane is introduced below the site concrete, a 150 mm thick slab and screed would take at least six months to dry sufficiently for a moisture-sensitive finish to be laid. A device for testing the dryness of a screed is described in Digest 18.

Continuity

All damp-proof layers must be continuous with the damp-proof courses in adjoining walls and with damp-proof membranes in adjacent floors. Where necessary, a vertical damp-proof course must be provided to link membranes at different levels, as shown in Fig 4.

A floor that is finished in part with material that needs no protection against ground moisture and elsewhere with material that does require protection, must be provided with continuous damp-proofing of the whole area, or each area of moisture-sensitive flooring must be protected by tanking—*see* Fig 5.

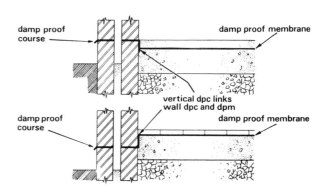

Fig 4

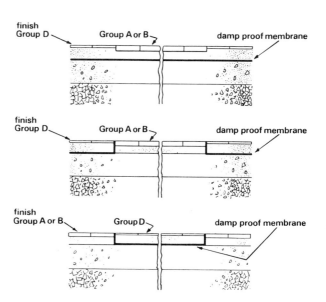

Fig 5

Clay tile flooring

This digest describes methods of laying clay floor tiles to avoid risk of failure by arching or ridging. Cement mortar bedding on a separating layer of sheet material gives satisfactory service. This method, and the newer ones of laying by the 'thick bed' (also sometimes referred to as 'dry bed' or 'semi-dry bed') technique or by using thinly-applied adhesive compounds, are described below. More detailed guidance can be found in BS CP 202: 1972, Tile flooring and slab flooring.

Classes of tile available

For general use

Two classes are available, floor tiles and quarry tiles the difference being as stated in BS 1286:1974: 'floor tiles are manufactured to narrower limits than quarries and are made by the compaction of powder method, usually from refined and blended ceramic powders but some are made from neat clay powders; quarries are made from stiff plastic clays by extrusion or other plastic process'. Both types are divided into two classes, as shown in the following table:

	Maximum water absorption (%)
Ceramic floor tiles	
fully vitrified	0.3
vitrified	4.0
Quarry tiles	
class 1	6.0
class 2	10.0

For special uses

Slip resistance. Improvement in slip resistance can be obtained with ribbed or studded surfaces, particled surfaces (shot-faced or pin-head finish) or with non-slip aggregates incorporated in the wearing surface. 'Slip-resistant' tiles are more difficult to keep clean. In some areas, industrial kitchens, for example, there is always the possibility of greasy films being formed on the surface, and unless extra care is taken to eliminate these films, the benefit of the special surfaces will probably be nullified.

Chemical resistance. Clay tiles in general have good resistance to chemical attack but for use in severe conditions tiles should meet the requirements of BS 3679: 1963.

Frost resistance. Most floors will not be subjected to frost attack in normal service but if this is likely, e g if used externally, the frost resistance of the' tiles should be verified by reference to the manufacturer. There is no standard method of test.

Bases for tiling

Rigidity

The base on which the tiling is to be laid must be rigid and stable, e g concrete slabs, precast concrete or hollow clay units; most wood joist-and-board floors are not suitable.

Falls

Any falls required in the finished floor should be formed other than in the bedding of the tiles although the thick semi-dry method of bedding offers some opportunity to form slight falls in the thickness of the bedding.

Prepared at Building Research Station, Garston, Watford WD2 7JR
Technical enquiries arising from this Digest should be directed to Building Research Advisory Service at the above address.

Smoothness

Thick semi-dry bedding can be applied directly to a good 'spade-finished' surface of concrete. The thickness of bed can accommodate some irregularity in the surface of the base. For other methods of laying, the base must have a smooth surface; a structural concrete slab can be finished to a satisfactory surface by mechanical means but it is more usual to apply a screed or levelling compound.

Methods of laying

Good laying techniques are designed to prevent bonding between the bedding and the base so that relative movement between them is not restrained.

Bedding on a separating layer (see Fig 4).

A separating layer of sheet material such as polythene or building paper is spread over the base—whether concrete slab or screed. Adjacent sheets should be lapped 100 mm to prevent any bond between bedding and base. The tiles are then laid on the sheet in as thin a bedding of cement and sand mortar as will produce a level floor. A thickness of 13 mm is common but a thinner bed, say 10 mm, may be possible on a smooth base. Where heavy traffic or sharp impacts are likely, the thickness of bedding may be increased to a maximum of 20 mm but its thickness should be less than that of the tiles. The only purpose of a separating layer is to avoid forming a bond between bedding and base. Tiles may therefore be bedded directly on to a damp-proof membrane or on to any surface treated so as to eliminate bonding, e g surfaces coated with curing compounds. An exception is mastic asphalt, where a separating layer lapped 50 mm is required wherever cement/sand bedding layers are used.

'Thick bed' method

No special preparation of the base is required but it may be necessary to dampen the surface to reduce suction. A semi-dry mix of cement and sand not richer than 1 : 4 should be packed on to the base to a thickness which should not be less than 20 mm but may be as thick as 75 mm; a thickness of 40 mm produces good results. The area of bedding placed in one operation should allow grouting and tiling to be completed whilst the bedding is still plastic. The surface of the compacted bedding should be spread with a 1 : 1 cement and sand slurry about 3 mm thick. The floor tiles are normally laid dry and are tapped into the slurry. A separating layer is not required with this method.

'Thin bed' (adhesive) fixing

Proprietary cement-based and other types of adhesive are available. They should conform to the requirements of Appendix B of Part I of BS CP 212. They should be used according to the instructions of the manufacturer, at a thickness not exceeding

Fig 1 Arching of floor tiles

Fig 2 Ridging of floor tiles

5 mm. Adhesives bond the tiling to the base but the bedding material is sufficiently resilient to tolerate some slight movement between tiling and base without ill effect.

Arching of tiles

The above methods of laying avoid risk of failure of floor tiling by arching or ridging (see Figs 1 and 2). A feature of this type of failure is the way in which the tiles separate cleanly from the bedding; there should be no risk of confusion, therefore, with failures caused by sulphate attack on the concrete base, where the whole floor may bulge upwards (see Digest 75).

Shrinkage of the screed

A newly laid screed shrinks during drying, the tiles do not; indeed some tiles may undergo a small but non-reversible expansion early in their life. If the tiles are firmly bonded by their bedding to the screed surface, considerable stresses can be set up which in the most severe cases are eventually relieved by areas or rows of tiles lifting. In typical instances, failure would occur during the first year after laying. Thin tiles rise more readily than thick ones.

Thermal movements

Failures similar in appearance can be caused by thermal movement in conditions that exclude screed drying shrinkage as a cause of failure, that is in new tiling laid on an old concrete base, or in tiling which has behaved satisfactorily for many years. It may occur after a prolonged cold spell because concrete contracts two or three times as much as clay tiles and a sufficiently low temperature may produce sufficient stress in the tiling to cause lifting. Drying shrinkage and differential thermal movement often act together in causing failure; the stresses set up by one may be insufficient to produce lifting until augmented by the stresses of the other.

Expansion of tiles

In common with most ceramic materials clay tiles may expand slightly due to gradual uptake of moisture, although with highly vitreous low porosity tiles the expansion is insignificant. The mechanism of expansion is not fully understood but it probably involves both physical adsorption of water vapour and chemical hydration. Expansion is most rapid in the first few days after manufacture but can continue at a reduced rate for many years. Long-term expansion is the most likely cause of failure of tiled flooring when this occurs after some years of satisfactory service (see Fig 3).

Special requirements for bedding

Bitumen bedding

If the base is to be subjected to high temperatures, e g around boilers and heating installations, bituminous bedding is recommended. This should consist of 1 part of aqueous bitumen emulsion and $2\frac{1}{2}$ parts of soft dry sand by volume, The bedding should be laid only on a dry surface, primed by brushing a coating of bitumen emulsion over it. The minimum of water should be added to the composition to improve the workability of the mix.

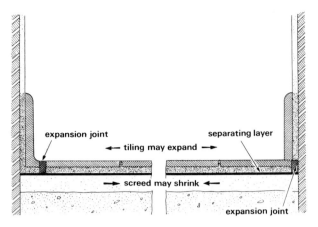

Fig 4   Use of expansion joints
(left) between tiling and skirting and
(right) between tiling and wall

Corrosion-resistant bedding

Where there is risk of chemical attack, special corrosion-resistant jointing compounds should be used and in the severest cases the compound should be used for bedding as well as jointing. More detailed recommendations are given in Digest 120. It should be borne in mind that chemical attack can derive from seemingly harmless liquids such as milk and fruit juices.

Expansion joints

Expansion joints with suitable compressible material should be provided around the perimeter of every clay tiled floor and at abutments against piers, machine bases, etc. They may be formed either between tiling and coved skirtings, or against walls, where they are lapped and concealed by a skirting (see Fig 4). If the area of flooring requires it, additional expansion joints should be provided at intervals of about 4.5 m across both the length and width of the floor.

Heated floor

Clay tiling is suitable for use on floors that incorporate a heating system. If the bedding is to be other than cement and sand, its suitability for use on a warmed floor should be verified with the manufacturers. The thermal resistance of the tiles is not significantly different from that of concrete but the heating engineer should be informed of the proposed thickness of tiles and bedding. The provision of expansion joints as outlined in the preceding paragraph is important.

Fig 3   Failure caused by long-term expansion of tiling

Sheet and tile flooring made from thermoplastic binders

Sheet and tile floor finishes for non-industrial premises are nowadays frequently made from mixtures consisting essentially of fillers, pigments and thermoplastic binders. This Digest discusses materials other than linoleum and natural rubber together with some of the problems that have arisen in their use, and the sub-floor requirements. A section at the end describes the constitution of the various types of material, and their manufacture and availability, and will provide a background for an understanding of the problems discussed in the earlier sections.

The information given on the composition, manufacture and uses of flooring made from thermoplastic binders should be read in conjunction with the relevant British Standard Specifications and Codes of Practice. These are as follows :

BS 2592 : 1955   Thermoplastic flooring tiles
BS 3260 : 1969   PVC (vinyl) asbestos floor tiles
BS 3261 : 1960   Flexible PVC flooring
BS CP 203 : 1969   Sheet and tile flooring

In addition to the materials listed above, brief reference is made in this Digest to PVC floorings not covered by BS 3261, and to synthetic rubbers. The latter are introduced for the sake of completeness, though the Station's experience of their behaviour in practice is not yet sufficient to provide detailed information.

Sub-floors

All the types of flooring described will conform to the contours of the sub-floor which should, therefore, be even, smooth and rigid. Otherwise the appearance of the finished floor will be affected and any raised portions will show signs of wear more quickly than the rest of the floor. Any sub-floor can be levelled and smoothed, and suspended timber floors can be made more rigid by the use of suitable underlays. The choice of these depends on the situation in which they are to be used and detailed consideration of underlays such as mastic asphalt,

emulsion/cement mixtures, plywood and hardboard is given in BS CP 203 : 1969.

Whilst these sub-floor requirements are comparatively easily met, the most difficult problem associated with sub-floors is the exclusion of moisture. Dampness in sub-floors is the commonest cause of premature failure of floorings fixed with adhesives. The problem arises because the finishes, the adhesives and in some cases the sub-floor (e.g. magnesium oxychloride cement or timber) can be affected by moisture. The commonest sub-floor for any of the materials under discussion is, however, concrete used in the form of a screed (see Digest 104). It is with moisture in this screed that the following remarks are concerned.

Moisture in the screed can derive from water used to mix the screed or base concrete on which it is laid, and from water that can on wet sites rise through concrete in contact with the ground. In each case the water contains alkalis derived from the Portland cement, and can soften all adhesives normally used and give rise to considerable moisture expansion of some of the finishes. With thermoplastic and vinyl asbestos tiles, alkaline moisture produces a curious effect which will be discussed later.

Water rising from the ground or from the base concrete can be prevented from reaching the screed by taking the precautions discussed in Digest 54 and detailed in BS CP 102, Protection of buildings against water from the ground.

In making the cement/sand screed the amount of water used is always much greater than that required to hydrate the cement. Nearly all the excess water must be removed before the floor finish is laid, irrespective of whether the finish, e.g. thermoplastic and vinyl asbestos tiles, has good tolerance to moisture. The only way to eliminate excess water from the screed is to allow it to evaporate. No particular drying period can be specified because the time required will depend on many factors, such as the quality and thickness of the screed, and the heating and ventilation within the building. A rule-of-thumb method often quoted is that one month should be allowed for every inch of the screed thickness. This figure is useful for forward planning of building operations but no finish should be laid until the screed is shown to be sufficiently dry by a reliable moisture test. Various test methods have been devised and of these a method based on the use of a paper hygrometer fitted into an insulated box has been found by the Station to be both simple and reliable. Details of the apparatus and method of use are given in Digest 18 and BS CP 203 : 1969.

Tests that are of little value are those relying on the use of anhydrous calcium chloride, anhydrous copper sulphate or phenolphthalein. In the presence of moisture, calcium chloride becomes visibly damp and copper sulphate turns blue, but the amount of moisture necessary to produce these changes is so small that they can occur even when the screed is sufficiently dry to install the floor finishes. It is generally believed that drops of an alcoholic solution of phenolphthalein placed on concrete will always turn purple when the concrete is too wet to lay the finish. Unfortunately, the colour change can occur even when the concrete is sufficiently dry, and in certain circumstances it will even remain colourless on wet concrete.

The effect of alkaline moisture is the same for all flexible floorings. The edges of the sheet or tile lift and bubbles appear in the surface. Usually the adhesive remains firmly attached to the underside of the finish but leaves the concrete surface completely. Occasionally the adhesive is attacked so severely that it is converted to a brown or black liquid that oozes up between the joints.

Thermoplastic and vinyl asbestos tiles are much more resistant to alkaline moisture but sometimes the adhesive is attacked in the manner just described. Alkalis can, however, produce failure peculiar to these tiles. Water rising through the base concrete penetrates the joints and on evaporation deposits salts, mainly sodium carbonate, from the concrete on the edges of the tiles; the salts tend to creep inwards from the joints over the surface of the tiles, and when dry, characteristic white bands about 25mm wide are formed around the edges, which have been described as 'window framing'. This condition, though unsightly, is not necessarily harmful, and the salt deposits can be removed by careful cleaning. In severely damp conditions, however, thermoplastic tiles can absorb these salts, and the pressures set up within the tiles as the salts crystallise are sometimes sufficient to cause delamination and ultimately powdering of the edges of the tiles.

Uses

Thermoplastic tiles may be used in most non-industrial situations. The tiles are not resistant to grease and oil but are satisfactorily used in domestic kitchens.

Vinyl asbestos tiles tend to have better abrasion resistance than thermoplastic tiles. They have good grease and oil resistance and are more suitable for domestic kitchens or even industrial canteens: they are not, however, suitable for industrial kitchens.

Flexible PVC flooring is produced in such a wide variety of forms that a suitable type can be found for most non-industrial situations and in some instances for industrial situations also. Some are tough enough to withstand truck traffic but it is difficult to fix them so as to prevent the stretching and splitting this produces. In places where a jointless floor is desirable, such as in industrial chemical laboratories or hospitals, it is possible to make a continuous floor finish impervious to liquids by hot air welding of adjacent sheets. Sometimes sheets are butt jointed and welded; in other cases a rod of material of similar composition to the sheets is welded into a gap left between the sheets or one formed by edge trimming.

A disadvantage of PVC flooring is that it is more easily damaged by cigarette burns than some other materials, but it is doubtful whether any floor finish should be expected to withstand abuse of this kind.

The characteristics of synthetic rubber flooring are much the same as those of natural rubber flooring but they have the advantage of higher resistance to solvents, grease and oils, and freedom from the surface crazing often associated with natural rubber flooring.

Adhesives

There are few difficulties associated with adhesives for flooring so long as it is realised that adhesives cannot act as damp-proof membranes. Even on a dry base there are some problems involved in laying flexible PVC flooring on adhesives. Tar from an adhesive can diffuse slowly through the thickness of the flooring to produce indelible brown stains on the surface. Adhesives containing tar are not therefore recommended.

Some adhesives cause flexible PVC flooring to shrink and produce unsightly gaps around the tiles. This shrinkage is quite different from that shown by dimensionally unstable material (BS 3261 : 1960 includes a test for this) and is produced by movement of plasticiser from the tile into the adhesive. The shrinkage is high (0·7 per cent has been observed) and because the plasticiser softens the adhesive there is a tendency for the tiles to move under traffic and for very wide gaps to appear.

The problem can be solved by using an adhesive that is resistant to plasticisers. Water emulsions of synthetic resins or synthetic rubbers form the basis of most suitable adhesives but the choice of adhesive must normally be left to the manufacturer of the flooring, since he is likely to use a range of plasticisers any of which might bleed into particular adhesives.

Maintenance

To retain the initial appearance of the floor finishes discussed in this Digest it is necessary to maintain them by polishing. The polishes available may be divided into two categories: (i) emulsions in water of resins, waxes or blends of these; and (ii) pastes or liquids in which wax is dissolved in white spirit, turpentine or other solvent. Emulsion polishes can be used on all the materials without risk of damaging the finish, but solvent-based polishes should never be used on thermoplastic tiles since the solvents soften the binders in these. Excessive use of polish should always be avoided, since it leads to slipperiness and high dirt retention. Worn or dirty coats of polish can be removed by washing with a solution of a neutral detergent and subsequently rinsing with clean water.

Two common kinds of markings which may present problems of flooring maintenance are those produced by black rubber in footwear, castor tyres and protective thimbles on the legs of metal furniture, and those produced on the floorings of motor showrooms by rubber tyres.

The scuff markings first referred to can be removed by rubbing with scouring powder and fine steel wool and, on materials other than thermoplastic tiles, by wiping with a cloth moistened with turpentine or white spirit. The markings in motor showrooms, however, are indelible as they are caused by interaction between the antioxidants in the rubber tyres and the floor finish. Here, prevention is the only real answer, although careful choice of pattern in the flooring can help to mask the effect. Mats, metal strips, or thin sheets of polyethylene are effective safeguards in preventing contact between tyres and floors.

Composition

Thermoplastic binders

These are termed thermoplastic because they soften when heated and harden again on cooling. At normal temperatures they are usually brittle unless blended with plasticisers. Large quantities of flooring employ the following binders:

Pitch and petroleum bitumen—dark brown to black substances obtained from the distillation of coal and petroleum respectively.

Gisonite—a dark brown naturally occurring asphaltic material.

Coumarone resins—pale yellow substances found in coal tar naphtha. Extensive processing, including polymerisation, is necessary before they can be used for flooring.

Vinyl resins—white resins synthesised from acetylene or ethylene. Important members of this group are polyvinyl chloride (PVC), copolymers of vinyl chloride and vinyl acetate containing up to 15 per cent of the acetate, and copolymers of vinyl chloride and vinylidene chloride.

Plasticisers

Plasticisers are usually oily liquids having high boiling points and low volatility. They are used to increase the pliability of the binder during the manufacturing process and to provide some measure of control over the flexibility of the finished product.

Fillers

These are used mainly to reduce material costs but they have subsidiary uses, e.g. carbon black may sometimes act as a reinforcing agent or even as a means of providing an electrically conducting material, and asbestos fibre helps to improve the handling properties of hot material during the manufacturing process. Most of the powdered fibres used are of mineral origin, e.g. calcium carbonate and china clay. Cellulosic fillers such as sawdust are seldom used since products containing them are more sensitive to moisture: further, they sometimes lead to high dirt retention by the finish.

Stabilisers

Stabilisers are used mainly to prevent degradation of some of the thermoplastic binders during manufacture, but they also protect the finished flooring subsequently when this is exposed to strong sunlight.

Manufacture and Availability

Thermoplastic flooring tiles

Thermoplastic tiles are made by heating and masticating binders, plasticisers, short-fibre asbestos, powdered mineral fillers and pigments. The resulting hot mass is passed between rollers, which combine heat and pressure, to produce a sheet of appropriate thickness from which the tiles are produced, usually by die-cutting. At ordinary temperatures the material is brittle so that it cannot be marketed in sheet form. The binders range from petroleum bitumen and pitch in the very dark coloured tiles through gilsonite to coumarone-indene and coumarone-styrene resins in the lightest colours. Many of these tiles are now produced with a small proportion of plasticised PVC; they are more flexible and more resistant to grease. The dark binders and their associated fillers and pigments are cheapest and this is reflected in the lower cost of the dark tiles. They are produced in a variety of plain colours and marbled patterns; other patterns, e.g. one simulating the grain and colour of timber, have been made.

PVC (vinyl) asbestos tiles

PVC (vinyl) asbestos tiles formed a natural development from thermoplastic tiles. They are manufactured in the same way with approximately the same ratio of binder to filler: the difference lies in the binder, which consists mainly of vinyl chloride polymer or of copolymers of vinyl chloride with vinyl acetate. The binder allows the production of tiles having clearer, brighter colours and greater flexibility than thermoplastic tiles, though the material is too inflexible to allow of its marketing in sheet form.

Flexible PVC flooring

Flexible PVC flooring is made in both sheet and tile form and in the same thicknesses as vinyl asbestos tiles. The binders used are polyvinyl chloride, copolymers of vinyl chloride or blends of these. It should be noted that although the binding medium may not be entirely polyvinyl chloride it is common practice to refer to the binders as PVC: to avoid confusion this description will be used here. Powdered minerals are the most commonly used fillers but some flooring contains a small proportion of asbestos fibre. The ratio of binder (plasticised resin) to filler can vary very widely; some materials contain as much as 85 per cent of binder, whereas others may contain only 25 per cent or even less. The prices of the finished products when compared on the basis of equivalent thicknesses give some indication of the proportion of binder, as this is the most expensive ingredient.

The most important processes in the manufacture of PVC flooring include the following:

(1) The binder and its compounding ingredients are heated and masticated to form a hot mass from which sheets are produced by calendering. Sheets up to 3 mm thick can be satisfactorily produced in this way, but it is often easier to manufacture thinner sheets which are then pressed together in layers or laminated with other materials such as bitumen-saturated paper felt, cellular rubber and cellular PVC. When similar sheets of thin material are laminated together it is often difficult and sometimes impossible to distinguish the finished product from one made to the full thickness in one operation. Frequently the backing has the same composition, apart from pigmentation, as the face, so as to allow trimmings or offcuts, which would otherwise be scrapped, to be re-used.

(2) A cold paste of the plasticised binder is spread on to a supporting layer such as needleloom felt or hessian. The paste is then heated and a tough film is formed when it gels. This process lends itself to the production of embossed patterns.

(3) Pelletised material is formed into blocks and these blocks are sliced into tiles. Particular patterns, e.g. simulated terrazzo, can be produced by this method.

Methods (1) and (2) are used for the production of PVC flooring having a jute hessian backing. Hessian may also be used to support material during production, in which case it is stripped from the product before it is distributed.

Synthetic rubbers

There is a small but increasing use for flooring of a group of materials generally referred to as synthetic rubbers. These materials resemble natural rubber flooring in appearance and can be produced on conventional rubber manufacturing equipment. Tiles may be cut from calendered sheet or produced individually in moulds to give the same wide range of thicknesses and sizes that are available for natural rubber flooring. The binders used include chloro-sulphonated polyethylene, styrene-butadiene copolymers, and butyl and nitrile rubbers.

Built-up felt roofs

Built-up bitumen felt roofing is an efficient and durable form of roof covering provided it is properly laid. Many roofs of this kind have remained serviceable for 20 years or more with little need for maintenance or repairs. There are others, though, which for a variety of reasons, have become defective, sometimes quite early in their life, causing leakage and other troubles.

With due care, difficulties can be avoided; this digest explains the reasons for the defects and shows how they can be overcome. The recommended precautions are included in British Standard Code of Practice CP144 Roof coverings, Part 3:1970, Built-up bitumen felt.

Roofing felt may be used as a single thickness for temporary structures, such as sheds, but for permanent construction three layers of felt are usually bonded together on site with hot bitumen to form 'built-up' felt roofs.

Types of felt

Roofing felt consists of a mat of organic or inorganic fibres impregnated and usually coated with bitumen. BS 747 Roofing felts Part 2 : 1970 groups the felts into four classes, sub-divided as follows:

Class 1. Bitumen felts (fibre base)
  1A Saturated
  1B Fine sand surfaced
  1C Self-finished
  1D Coarse sand surfaced
  1E Mineral surfaced
  1F Reinforced

Class 2. Bitumen felts (asbestos base)
  2A Saturated
  2B Fine sand surfaced
  2C Self-finished
  2E Mineral surfaced

Class 3. Bitumen felts (glass fibre base)
  3B Fine sand surfaced
  3E Mineral surfaced
  3G Venting base layer

Class 4. Sheathing felts and hair felts
  4A(i) Black sheathing (pitch)
              Black sheathing (bitumen)
  4A(ii) Brown sheathing
  4B(i) Black hair
  4B(ii) Brown hair

Durability

As already stated, built-up bitumen felt roofing of reputable quality, when properly used, can be expected to last for many years. Some of the felts made under the 'austerity' conditions of the last war gave poor service, but these are not representative of the general run of production before or since.

When felt roofing fails to give satisfactory service, the failure is generally due to incorrect use of the material, or neglect of the necessary precautions, rather than to poor quality felt. If, for example, no suitable provision is made against the movements of the sub-structure of the roof that result from drying shrinkage or thermal changes, the felt may be stretched beyond its capacity, and crack or tear.

Again, defects may arise through the entrapment of large amounts of water under the felt, or through excessive condensation on the underside. Effects such as these usually occur long before the felt shows any serious deterioration as a direct result of exposure to the weather.

The long-term effect of exposure is to cause a gradual loss of bitumen from the surface; crazing and pitting may eventually occur, allowing access of moisture to the fibre, and deterioration may then be accelerated. The felt also loses flexibility on exposure and so becomes more liable to crack. Walking on old felt that has become blistered or wrinkled may cause cracking and subsequent leakage.

The slope of the roof has an important influence on the durability of the felt. If rain water is not able to drain off completely, but stands on the roof in pools, it hastens the breakdown of the felt and may also cause pimpling or blistering, and loosening of grit from the protective surface dressing. Built-up bitumen felt roofing, therefore, should never be laid on a completely flat roof; a true fall, including allowance for deflection, of not less than 1 : 80 is essential, with provision for complete drainage.

Organic fibre felts can be used on dry roof decks and insulation, but are not recommended as the first layers on concrete or screeds. Felts based on asbestos or glass have better dimensional stability than those based on organic fibres, and so are less liable to cockle where the felt is not fully bonded to the roof.

Choice of felt

Built-up felt roofing will generally consist of three layers of felt bonded with hot bitumen.

If self-finished felt is used, some roofing contractors prefer to use a felt coated with a light dusting of sand instead of the talc normally used to prevent sticking in the roll, because they consider that the sand coating gives a better bond to the roof deck and so helps to avoid blistering. In that event, allowance of 0·35 kg/m² for fine sand and 1·1 kg/m² for coarse sand should be made for the additional weight of the sand in specifying the weight of the roll. Saturated felts, particularly those based on organic fibres, are not recommended for the lower layers of a built-up roof in damp climates, because they tend to hold moisture and may cause blistering.

The type of felt for the top layer depends to some extent on the slope of the roof. On roofs with a slope of not less than 10 degrees, mineral-surfaced felt type 1E can be used, whilst types 2E and 3E are suitable for slopes not less than 5 degrees. On slopes less than 5 degrees the protective mineral chippings should be applied *in situ*, secured with an adhesive of 'cut-back' bitumen (a solution of bitumen in a volatile solvent), blinded with 5 or 10 mm mineral chippings. The chippings should preferably be white or light in colour, so as to keep the felt and the underlying structure cool in sunny weather and so minimise thermal movements.

Fire protection

Although bitumen felt is a combustible material, the degree of fire protection afforded by a built-up roof depends upon the roof structure as a whole. Requirements relating to the ability of a roof covering to afford protection against the spread of fire into the building or to adjoining buildings are laid down in both the English and the Scottish Building Regulations, and examples are quoted of various felt-covered roofings that would be deemed to satisfy these regulations.

The requirements are two-fold:
(1) The roof shall resist penetration of fire.
(2) The roof shall not encourage the spread of flame.

Each requirement is classified from A to D, representing minimum to maximum hazard; thus an 'AA' roof resists penetration of fire for one hour and the flames will not spread. Details of fire resistance for pitched and flat roofs will be found in Table A3 of CP144 and in the Building Regulations.

Roof construction

The various kinds of roof decks on which built-up roofing can be laid are listed in **Table 1** with the appropriate methods of treatment. For example, some that are thermally insulating in themselves require a topping of cement and sand, and the felt is laid on this; with others, the thermal insulation, where necessary, is provided by means of materials such as fibre insulating board, or cork, on which the felt can be laid direct.

In the construction of roof decks, the following three points call for special consideration since they have an important bearing on the performance of the felt covering and the efficiency of the roof as a whole.

Felt roofs must not be laid without falls

Moisture and thermal movement

It was mentioned earlier that tearing of the felt can be caused by movement of the underlying structure, especially drying shrinkage and thermal movements. Since these cannot be eliminated entirely, special precautions are necessary in laying the felt to minimise their effect and these are indicated under **Preparation for fixing**; in addition, everything practicable should be done to ensure that the movements themselves are kept to a minimum. To control the drying shrinkage in screeds or topping the mix should not be richer than 1 : 4 and it is important that the sand should be clean, well graded and fairly coarse. The water content of the mixes should be no more than is necessary for placing, compacting and finishing. The laying of screeds over weak insulating materials supported on roof decks is not recommended. Drying shrinkage of the screed is unrestrained and the screed is liable to crack and curl during drying, and the screed and the insulating material can become waterlogged during the hardening period for the screed.

Thermal movements of a concrete decking or topping are best controlled by a white or light-coloured treatment applied to the felt after it is laid, e.g. a layer of light-coloured grit or stone chippings, or decking slabs; movement joints should also be provided in large areas of concrete decking.

Constructional and rain-water

The average weekly rainfall in the driest part of the United Kingdom is approximately 12 mm; an evaporation rate of 12 mm per week is achieved only in fine summer weather. Porous decking or screed exposed to the weather is more likely therefore to increase its moisture content than it is to dry out.

Once felt has been applied the entrapped water, whatever its origin, can escape only very slowly, and its effects may continue for many months or even years. Apart from any visible effect, moisture retained in the structure reduces the thermal insulation and so encourages condensation, thus defeating the purpose of the insulation. It may, moreover, create a serious nuisance by causing stains, or even appearing as drips, on the ceiling below; also, in sunny weather, the pressure of water vapour may cause the felt to blister. Every practicable step should therefore be taken to reduce the water content. Drainage tubes, inserted in the structural roof and left open until the ceiling is plastered, are of great benefit in reducing the amount of water retained.

A practice known to have given satisfactory results is as follows. The structural deck is drained so that no ponds can form on it. This may be done by inserting drainage tubes at the time of construction; alternatively, the roof may be flooded and the deck punctured at the centre of all ponds. An insulating screed consisting of cement and no-fines lightweight aggregate (e.g. sintered pulverised-fuel ash) is then laid, followed by a thin 1 : 4 cement/sand topping, just sufficient to bring the screed to a fair face. The screed can then be allowed to mature until conditions are suitable for the roofing felt covering to be laid.

Although most of the rain penetrating the screed will drain away, even a drained screed will retain some moisture, and provision must be made for its escape. Small pressure release vents can be provided every 20 m², or when a lot of moisture is trapped brick box ventilators as shown in **Fig. 5** can be used. Various types of proprietary ventilators are available as alternatives to the brick box. One system uses tubes set into the screed and connecting the ventilators. The use of a spot-bonded ventilating felt as the first layer of built-up roofing will also encourage evaporation.

A system of pumping air through porous screeds has been developed in the last few years. Some success has been reported, but it cannot be expected to dry out in a few weeks a screed that may contain 1000 kg of water.

If lightweight concrete were made water-repellent, the absorption of mixing water and rain would be much reduced, and a no-fines screed laid on a drained roof deck would then hold very little water. Trials have shown this practice to be feasible with little or no loss of strength, and British Patent No. 824592 has been taken to cover the process. At present, though, it has not been successful; there has been insufficient demand for the treated aggregate to allow it to be marketed at a realistic cost.

Lightweight concrete slabs, insulating boards, compressed straw panels, wood-wool slabs and other absorptive materials intended to be incorporated in the roof structure should be stored under cover and should be fixed in sections as the roof covering is proceeded with, so that each section may be covered without delay. Wherever possible, tarpaulins or polythene sheets should be used to protect uncovered sections in wet weather.

Condensation

Moisture condensing within the thickness of a roof structure under built-up roofing can, if the condensation is heavy and long-continued, produce the same effects as entrapped construction or rainwater. This is not confined to high humidity buildings such as mills or laundries, it is common in dwellings. Two methods of preventing trouble are possible; to fit a true vapour barrier over the structural roof covered by thermal insulating material and waterproof covering. The vapour barrier should consist of one layer of bitumen felt fixed with hot bitumen using the 'pour and roll' technique, with the insulating material stuck to the vapour barrier with more hot bitumen. The whole job, from vapour barrier to covering, should be completed at one time, with precautions taken to protect raw edges overnight. The other technique is to use a vapour check at ceiling level, combined with ventilation of the roof space. The ventilation of the roof is necessary because it is impossible to make a true vapour barrier at ceiling level, but the ceiling should be as free as possible from gaps and holes, and should have a low vapour permeability. A ceiling could, for example, be constructed of foil-backed plasterboard, or have a polythene membrane immediately above it. The minimum ventilation is given in CP144 as 1000 mm² opening per metre run of eaves on two opposite sides of the building. Air must have a free passage from one side to the other, and if the roof is wider than 12 m, the size of the openings should be doubled. With some types of roof slab, especially those of cellular concrete, these precautions can be relaxed. The slabs give satisfactory service in most situations without a vapour barrier beneath them.

Preparation for fixing

Splitting of the covering can be avoided by careful design. Research into the behaviour of bitumen felt in tension has indicated that it will tear at about 5 per cent extension, so if in the design a limit of 2 per cent is adopted, the risk of tearing would be avoided. Thus, if a crack or joint is likely to open 2 mm, the width of felt left unbonded over the crack or joint should be 100 mm.

Recommended preparatory measures for roofs of different kinds are outlined in **Table 1** and particular attention is directed to those relating to lightweight concrete screeds and woodwool slabs.

Observations on roofing felt laid on these materials demonstrate that the practice of bonding the felt to a blinding coat of slurry often leads to cracking of the felt in places where shrinkage cracks develop in

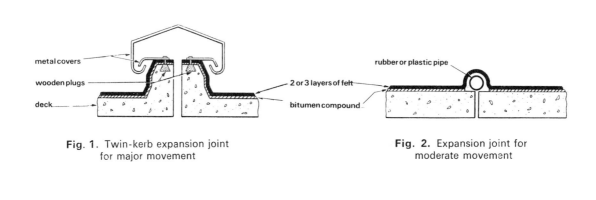

Fig. 1. Twin-kerb expansion joint for major movement

Fig. 2. Expansion joint for moderate movement

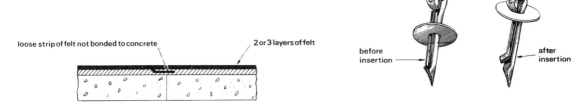

Fig. 3. Flat expansion joint for minor movement

Fig. 4. Expanding nail

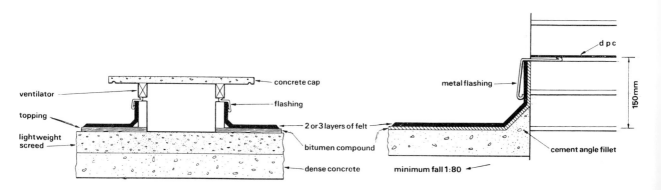

Fig. 5. Brick box ventilator

Fig. 6. Treatment of upstand

the roof structure. Felt laid directly on aerated concrete is sometimes prone to blister.

For these reasons it is recommended that a 12 mm topping of one part of cement to four parts of clean coarse sand should be used, and that this should be laid in alternate bays, each of not more than 10m². For aerated concrete screeds, however, some contractors prefer to prime the surface with a bitumen primer instead of using the topping, and this is permissible.

Since shrinkage cracks often develop along the line separating two areas of roofing of different widths, or at junctions between lengths of roof, or in places where the run of the roof is interrupted by roof-lights, it is further recommended that cuts should be made in the topping and preferably through the full depth of the screed along the lines of such junctions and along lines joining the adjacent corners of roof lights, and that any large areas of topping should be similarly subdivided at junctions between the bays.

Apart from providing a fair surface for adhesion of the felt and facility for correcting any inadequacy in fall, the purpose of the topping is two-fold. It aims to restrain the drying shrinkage of the woodwool slab or lightweight concrete screed and also to encourage any cracking of the topping to occur along the lines of the cuts rather than in random directions across the slab. Subsequently, loose strips of felt should be laid along the lines of the cuts, **Fig. 3,** to prevent adhesion of the overlying felt for a distance of about 100 mm on either side. The aim here is to allow the felt to stretch rather than tear in response to any small movements that may occur in the topping. The method illustrated in **Fig. 2** is better where considerable movement is likely. Expansion joints in the roof structure should preferably be of the twin-kerb type, **Fig. 1.**

Fixing

Methods of fixing are also set out in **Table 1.** The surface should be clean, free from dust or debris, and at least surface-dry at the time of laying. Except for wooden boarded roofs, where the first layer is nailed and should not be bonded to the boards, roofing felt is customarily bonded to the roof with hot bitumen spread at the rate of about 1·5 kg/m². On highly absorptive surfaces, this is preceded by an application of a bitumen primer to reduce frothing of the bitumen and assist adhesion. The primer must be allowed to dry before proceeding.

Table 1   Recommended constructions

Roof decks	Treatment before laying felt	Method of fixing first layer
Aerated concrete screeds, or lightweight aggregate concrete screeds, on dense concrete slabs, precast concrete beams, hollow pots, etc.	12 mm topping of 1 : 4 cement : clean coarse sand, laid in alternate bays not exceeding 10 m²*. Drain tubes through the deck and ventilators may also be required.	Partial bonding. Where cuts are made in the topping (see text), strips of felt to be laid along the cuts.
Asbestos-cement	Fibre insulation board, laid to break joint, bonded with hot bitumen to a vapour barrier	Bonding overall
Dense concrete, shell roofs, etc.	Nailing battens should be provided at the top of steep slopes. Fibre or cork insulation board may, if required, be bonded to the roof over a vapour barrier	Bonding overall, unless cracking is expected
Metal deck	Fibre insulation board, laid to break joint, bonded with hot bitumen to a vapour barrier	Bonding overall
Compressed straw slabs	Tape joints	Bonding overall
Wood boards	If additional insulation is needed, insulation board, laid to break joint, may be fixed	Nailing
Woodwool slabs	12 mm topping of 1 : 4 cement : clean coarse sand, laid in alternate bays not exceeding 10 m²	Partial bonding. Where cuts are made in the topping strips of felt to be laid along the cuts.

*With aerated concrete screeds, some manufacturers recommend priming the surface in preference to a cement : sand topping; either is permissible.

It is seldom necessary to bond the felt overall, but there should be sufficient bonding to prevent lifting and tearing of the felt in high winds. Where there is a substantial loading of tiles or stone chippings, it may be enough to bond the edges of the strips of felt. For fixing to the cement/sand topping recommended for use over lightweight concrete screeds or woodwool slabs, partial bonding at the edges and in strips or spots elsewhere is preferable to overall bonding, since this gives the felt more scope for stretching in response to any differential movement in the roof slabs.

The suggestion for partial bonding applies only to the first layer of felt. Partial bonding is essentially a precautionary measure imposed by the impossibility of predicting precisely where cracking may occur. It is not necessary or desirable to use partial bonding where the felt is laid on fibre insulating board, cork or compressed straw slabs.

Table 2 Defects in built-up felt roofs

Defect	Cause	Remedial treatment
Tearing or cracking	1. Differential movement at cracks or joints in the substructure	1. Adopt details shown in Figs. 1, 2 or 3. If defects extensive, re-lay over fibre insulating board
	2. Perforation of unsupported felt	2. Provide a supporting fillet and patch with felt
	3. Perforation of blisters by traffic	3. Cut, bond down and patch over blister
	4. Sharp bends in felt	4. Round off and patch, or use a metal flashing
Pimpling on top layer of felt, eventually breaking open and exposing fibres	Expansion of more volatile fractions of bitumen, or of air or water, in sunny weather. May occur with self-finished felt, particularly where pools of water can stand on it, or with mineral-surfaced felt laid at too low a pitch	In serious cases on felt roofs, dress with cut-back bitumen and grit
Blisters between layers of felt	Expansion, in sunny weather, of entrapped air or water	Cut the blister, re-bond and patch. If the trouble is persistent, a heat-reflecting treatment, or the weight of a heavy dressing, may help
Blisters between felt and deck	Expansion in sunny weather, of entrapped air or water. Particularly liable to occur on surfaces such as lightweight concrete screeds or asbestos cement, if not dealt with as in Table 1	
Cockling and rippling	Moisture movement of either felt or roof, especially where felt is not bonded	Little can be done, except to relay. Site dressing, using a fair weight of grit, may make the defects less conspicuous
Lifting of laps	1. Bad bonding initially 2. Pulling as a result of formation of blisters	1. Re-bond 2. Cut, bond down and patch
Local deterioration associated with ponding	Inadequate fall, or obstruction of outfall	Clear outfalls. Site dressing with cut-back bitumen and coarse grit may limit further damage
Arching of tiles, screeds, etc.	Inadequate allowance for thermal or moisture movement	Provide 25 mm gaps around bays of about 9 m² and fill with a bitumen compound. If necessary, rake out old compound and re-point
General deterioration and embrittlement	Premature deterioration indicates inadequate falls, wrong choice of felt, neglect of any recommended surface dressing, or wrong laying	Re-lay if deterioration is far advanced; if not, site dress with cut-back bitumen and grit
Loss of grit	1. Site dressing in adverse weather conditions 2. Use of hot bitumen or emulsion instead of cut-back bitumen 3. Inadequate fall	Site dress, using cut-back bitumen and fairly coarse grit

Partial bonding may also be achieved by using a proprietary underlay perforated with holes about 12 mm in diameter and gritted on the undersurface. Hot bitumen is spread over this so that the bonding of the felt to the roof is restricted to the areas of the holes in the underlay. The gritted under-surface provides a continuous air space through which vapour can escape at the verges, thus preventing a build-up of pressure beneath the felt.

A form of expanding nail, **Fig. 4,** has been introduced for nailing felt to lightweight concrete of medium strength without a topping, but there has not yet been much experience of its use. Because of the alkaline character of concrete, nails in an aluminium alloy would be unsuitable for this purpose.

Upstands at parapet walls, etc., need careful detailing to exclude rain. The upstand, which should be at least 150 mm high, should preferably be covered with a metal flashing as shown in **Fig. 6.** Where there is a damp-proof course in the wall, the flashing should be made continuous with it. Bends in the felt in these or similar circumstances should be supported, preferably with a wood or mortar fillet.

Where the edges of a roof are finished with a kerbing under the felt, the development of shrinkage cracks in the joints of the kerb may lead to tearing of the felt. Laying a loose strip of felt over each joint, **Fig. 3,** to break the bond with the overlying felt will reduce this risk. A metal trim should be firmly anchored at close centres to a substantial member in the roof deck.

Roof paving

Where a built-up roof has to carry much traffic, a more substantial surface is needed. This may be of tiles bedded in bitumen, or a topping of bitumen macadam not less than 12 mm thick or a mortar screed not less than 25 mm thick. Since there must be enough freedom of movement in tiling or screed to prevent lifting or arching under the combined effects of thermal and moisture movement of the roof structure, tiling or screed should be laid in areas of not more than 10m² and these areas should be separated by 25 mm joints. Tiles should be butt-jointed. Each area of mortar screed should be sub-divided into units not larger than 0·6 m by 0·6 m by

cutting through the full thickness of the screed before it has set and hardened. Subsequently these cuts and the joints between the separate areas should be filled with a bitumen jointing compound.

Treatment of defects

The appearance of dampness, or even of water drips below a built-up roof does not necessarily mean that the roof covering is leaking, for these defects can also be produced, as already explained, by construction water, by rainwater or by heavy condensation within the roof structure. If, therefore, on careful inspection, the felt covering appears to be intact, these possibilities should be considered, remembering that water can remain entrapped for many months after the covering has been laid.

There is no quick way of drying out a roof that, from any cause, has become waterlogged. If water is dripping from points in the ceiling or, as often happens, from electric conduits, holes may be bored near the places affected to assist drainage. Drying can also be assisted by building brick box ventilators, **Fig. 5,** on the roof at appropriate places, or by the other methods already described.

If the conditions within the building are warm and humid, condensation may be suspected; if it is in fact the cause of the dampness, the only remedy, in severe cases, may be to provide more thermal insulation over an effective vapour barrier. In milder cases it may be sufficient, if practicable, to improve the ventilation of the building.

Sources of dampness caused by cracking or deterioration of the felt or failure to cover upstands with flashings can usually be traced by inspection. Where the felt has become torn or cracked but is otherwise in good condition, patching on the lines indicated in **Figs. 2** or **3** will be well worth trying; it can best be undertaken by a specialist contractor. Other defects can be dealt with by the methods given in **Table 2.** If there is reason to think that thermal movement of the roof has been a contributory factor in damaging the felt, it may help to prevent a recurrence if, after repair, the felt is covered with a layer of light-coloured grit to reflect solar heat.

Further reading

BS 747 Roofing felts Part 2 : 1970
BS CP 144 Roof covering Part 3 : 1970 Built-up bitumen felt
Built-up roofing; Felt Roofing Contractors Advisory Board: 1966

Asphalt and built-up felt roofings: durability

A study of flat roofs covered with mastic asphalt and built-up bitumen felt roofing has disclosed the most common causes of failure and made possible an assessment of these roofings when properly designed and laid. It is suggested that they should be inspected at least annually so that action can be taken to deal with defects early enough to prevent their leading to failure.

Although many complaints are made about leakage and maintenance costs of flat roofs, these still remain popular with designers. A survey of flat roofs on Crown buildings covered with mastic asphalt and built-up bitumen felt was therefore mounted by the Building Research Station at Garston in order to provide more detailed information about the frequency and causes of failure and success. Figures 1 and 2 show the number of examples studied and the age and performance of each up to the date of the survey. The failures recorded could all be attributed to failure to comply with published recommendations for design and installation (*see* 'Further reading'). A study of similar roofings on local authority dwellings in Scotland is also nearing completion. Failure to comply with published recommendations, particularly in regard to edge details, at verges, curbs and parapets was also noted. A further publication incorporating the details of the lessons to be learned from both surveys is planned.

General characteristics

A flat roof is normally a composite structure. Its functional requirements are met partly by the load-bearing deck and insulation, partly by the covering and, where appropriate, by a vapour barrier under the insulation. Only the covering is considered here.

Mastic asphalt Asphalt to BS 1162 tends to develop a grey appearance when weathered whereas the BS 988 material remains dark in colour, though finishing by sand rubbing lightens its appearance; the two are visually indistinguishable when given a solar reflective treatment. In direct sunshine, both types harden gradually and shrink slightly; this causes shallow surface crazing which does not usually develop into cracks. Cracking from other causes, such as the drying shrinkage of a coating of unsuitable paint or the differential movements of paving tiles not laid on a separating layer, may progress through the full thickness of the asphalt.

Asphalt being, in effect, a stiff liquid can tolerate slow movement involving the full thickness of the material, but otherwise it behaves as a brittle solid and is liable to crack under any suddenly applied strain, particularly under impact and in cold weather. Because of its high coefficient of thermal expansion, and because partial bonding to a roof deck of 'wet' construction tends to cause blistering due to concentrated vapour pressure, it is now usual to separate the asphalt from any substrate, except bitumen-bonded lightweight aggregate screeds, by an isolating membrane of sheathing felt. The purpose of this is to avoid blistering or cracking and to bridge discontinuities, but where significant movement may occur, for example at a butt joint in the deck, it is desirable to break the continuity of the asphalt by means of a movement joint. The dead weight of the roofing, including sheathing felt, is about 40 kg/m^2, and this, with proper edge detailing, is usually sufficient to prevent uplift by wind suction in the UK.

Built-up bitumen felt roofing The early felts were based wholly on organic fibres which were very strong when new but dimensionally unstable, and could rot, when moisture eventually penetrated the bitumen coating. The asbestos-based felts are more stable but they may still include up to 20 per cent of organic fibre. Bitumen felt based on glass fibre is stable and rot-proof but the glass fibre is in the form of a bonded tissue, not a woven fabric, and does not provide very high strength, so that the felt needs careful handling. The merits of each type can be exploited by correct design, often using two or more types in the same system. None of these three standard types can be stretched, before splitting, more than about 5 per cent (say 2 per cent for design purposes) and if fully bonded to a substrate which subsequently cracks they will split. On concrete and screeded surfaces, it is now usual to fix the first layer by only partial bonding to a pattern that allows the escape of water vapour, during drying, and reduces the risk of splitting. The felt can be fully bonded to dry insulation materials; on a wooden deck, the first layer is fixed by nailing.

If exposed to the weather, a bitumen surface is gradually attacked by solar radiation, both ultraviolet and heat-producing, and by atmospheric oxidation; the effects are increasing embrittlement and crazing, or superficial pimpling, leading to exposure of the fibres and progressive attack of the bitumen underlying them. Some form of surface protection is therefore necessary. Unless a special finish for solar reflection or foot traffic is required, the roofing should be given a surface dressing of bitumen compound and mineral chippings; in the Scottish study it was found that stone chippings smaller than 25–32 mm grade are liable to be scoured by the winds to expose the bitumen surface below. By its added weight this dressing reduces the risk of lift by the wind; it also contributes to the fire grading of the roof. To reflect solar heat, white chippings may be used. The weight of built-up felt roofing varies with the nature of the surface dressing and the risk of uplift by wind suction may limit the proportion in area that can be safely left unbonded.

For more detailed recommendations for built-up felt roofs, see Digest No 8 (1970 edition).

Performance

Not all of the sites were visited and though a great deal of information was obtained by technical questionnaires some of the detail requested, particularly as to falls, was not provided. Official records of minor repairs (under £100) are almost non-existent and some reliance had to be placed on the memories or personal notes of the maintenance personnel. Published guidance has undergone some changes, for example in the revision of Codes of Practice, the effects of which could not in all cases be isolated.

About one-third of the roofs studied from Garston had 'failed', this being defined as a roof, or its weathering detailing, that has permitted water to penetrate at some time. The roofs shown in Figs 1 and 2 to be 'defective' exhibit visible imperfections such as blisters, cockling and ponding which could lead to failure though this has not yet occurred.

The incidence of failure seems to vary between the two types of roofing mainly in that the probability of failure remains practically constant throughout the life of an asphalt roof but increases steadily during the life of a built-up felt roof.

Asphalt roofing, properly designed and laid, should prove capable of lasting 50–60 years; the natural ageing of bitumen felt is likely to limit its life to about 20 years.

Mastic asphalt Of 123 coverings, 34 were classified as having failed: 20 by splitting, cracking or tearing under strain, as by differential movement of a deck from which the covering was not properly isolated; 14 due to disruption of associated weathering, skirtings or flashings, at parapet walls, roof lights or around rainwater outlets. After repair, none of these failed coverings had needed to be replaced.

Built-up bitumen felt Of 200 coverings, 77 had failed. Most of these were due to the same causes that damaged the asphalt roofs, inability to accommodate movements in the roof decks (37 roofs) or disruption of weathering (26 roofs). A few failures attributable to entrapped moisture or condensation had also resulted from avoidable inadequacies in design or workmanship. A single instance of wind damage could be ascribed either to inadequate fixing or to a gale of abnormal severity. Five of the roof coverings had been replaced after 20–30 years of service (see Fig 2) because of deterioration by natural ageing.

Findings common to both types

Use and location of building No correlation was found between the performance of the roof covering and the function or structural type or form of the building, or with the exposure and topography of the site.

Falls There was no evidence that the provision of falls had any effect on the life of the coverings. But a truly flat surface is unlikely to be achieved in practice, and ponding is likely to occur unless a fall sufficient to drain depressions is provided. Ponding is less harmful to the covering than was at one time supposed but if a leakage occurs in a ponded area water will enter the building in greater quantity than through an effectively drained surface.

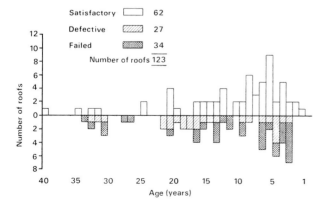

Fig 1 Mastic asphalt coverings

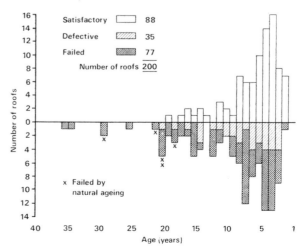

Fig 2 Built-up bitumen felt coverings

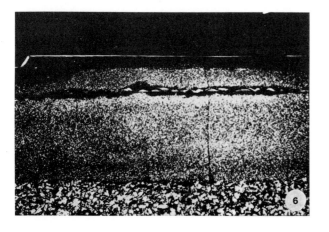

Visual appraisal of defects

Roofings should be inspected at least annually by a maintenance surveyor to ensure that rainwater outlets are kept clear and to decide on any action necessary to prevent defects from becoming failures. The photographs (3–9) may assist in identifying defects.

Mastic asphalt

Ponding: Slight localised deflections below the general plane of the drainage falls can result in ponding. In asphalt roofing, this can cause crazing which may be only shallow and in the condition illustrated (3) does not warrant the cost of remedial measures on technical grounds alone though it might do so on grounds of appearance.

Cracking: Differential movement between precast concrete roofing units can cause cracking (4). This might have been avoided had the perimeter of the asphalt not been bonded directly to the concrete beyond the edges of the sheathing felt, which stops short as can be seen from the change in level of the surface. Rain has not yet penetrated but it could do so by capillary action. Repair is desirable, but not urgent.

Blistering: (5) shows a combination of blistering and sagging in an asphalt skirting. The most likely sequence of events was that, during hot weather, vapour pressure from water leaking into the parapet wall produced the large blister and in so doing either fractured the tucked-in portion above the blister or pulled it out of its chase. The detached portion of the asphalt when warmed by the sun would tend increasingly to sag under its own weight and so produce the fold seen below the blister. If not arrested the sagging will progress and rainwater will enter the building. The damaged area should be cut away and made good without delay.

Built-up bitumen felt covering

Splitting: Tearing (6) occurred over an edge or verge curb, the capping of which is of plywood; the plywood has delaminated as a result of entrapped moisture and as it distorted it imposed sufficient tensile forces to split the felt. Adherence to recommended details would avoid this defect. Metal edge trims were found also to split the felt at or about the butt joints in the trims.

Cracking: A portion of replacement felt at the northeast corner of a roof (7) shows cracking of the type sometimes called 'crocodiling'. The horizontal area of felt is protected by mineral aggregate dressing but on the fillet at the base of the upstand to the parapet wall the felt suffers maximum exposure to the sun. The combination of solar heating, ultra-violet radiation and atmospheric oxidation has crazed the coating of bitumen, applied generally to the area to stick down the mineral aggregate and then cracked the top layer of self-finished felt. Further progress of the

Further reading

Mastic asphalt:

BS 988 Mastic asphalt for roofing (limestone aggregate)
BS 1162 Mastic asphalt for roofing (natural rock asphalt)
BS CP 144 Roof coverings Part 4:1970 Mastic asphalt (metric units)
Application of mastic asphalt; Mastic Asphalt Advisory Council:1967

Built-up bitumen felt:

BS 747 Roofing felts Part 2:1970
BS CP 144 Roof covering Part 3:1970 Built-up bitumen felt
Built-up roofing; Felt Roofing Contractors Advisory Board: 1966

cracking into the underlying layers of felt can be arrested by a reflective treatment, and as the roofing is laid on insulation of vegetable origin this should be done immediately.

Blistering: The brick indicates the size of the blisters (**8**)—up to about 1 m long and 75 mm high. The top layer of the three-layer roofing is mineral-finished. Cutting open a blister revealed that the bottom layer of felt is adhering firmly to the base and the middle layer is firmly bonded to the top; the blisters have developed between the middle and bottom layers. This could result from insufficient pressure when rolling the middle layer into the hot bitumen bonding compound, or from moisture entrapped between the two layers (either rain or dew). As none of the blisters shows signs of bursting, and the bottom layer of felt will still provide cover if they do, repair can be delayed. Meatime, the alternating expansion and contraction of the blisters resulting from thermal variations, particularly in sunny weather, can be reduced by the application of a lime/tallow wash, taking care not to tread on the blisters during application.

Ruckling, rippling, cockling: Undulations (**9**) to which these descriptions have variously been applied can result from inadequate pressure on the roll or insufficient or badly distributed bitumen compound. It is particularly important to avoid these faults in the intentional partial bonding of the first layer. But this did not apply to the present case in which the bottom layer of felt was fully bonded to a fibreboard underlay. Asbestos-based felt type 2A was specified for the bottom and middle layers, but type 1C, which can contain a considerable proportion of vegetable fibre, for the top layer. The vegetable fibre in the top layer of felt could, therefore, have been exposed to the ingress of moisture and the resulting dimensional changes would then aggravate the effects of vapour pressure corresponding to variations in ambient temperature. However, the regular, parallel pattern of the undulations suggested that most, if not all, of the blame stemmed from not allowing the top layer of felt to flatten before fixing.

Except in one case where an undulation is associated with partial lifting of a lapped bond in the felt, which needs to be re-sealed, no immediate repairs are considered necessary so long as the undulations are not likely to be trodden on by maintenance staff servicing plant on the roof.

Condensation in roofs

Although most roofs perform well, problems of condensation are increasing. The risk is greatest in roofs that have impermeable sheet coverings, and flat roofs in particular have frequently given rise to problems. With newer forms of construction, lower roof pitches, and changes in standards and forms of heating, similar problems are now being met in pitched roofs.

This digest discusses design principles for minimising the risk of condensation and consequential damage to decorations or structure.

Design principles

The simplest roof is no more than a rain shield but many designs include a lining or a ceiling, separated from the rain shield or cladding by an air space and insulation. If warm moist air from the building can enter the air space, it will condense on any surface whose temperature is below its dewpoint. This is most likely to be the underside of the cladding, from which moisture can drip on to the ceiling or damage the roof structure. The design should therefore aim to balance temperatures and humidities so that the surface temperatures of critical component parts of the roof remain above the dewpoint of the surrounding air for most of the time. Practical measures that can be taken are:

a provide a vapour barrier at the warm side of the roof structure to prevent the entry of moisture from the building.

b provide a rain shield that is permeable to water vapour, to allow for the transfer of moisture to the outside.

c ventilate the roof space to the outside air.

d blow 'dry' air into the roof space under pressure and thus prevent moist air from entering it.

The practical difficulties of achieving these measures vary from one type of roof to another, and methods appropriate to different roof types are discussed later. For instance, it is very much easier to achieve a permeable rain shield on a pitched roof than on a flat one; it is also easier to form an impermeable membrane above a flat roof deck than below it.

Digest 110 *Condensation* sets out procedures for steady-state calculation of internal temperatures and dewpoints in roofs which do not incorporate ventilated air spaces, and these procedures enable the risk of steady deposition to be assessed for lightweight (low thermal capacity) roofs. An estimate has to be made of the most adverse external and internal temperatures and humidities that will occur at any time.

Such calculations cannot be made for heavyweight (high thermal capacity) roofs such as concrete roofs, which take some time to warm up and cool down, but it is possible to assess whether a steady deposition in concrete roofs is likely by making steady-state calculations based on the most adverse *daily mean* temperatures and humidities.

It is not generally possible to calculate with certainty the risk of condensation in roofs with ventilated air spaces.

Even if there is no steady deposition of water, intermittent condensation can occur. If the roof incorporates absorbent materials that are unaffected by moisture, small amounts of moisture may be deposited for short periods and can later evaporate without causing trouble. Care must be taken to avoid situations where water might drain to where it can cause damage and the ventilation must be good enough to encourage drying during favourable atmospheric conditions.

Condensation is not necessarily troublesome; on the upper side of undertiling felt it is usually harmless as it can normally drain away, but on the underside it is likely to cause trouble either by dripping on to the ceiling below or by draining to a point where it can wet the structure.

Particular attention has to be paid to the possibility of condensation on cellulosic materials such as flaxboard, strawboard, fibreboard or chipboard, which permanently lose mechanical strength or rot when they become wet. Untreated timber is susceptible to fungal attack when its moisture content exceeds 20 per cent by weight. Where there is any risk that it might reach this condition, it should be pressure impregnated with preservative, but timber that has been treated with preservation salts may, when it gets wet, cause corrosion of metal fastenings.

Types of roof

Various forms of roof are now discussed to bring out the factors affecting condensation. The order of presentation is not related to the frequency of occurrence of the roofs, but is chosen to illustrate the principles in a convenient manner.

Sheeted roofs (Fig 1)

Sheeted roofs, which are commonly used in factories, consist of an outer cladding of, say, corrugated metal or asbestos-cement and an inner lining, often fibreboard or plasterboard, with an air space between cladding and lining which may incorporate some additional thermal insulation. In adverse conditions, moisture can enter the air space from the building through gaps between the lining boards or by diffusion through the lining itself, condense on the underside of the cladding and drip on to the insulation or the lining. The problem is reduced if air can flow through gaps between the cladding sheets; spacers can sometimes be used to increase the size of the gaps. Ventilation of the air space can reduce the moisture content of the air within it, and hence the risk of condensation and dripping; it also promotes drying during favourable conditions.

Though sheeted roofs with ventilated air spaces are suitable for most factories, there can be problems in factories where high humidities occur, eg breweries, dye-houses, etc. These can sometimes be overcome by providing a vapour check at the inside of the structure. The best available method of forming a vapour barrier at ceiling level is to spray the underside of the lining with a suitable plastics coating. This treatment is, however, expensive and the film might be ruptured by roof movements. Nevertheless, some form of vapour barrier should be provided as it will reduce the amount of water vapour entering the roof.

Lightweight flat roofs (Fig 2)

Lightweight flat roofs comprise a waterproof membrane covering a structural deck, an air space and a lining or ceiling; they may also incorporate insulation. The air space cannot be ventilated through gaps in the cladding, neither can water vapour diffuse through the waterproof covering which is usually bitumen felt, asphalt or sheet metal. Moist air which finds its way into the air space therefore condenses on a metal deck, or diffuses through a timber roof deck, wetting the deck and condensing on the underside of the waterproof covering. The condensation risk depends on the roof design and because of this all timber used in flat roofs should be pressure impregnated with preservative.

Cold roof   In the roof illustrated in Fig 2a, the insulation is placed on top of the plasterboard; this will prevent surface condensation on the ceiling but there is a risk of condensation on the underside of the waterproof covering. This type of construction is

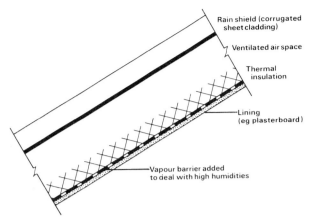

Fig 1 Sheeted roofs

commonly referred to as a 'cold' roof, because for much of the year the temperature of the air within the roof space is lower than the temperature inside the building. The amount of water vapour entering the roof structure can be restricted by a vapour check, eg sheet polythene at ceiling level.

The only way in which the air spaces in a lightweight flat roof can be ventilated is through gaps or grilles at each end of every air space but there is a fairly high resistance to the flow of air in these long narrow air spaces, particularly if they are partially obstructed by stiffeners. If the roof overhangs the external walls, ventilation openings can be provided in the soffit but if the roof finishes flush with the external walls, grilles have to be built into the walls. Neither the air flow through the roof spaces nor the moisture flow into the roof can be estimated with any accuracy. Furthermore, if water is trapped between the timber deck and the waterproof covering, one cannot rely on this being removed by evaporation. Experience has shown that there is a relatively high risk of condensation in this type of roof.

Warm roof (Fig 2b) The behaviour of a lightweight flat roof in respect of condensation is improved if the insulation is placed above the deck and a vapour barrier added between the deck and

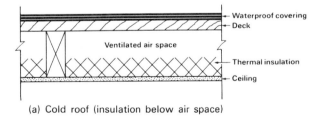

(a) Cold roof (insulation below air space)

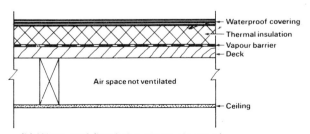

(b) Warm roof (insulation above air space)

Fig 2 Lightweight flat roofs

the insulation. The air in the deck spaces is warmer than the outside air and this type of roof is commonly referred to as a 'warm' roof. In this form of construction with overdeck insulation, no attempt is made to ventilate the roof spaces. If the temperature of the vapour barrier is kept above the dewpoint of the air, condensation will not occur within the roof structure. When it is possible to specify the most adverse temperatures and humidities both inside and outside, the amount of insulation required above the vapour barrier can be calculated.

In housing, the internal conditions are not known but experience has shown that if the roof insulation meets the requirements of the Building Regulations, with most of it located above the vapour barrier, the risk of condensation within the structure is small.

The vapour barrier normally consists of bitumen felt (not less than 13 kg/10 m²) well lapped at joints and nailed or spot bonded to the structural deck in compliance with BS CP 144. An all-over coat of hot bitumen mopped on to the top of the bitumen felt completes the vapour barrier and also provides a means of sticking down the thermal insulation. With this form of construction it is essential that the insulation is kept dry. The insulation boards must also be closely butted since there is a high risk that coverings like bitumen felt or asphalt will fail over gaps. At the perimeter of the roof the vapour barrier must be turned up and sealed to the rain shield to prevent ingress of moisture at the edges of the insulation boards. Similar measures are needed at any breaks in the roof such as at roof lights, around pipes, etc. On large roofs it is also advisable to divide the insulation into sealed compartments.

Lightweight pitched roofs (Fig 3)

Lightweight pitched roofs can be constructed in a similar way to lightweight flat roofs, with a sloping waterproofed deck, a ventilated roof space and a ceiling. Fig 3 illustrates a typical construction with a timber deck and insulation between joists. The roof space can be ventilated by suitable openings at eaves or gables.

The roof illustrated in Fig 3 is a 'cold' roof; the insulation is at ceiling level and the roof space is cold. As with the similar flat roof there is a high risk of condensation on the underside of the water-proof covering. It is more satisfactory to fix the insulation on the slope of the roof, as in the 'warm' flat roof. There is then little risk of condensation if a vapour barrier is placed below the insulation.

Tiled or slated roofs (Fig 4)

The tiles or slates of traditional pitched roofs were often laid only on battens on rafters, or fixed direct to timber sarking, so that the roof space was freely ventilated through gaps between the tiles or slates. It is now usual to provide an underlay to the tiles or

slates, usually of bitumen felt. If the underlay is permeable, either because it is not saturated with bitumen or because of gaps at the lapped joints, there is still very little risk of trouble from condensation. Moist air which enters the roof space can escape through the permeable covering, and any intermittent condensation in the roof is absorbed by the timber or felt and later re evaporated. If timber sarking is used above the rafters it provides further absorbent material.

However, impermeable materials such as saturated bitumen felt, PVC and polythene are now extensively used for underlays. These reduce the rate at which moist air can escape from the roof space so that condensation problems are becoming more common. Water condensing on the underside of an impermeable underlay may drip on to the ceiling or drain down the roof slope, wetting timbers at the eaves and causing damage to the structure. If timber, chipboard or other organic material used as sarking has an impermeable underlay above it, the

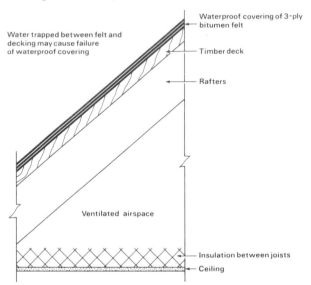

Fig 3 Lightweight pitched roof ('cold')

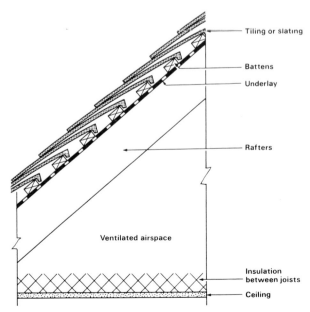

Fig 4 Tiled or slated roof

sarking material may be damaged by condensation; this could usually be avoided by substituting a 'breather' felt for the impermeable underlay and ventilating the roof space.

Concrete roofs

Concrete, either cast in situ or precast, can be used as a structural deck. A lightweight screed is sometimes used to provide falls (though these are better formed in the structural deck) and additional insulation. The deck is usually covered with an impermeable waterproof covering, such as bitumen felt or asphalt.

In wet districts it is not easy to dry out the construction water or to prevent further wetting before the waterproof covering is laid. Moisture can diffuse through the concrete or any cracks in it and condense on the underside of the waterproof covering. Condensed water may flow between the waterproof covering and the concrete to drip down through joints or cracks in the concrete deck. The condensed water may also saturate any insulating screed, thus greatly reducing its value as insulation. These roofs can, nevertheless, perform satisfactorily if the concrete is dry before they are covered and if the internal humidity in the building is low.

The waterproof covering may also be damaged by blisters caused by vaporisation of water entrapped below it. Properly designed breather vents, in conjunction with a pressure-releasing layer beneath the rain shield, can overcome this problem but they are not very effective in preventing trouble from condensation.

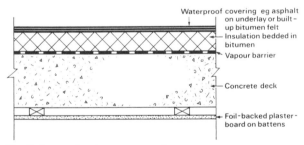

Waterproof covering eg asphalt on underlay or built-up bitumen felt
Insulation bedded in bitumen
Vapour barrier

Concrete deck

Foil-backed plasterboard on battens

Fig 5 Conventional concrete roof

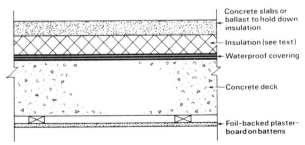

Concrete slabs or ballast to hold down insulation
Insulation (see text)
Waterproof covering

Concrete deck

Foil-backed plasterboard on battens

Fig 6 'Inverted' roof (waterproof covering *below* insulation)

An effective method of avoiding condensation, at least in continuously heated buildings, is to provide overdeck insulation as shown in Fig 5. There may be some temporary condensation on the underside of such concrete roofs in intermittently heated buildings, but this can usually be avoided by using a lightweight battened out ceiling, preferably using foil-backed plasterboard, to avoid staining during the drying-out period.

The 'inverted roof' (Fig 6) operates on the same principle as overdeck insulation but uses materials that are unaffected by moisture, such as foamed glass or extruded polystyrene, above the waterproof covering. The insulation is not covered with a waterproof layer as with overdeck insulation, but simply weighted down by gravel of a suitable size or concrete paving slabs.

Pressurised roof space

A suspended ceiling may be used to provide a roof space to accommodate machinery, or for appearance, or for acoustic absorption (Fig 7). This introduces an air space which must be taken into account in assessing the condensation risk. For instance, the thermal insulation of an acoustic ceiling may be high enough to reduce temperatures within the structure below the dewpoint of the air within the building.

In such cases, warm 'dry' air can be blown into the roof space to ensure that the dewpoint of the air within it is kept below the temperature of any part of the structure. The air pressure in the roof space has to be high enough to prevent the entry of water vapour from the building, and to ensure a downward flow of air through gaps. It 's desirable to incorporate a vapour check at ceiling level to reduce the diffusion of water vapour into the roof space and to reduce the gaps through which air is lost. The excess pressure can then be kept to a minimum, to save on the cost of fans and energy.

This technique is normally justifiable only for buildings with abnormally high internal humidities, such as swimming pools.

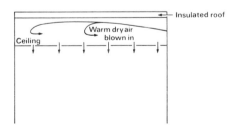

Insulated roof
Warm dry air blown in
Ceiling

Fig 7 Pressurised roof space

Design of timber floors to prevent decay

Most species of timber, especially softwoods, are liable under certain conditions to attack by the 'dry rot' fungus, *Merulius lacrymans,* which feeds on the timber, destroying it in the process. In persistently wet conditions, wood may be attacked by the 'cellar fungus', *Coniophora cerebella*; the effect is often called 'wet rot'.

An outbreak of dry rot can spread quickly, cause serious damage, and prove troublesome and costly to eradicate; prevention, therefore, is all-important. There are two possible courses—use timber that is naturally resistant to dry rot (eg Western red cedar, Californian redwood or yellow cedar) or take precautions in design and construction with less resistant species. To be immune from attack, the moisture content of the timber must be kept below 20 per cent (based on its oven-dry weight). Accordingly, the timber must be nearly in this condition at the time of fixing and everything possible must be done to keep the moisture content below 20 per cent thereafter. For the most part, this can be achieved by careful attention to the principles of good building construction—full provision against the entry of rain and ground moisture, thorough drying of the structure on completion, and efficient heating and ventilation to minimise condensation. Nevertheless, in the more inaccessible parts of a building—under floors, behind skirting and panelling, etc.—unsuspected damp conditions may persist unless precautions are taken.

Selection and storage of timber

Only sound, well-seasoned timber should be used; any that shows signs of incipient decay should be rejected. If possible, the conditions under which it has been stored should be ascertained and nothing allowed on the site which comes from a yard in which careless stacking or unclean conditions are tolerated.

Care taken in storage at the timber yard will be largely wasted unless it is matched by similar care on site. If the timber cannot be stored inside a building, it should be stacked on bearers so as to avoid contact with the ground. Dry, well-seasoned timber should be closely stacked, to minimise absorption of atmospheric moisture, and wholly covered with tarpaulins or polythene sheeting around and under the stack as well as over it.

If the timber is moist when it reaches the site, it should be open-piled so that air can circulate round each piece to promote further drying; the stacks should have top cover but the sides should be left open so as not to hinder air flow through the stack. If the stacks are within a building, windows should be left open.

Timber that has been treated with water-borne preservatives will not have been re-dried in a kiln unless this was specially ordered; normally, therefore, it will need to be open-piled and air-dried.

The moisture content of floor joists and battens should not exceed 22 per cent at the time of fixing; under normal drying conditions it will then quickly fall to 20 per cent and lower.

To prevent undue drying shrinkage, floor boarding and blocks, at the time of laying, should have a moisture content not more than about 2 per cent higher than they are expected to attain in use in a dried-out building; this final value is about 14 per cent where heating is intermittent, or 12 per cent where heating is continuous; softwood boarding may be fixed at a moisture content of up to 18 per cent if some gapping of the joints is acceptable.

Types of floor
Unventilated ground floors
Wood block floors. Wood blocks laid in hot-applied bitumen or pitch adhesive require no additional

protection against rising moisture; the adhesive, in which the blocks are dipped, should form a continuous layer and keep them out of contact with the concrete. Cold bitumen emulsions, however, cannot be relied on to give adequate protection, and blocks laid with this type of adhesive should be protected by a sandwich type damp-proof membrane (*see* Digest 54) or by an underlay of mastic asphalt, using an adhesive which is compatible with the asphalt.

Board or strip flooring. Board and strip flooring may be nailed to battens fixed to the concrete sub-floor by one of the methods illustrated in Fig 1. Protection by an impervious membrane is essential for these floors.

A surface membrane will protect the floor against rising ground moisture and also against the effects of residual construction moisture in the screed, but it will be pierced by the legs of the flooring clips or by the flooring nails. A sandwich membrane need not be pierced but sufficient time must be allowed for the concrete above the damp-proof layer to dry before the boards are fixed. The time necessary for this will depend on the density and thickness of the concrete and on the drying conditions, but since in the absence of heating facilities it may be a very long period, the sandwich method is perhaps less useful in practice. Failure to dry out the floor screed thoroughly may lead to decay in these floors and the risk will be greatly increased if impervious floor coverings, such as rubber, linoleum, plastics, etc., are laid prematurely.

The damp-proof membrane should make a watertight joint with the damp-proof course in the walls, etc., the membrane being extended vertically if necessary. Materials suitable for use as damp-proof membranes are listed in Digest 54.

All battens should be impregnated with preservative. Brush application of a preservative to the underside of the boarding is also recommended; for this purpose it will normally be advisable to avoid creosote or any preservative which might creep or bleed through and disfigure the exposed surface of the flooring.

Tongued and grooved boarding should be used, so that water used for washing down, or spilled accidentally, will not readily pass through the joints. If any water reaches the underside of the boarding,

it will be slow to evaporate and dangerous conditions may persist for a considerable time.

Ventilated ground floors

Ground floors of boarding on joists have a relatively large air space beneath them. To minimise the evaporation of water into this space, the sub-floor should be covered with a bed of good-quality dense concrete or a hot applied damp-resisting coating (solum) to BS 2832; the latter should be laid on a well-compacted base of hardcore, blinded with ashes to form a level surface free from fissures. The surface of the concrete bed or solum should not be lower than the level of the surrounding ground, or alternatively, the site should be drained so that inundation of the area cannot occur. The air space should be thoroughly ventilated and, if this is efficient, no preservative treatment of the timber is necessary.

For efficient cross-ventilation, there should be a clear depth of 150 mm between the underside of the floor joists and the site covering and sufficient air-bricks to provide at least 3000 mm² *open area* per metre run of external wall. The airbricks should be placed as high as possible on opposite walls and sleeper walls should be built honeycombed. Care should be taken to avoid unventilated air pockets such as may occur near a bay window; ducts should be formed under hearths and under solid floors wherever these might interrupt cross-ventilation.

Airbricks should not be built in to the north walls of buildings which are situated in a frost hollow, particularly if the underbuilding or crawl-space is a deep one; otherwise, there is a risk that in some weather conditions condensation may occur on the underside of the floor near the airbricks. The risk will be greatest below rooms that are unheated or intermittently heated, such as bedrooms. On sloping sites where a deep underbuilding cannot easily be avoided, the need for a second damp-proof course near ground level should be considered. If a terrace around the building is cut into the hillside, it may be desirable to bring the level of the concrete bed or solum at least up to that of the terrace, for in these circumstances drainage of the terrace may not always be able to cope with the volume of rain-water run-off from the hillside. The concrete bed or solum should be stepped so as to coincide approximately with the finished level of the surrounding ground.

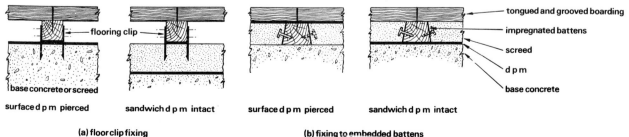

surface d p m pierced   sandwich d p m intact   surface d p m pierced   sandwich d p m intact

(a) floor clip fixing   **(b) fixing to embedded battens**

Fig 1 Board and batten fixing

Tongued and grooved boarding should be used because, if under-floor ventilation is as efficient as it should be, objectionable draughts would pass through the open joints of plain-edged boarding.

The thermal insulation of floors of this type can be improved by providing a layer of insulating material below the boarding. In a properly constructed and ventilated floor, this should not increase the risk of dry rot.

A damp-proof course should be provided in all sleeper walls and other supports that are in contact with the ground. The ends of joists should be cut back clear of the external walls (*see* Fig 2).

Upper floors

Dry rot in upper floors is rare because they are not exposed to moisture rising from the ground and the air above and below them is usually dry. No special precautions are required except that timbers built into walls that might become damp should be treated with preservative.

Board and batten floors (Fig 1) might be used on upper floors of *in situ* reinforced concrete, hollow beam or similar construction, but the damp-proof membrane would normally be omitted. However, structural floors of these types, possibly with the addition of a concrete screed, may contain a considerable quantity of residual construction water, and if a lightweight concrete is used the drying-out time will be substantially prolonged. Flooring should not be laid until drying-out is well advanced. Brush application of a preservative would then give temporary protection to the battens until drying-out is complete; the treatment could usefully be extended to the underside of the floorboards. Pressure impregnation, although not essential, would not only give protection during drying-out but would also continue to protect the battens from damage by accidental spillage, etc.

Wood block and parquet flooring laid on concrete, hollow tile or similar structural upper floors do not require special protection against fungal attack, but the concrete and screeds should be dry before the flooring is laid.

Floor coverings

Impervious floor coverings such as linoleum, rubber and plastics can safely be laid over floors that have been properly constructed in accordance with the foregoing recommendations, provided that residual construction moisture is not trapped below them. There may be some risk, however, in covering old timber floors, even when these have behaved satisfactorily for many years; the timber may have been kept at a safe moisture content mainly by evaporation from the upper surface, in which case the laying of an impervious covering might allow the moisture content to rise above the danger limit. Laying such coverings on a new boarded floor above a screed or slab which has not properly dried out could have a similar effect.

Skirtings

The absence of any protection on the back surface of a skirting and early painting of the exposed surface have the effect of raising the moisture content in skirting boards fitted to newly plastered walls that have not dried out. The risk of fungal attack is greatest when the wall is plastered right down to the floor and when skirtings are fixed above solid floors that are still wet.

All timber to be fixed in contact with new walls should, therefore, be given two brush-applied coats of preservative on the contact face. Impregnation would give still better protection; the use of preservatives that are soluble in water or certain organic solvents would allow for the normal painting of exposed surfaces.

Preservative treatment

Even with sound design and construction, it is necessary in some situations to treat the timber with a preservative. The effectiveness of this in eliminating or reducing the risk of attack will depend upon the thoroughness of the treatment. Any such treatment should be regarded as providing an extra margin of safety, the small cost of which, in comparison with the high cost and inconvenience entailed by fungal attack, is worth while in any situation where dampness, however slight, can occur. The treatment is further justified by the protection it affords against insect attack.

Timber to be treated with preservative should be clean and dry. The preservative may be applied either by brushing or by impregnation. Where permanent dampness cannot be avoided, timber

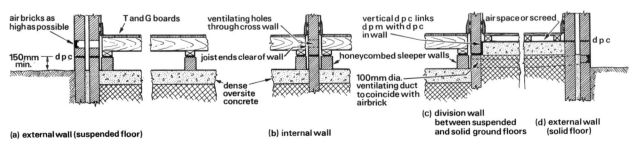

(a) external wall (suspended floor)   (b) internal wall   (c) division wall between suspended and solid ground floors   (d) external wall (solid floor)

Fig 2   Ventilated ground floors

should be impregnated. The maximum protection will be obtained if the timber is impregnated after all cutting and boring has been done; if this is not possible, preservative should be brushed liberally on to any cut surface.

Brush application gives less protection and should be used only where dampness is likely to be slight and temporary, as, for example, in those parts of a new building that can be expected to dry out fairly quickly.

Some care is needed in choosing the preservative to be used. In some situations the persistent smell of creosote and other preservatives of the tar oil type may be objectionable; also they tend to creep into and stain adjacent materials such as plaster. Alternatives are available in the organic solvent and water-borne types of preservative; see references below.

Method of determining the dryness of the sub-floor

A simple form of instrument measures the relative humidity of a pocket of air in equilibrium with the sub-floor (Fig 3). It consists of a paper hygrometer in a vapour-tight mounting housed in a well insulated box. Provision is made for sealing the edges of the instrument against the surface to be tested—Plasticine is a convenient material for this purpose—and for reading the hygrometer scale whilst the instrument is in position on the floor.

The instrument should be sealed firmly to the floor surface for not less than four hours to allow the entrapped air to reach moisture equilibrium with the concrete base before a reading is taken. A longer period is preferable and can sometimes be obtained conveniently by placing the instrument in position overnight and taking the reading in the morning. If readings are to be taken at several points with only one instrument available, subsequent positions may be covered by impervious mats (bitumen felt, polythene sheeting, etc.) about one metre square, laid down when the instrument is placed in its first position, to speed up the later readings.

When the hygrometer readings fall to 75–80 per cent, the sub-floor can be assumed to be sufficiently dry for flooring to be laid.

The use, instead of a hygrometer, of anhydrous copper sulphate (which turns blue in the presence of moisture) or of anhydrous calcium chloride (which liquefies), is not recommended.

Further reading

Decay in buildings—recognition, prevention and cure Tech Note 44 :1969 Princes Risborough Laboratory (free on application to Distribution Unit, BRE)

Decay of timber and its prevention K St G Cartwright and W P K Findlay; HMSO (London) 1967 : £2·47

BS 144 :1973 *Coal tar creosote for the preservation of timber*

BS 913 :1973 *Wood preservation by means of pressure creosoting*

BS 1282 :1959 *Classification of wood preservatives and their methods of application*

BS 3051 :1972 *Coal tar creosotes for wood preservation (other than creosotes to BS 144)*

BS 3452 :1962 *Copper/chrome water-borne wood preservatives and their application*

BS 3453 :1962 *Fluoride/arsenate/chromate/dinitrophenol water-borne wood preservatives and their application*

BS 4072 :1966 *Wood preservation by means of water-borne copper/chrome/arsenic compositions*

BS CP 98 :1964 *Preservative treatments for constructional timber*

BS CP 102 :1963 *Protection of buildings against water from the ground*

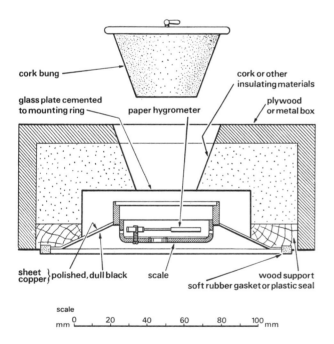

cork bung

cork or other insulating materials

glass plate cemented to mounting ring

plywood or metal box

paper hygrometer

sheet copper } polished, dull black   scale   wood support

soft rubber gasket or plastic seal

scale

mm 0   20   40   60   80   100 mm

Fig 3 Apparatus for measuring dampness

Prevention of decay in external joinery

An increasing number of reports of 'wet rot' in external joinery, particularly in new houses, suggests that the factors responsible are not as widely understood as they should be. This Digest examines the causes of decay and makes recommendations as to its prevention.

Incidence

Decay in exterior windows and doors has always occurred sporadically, but the number of reported cases of decay has increased appreciably over the past few years and is found even in joinery complying with current Codes of Practice and Specifications. Window joinery in newly built houses has given most cause for complaint; decay has sometimes become a serious problem within five or six years from the time of construction. Usually, decay has been noted earlier in the wetter, western areas of the British Isles though it has by no means been confined to these regions.

While decay may occur anywhere in opening lights and in frames permanently in contact with brickwork or blockwork, it is particularly marked in ground floor windows, especially kitchen and bathroom windows. The lower parts of these windows, ie the cills, the bases of jambs and mullions and the lower rails of opening lights, are particularly susceptible.

Type and symptoms

Almost invariably decay is of the wet rot type. This means that the fungi responsible, unlike the dry rot fungus, will not spread the rot to other woodwork in the building. Discoloration of the paintwork and 'cupping', or softening of the underlying wood, are the usual first symptoms of decay. Later, cross-cracking and dark discoloration of the wood itself may be observed. Sometimes in the later stages the wood becomes soft and stringy. There is no evidence of Baltic redwood having been infected prior to manufacture by the fungi responsible for wet rot.

Causes and prevention

Decay is caused by timber of low natural resistance becoming sufficiently moist to allow wood-destroying fungi to grow. Prevention of decay therefore depends on the selection of timber which is either naturally resistant to decay or which is otherwise protected by preservative treatment. Only heartwood has natural resistance to decay; sapwood* *must* be excluded where preservative treatment is not used.

---

* Sapwood cannot economically be excluded from joinery grade redwood.

Moisture control

Irrespective of the species of timber employed, adequate seasoning to remove moisture is essential before manufacture as joinery. A low moisture content restricts dimensional changes, permits satisfactory painting and contributes generally towards decay prevention. After seasoning, further access of moisture should be restricted:

by good design and careful fabrication of the joinery itself, particularly of the joints;

by storage indoors or raised clear of the ground and covered with waterproof sheets to protect the woodwork from exposure to the weather prior to final installation and painting;

by good detailing at the window/wall joint;

by thorough painting and regular maintenance;

by prompt attention to any necessary repairs.

Timber and its selection

Timbers for mass production joinery are chosen mainly because they are inexpensive and easily machined, not because they are particularly resistant to decay.

Baltic redwood (also known as red or yellow deal, red pine or fir) is the softwood most used for exterior joinery; its heartwood is more resistant to decay than its sapwood. The heartwood of Douglas fir is also used.

English oak is the traditional hardwood for exterior joinery, especially cills, in which greater resistance to decay is an asset. The hardwoods teak, utile, gurjun and agba have also proved acceptable. All these should be specified by name; merely to specify 'hardwood' can lead to the use of unsuitable timbers such as abura, beech, obeche and ramin (all with poor resistance to decay). The inclusion of perishable sapwood of an otherwise decay-resistant timber can be avoided by specifying 'Heartwood only'.

Suitable timber species and their properties are set out in Table 1 (on p. 129), extracted from CP 153: Part 2: 1970.

As Baltic redwood predominates in window joinery in the United Kingdom, the remarks which follow apply mainly to this timber. However, the principles of prevention and treatment of timber decay do not vary much between any of the different species used.

Preservative treatments

Care in design, construction, handling and maintenance can reduce but not eliminate the risk of decay. The obvious but often too costly remedy is to use naturally durable timber, excluding all sapwood. Alternatively, the risk of decay can be eliminated by adequate preservative treatment.

Recommended preservative treatments include:

Vacuum/pressure impregnation with water-borne preservative
Complete penetration of the sapwood of Baltic redwood can be achieved by this method. Treatment with an aqueous solution and the subsequent redrying that is necessary, however, cause the wood to swell and then to shrink; this can result in some raising of the grain and a risk of distortion.

Double-vacuum treatment with organic-solvent type preservative
The degree of treatment obtained can be controlled by varying the treating cycle used and it is possible to ensure that the net retention of the relatively high-cost preservative is adequate but not excessive. Complete penetration of sapwood is not usually obtained, but the average absorption and penetration achieved is about twice that from immersion treatment below.

Diffusion treatment This is carried out at the sawmill; after processing, seasoned treated timber can be supplied to the joinery manufacturer already penetrated throughout with a water-soluble preservative. This stock can then be converted and assembled in exactly the same way as untreated wood. Because the preservative is water-soluble, there is a risk that some may be leached out if the joinery is exposed to rain for months without paint or other protection.

Immersion treatment with organic-solvent type preservative Machined components or assembled units are submerged in a tank of preservative for three minutes. This provides satisfactory protection even though sapwood penetration is incomplete. Preservatives used for immersion, and for double-vacuum treatment, often contain water repellents: these improve the dimensional stability of the wood and hence benefit the performance of the joinery.

For further information on preservative treatment see PRL Technical Note 24, *Preservative Treatments for External Softwood Joinery Timbers*; this includes a list of the commercial processes and preservatives suitable for the treatment of external joinery.

Design and fabrication of joinery

Entry of water is most likely to occur at joints. Some modern joints loosen more easily than the old-style mortice-and-tenon joints with wedged tenons, and are therefore more vulnerable to water penetration. Joints are usually made with the grain of one member at right angles to that of another. Quite small fluctuations in moisture content stress these joints severely and once cross-grain movements begin, more water can enter and threaten decay.

The animal and casein glues permitted by some joinery specifications are likely to fail in persistently moist conditions. When this happens the joints in doors and opening sashes are less able to resist sudden stresses; the joints loosen, the paint film is broken, and penetration by moisture follows. The modern, synthetic resin glues are preferred because of their greater resistance to moisture. (See Forest Products Research Bulletin 38, *The efficiency of adhesives for wood.*)

The sectional sizes of timber scantlings accepted for windows have become smaller in recent years. It is bad practice to employ flimsy sections in window joinery, particularly where weather conditions are severe, as in some parts of Scotland. Such sections are prone to distort, permitting ingress of moisture, and they may not provide adequate space for the rebate. In opening lights the strength may be insufficient to prevent racking and consequent water penetration at the joints.

Window designs with horizontal surfaces which do not effectively shed water, still more those that actually entrap it, should be avoided. This applies both to rain-water on the outside of the window and to condensation on the inside.

The present-day omission of condensation channels and adequate means of drainage from them is to be deplored. Often water stands on the sill against the bottom of the frame and seeps into the joint between the two.

Cills present problems because they require timber of larger dimensions, and hence of greater cost, and also because they tend to present a higher decay risk. Whilst decay risk can be met by using more durable timber, increased cost is involved even if such timber is restricted to the cill alone. The current trend is to reduce costs by building up the cill from two smaller dimension timbers; the increased complexity of the two-piece unit calls for greater care in design and manufacture. However, even when Baltic redwood is used, a properly designed jointed cill effectively glued with suitable adhesives and preservative treated as necessary should give adequate service.

Fig 1 Complexity of joint design in a modern frame and cill. Result—joints expose a large surface area to risk of moisture penetration and facilitate decay

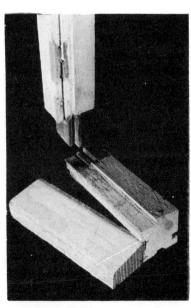

Weather protection before installation

Joinery is often to be seen exposed to all weathers while in transit or awaiting installation on building sites. This is thoroughly bad practice. All woodwork should be fully protected from the weather and stacked clear of the ground. Pink primer may look protective but it is rarely effective in preventing penetration of moisture—moisture which may later cause trouble if trapped by relatively impermeable coats of paint.

The window/wall joint

A further contributory cause of moisture penetration, and therefore of decay, may arise from contact between window frames and wet brickwork. There is rarely any damp-proof barrier separating them, nor is it usual to protect the backs of the frames with extra paint before installation. Even when the joinery is set in the inner leaf of brickwork there is risk of dampness continuing in the frames for as long as it takes the brickwork to dry out.

The more usual practice, however, except in Scotland, is to set the frame in the outer leaf of brickwork; not only is this brickwork often permanently damp, the window itself is much more directly exposed to the weather. Clearly this practice carries the greater risk of timber decay. Thorough priming—two full coats of an aluminium based primer—is needed on all timber surfaces that are to be in contact with external walls.

External and internal climates

The direct exposure of windows to driving rain and to rain-water run-off will depend on their regional location and position in the building, ie storey height and orientation (see Digest 127). That decay tends to be most marked in the lower, external parts of ground-floor windows is only to be expected. However, too little thought is given to the effects of internal climate on window joinery; this can be as damaging to the woodwork of single-glazed windows as the weather outside. In bathrooms and kitchens especially, temperature and humidity are often high, and in cold weather condensation on these windows is troublesome. Changed living habits and heating methods have aggravated the problem (see Digest 110). Often there is a pool of water along the lower edge above the back putty. This back putty is rarely as free from defects as that on the face, and water finds an easy entry. (The need for condensation channels at the base of the frame has already been mentioned.)

Fig 2
Outer glazing bead nailed—not glued or sealed. Result—free moisture penetration.

Grooves machined for outer glazing bead run right through mullion/transom joint. Result—void for collection of moisture

Fig 3 External part of mullion/transom joint held by nail. Result—water penetrates freely once the paint film is broken. Failure through decay began after three years' service

Painting and maintenance, primers
(*see also* Digest 106)

As noted, the ability of a single coat of primer, even a good quality lead-based type, to prevent ingress of water is greatly over-estimated. 'Pink' shop primers are of variable quality and many do little more than give the joinery a uniform appearance; after quite a short exposure they become weak or powdery and unfit to take further coats of paint. Many paint failures can be traced back to poor quality primers. Thus it is most important to store joinery under cover; if this is considered impossible much better priming than usual should be specified. A water-repellent preservative plus a good quality primer, or two coats of aluminium primer, would be suitable. (Since aluminium primers will also keep moisture in, they should only be used on correctly seasoned timber, or after the moisture or solvent from preservative treatment has dried out, otherwise blistering may occur.)

Lead-based pink priming paints (BS 2521 :1966) are among the best for durability, both as part of a full paint system and if left exposed on site. They are expensive and their toxicity makes their

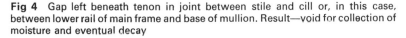

Fig 4 Gap left beneath tenon in joint between stile and cill or, in this case, between lower rail of main frame and base of mullion. Result—void for collection of moisture and eventual decay

Table 1 Timber species and properties

Standard name	Sapwood distinct	Heartwood durability†	Resistance to impregnation with preservatives	Woodworking properties		Amount of movement on re-wetting	Paint performance in service	Remarks
				Resistance in cutting	Blunting effect			
Afrormosia	Yes	Very durable	Extremely resistant	Medium	Moderate	Small	Good, provided paint is not affected by oily exudations	Non-ferrous fitments necessary
Afzelia				High	Moderate	Small	*	May discolour other building materials
Iroko				Medium	Fairly severe	Small	*	
Kapur				Medium (variable)	Moderate (occasionally severe)	Medium	*	Non-ferrous fitments necessary
Makoré				Medium	Severe	Small	*	Non-ferrous fitments necessary
Teak					Fairly severe (variable)	Small	Good, provided paint is not affected by oily exudations	Has been known to cause discoloration of granite
Western red cedar	Yes	Durable	Resistant	Low	Mild	Small	Good	Strength relatively low. Non-ferrous fitments necessary to avoid marked discoloration of the wood under clear finishes
Agba	Moderate			Medium	Moderate	Small	Moderate, but experience is limited	Log core may contain brittleheart. Resin exudation may occur with some parcels, especially if the timber has been air-dried
European oak, American white oak, Japanese oak	Yes		Extremely resistant	Medium (variable)	Moderate (variable)	Medium	Poor	Non-ferrous fitments necessary. Occasionally disfigures other building materials
Idigbo	Moderate				Mild	Small	*	Log core may contain brittleheart. May cause staining of other building materials
Sweet chestnut	Yes			Medium	Mild	Small	*	Non-ferrous fitments necessary
Utile					Moderate	Medium	Good	
Douglas fir	Yes	Moderately durable	Resistant	Medium	Medium	Small	Moderate	Non-ferrous fitments advisable
African mahogany			Very resistant	Medium (variable)	Moderate (variable)	Small or medium	*	Log core may contain brittleheart
Gurjun Yang			Resistant	Medium (variable)	Moderate (occasionally severe)	Large	Moderate	Resin exudation occurs with some parcels of these timbers (especially keruing); select material free from resin for painted work
Keruing						Medium	Moderate	
Red meranti Red seraya	Moderate					Small	*	Log core may contain brittleheart
Sapele	Yes		Extremely resistant	Medium	Moderate	Medium	Good	
Redwood	Yes	Non-durable or perishable	Sapwood permeable Heartwood moderately resistant	Low	Mild	Medium	Good	
Western hemlock	No		Sapwood and heartwood resistant	Low	Mild	Small	Good	
Whitewood								
American red oak	Yes		Sapwood permeable Heartwood resistant	Medium	Moderate	Medium	Poor	Non-ferrous fitments advisable
Beech	No		Permeable	Medium (variable)	Moderate (variable)	Large	Good	
Ramin				Medium	Moderate	Large	Moderate, but experience is limited	

† The sapwood of all species is either perishable or non-durable.

* Seldom painted; there is therefore little painting experience.

130

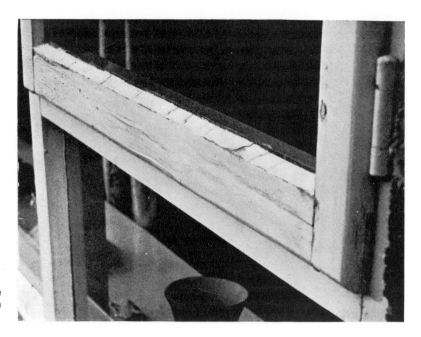

Fig 5 Cupping of paintwork and putty failure associated with decay in lower rail of an opening light

use indoors inadvisable where children could contact them (even under further paint). Acrylic emulsion-based primers are coming into use, because they offer convenience to the joinery manufacturers. Although their water repellency may be no greater than that of many oil-based primers, they appear, on the limited evidence available, to have adequate durability before and after painting.

If a thin, weak or powdery shop coat is present, it should be sanded and a further coat of good quality primer applied. End grain and surfaces in contact with brickwork or masonry should always receive an extra coat of primer. Poor quality putty cracks or loses adhesion easily and allows water to enter at the bottom rail: all putty should be completely painted, with a slight overlap on to the glass. Hardwood cills should have the grain filled with a knifing stopper or filler (not a water-mixed type), preferably between two coats of primer.

Shellac knotting, even if it holds back resin, usually permits adhesion failure of the paint coats; an aluminium pigmented knotting is preferable, but good practice requires knots to be cut out and the cavities to be stopped.

Treatment of decay

It is important that all decayed wood should be cut out and paint stripped from adjacent areas so that damp, but not rotten, timber can be given a chance to dry out. If decay is extensive the entire window unit may have to be replaced. Wood exposed by cutting should be treated liberally with preservative, again allowed to dry, then given a coat of primer. Depending on their size, holes should be made good with stopper (see above) or primed timber, suitably shaped. Another coat of primer should be applied to the new surface, followed by undercoat and finishing coats.

Recommendations

1 When making use of Specifications and Codes of Practice bear in mind that their requirements may not be adequate in every circumstance to ensure satisfactory durability of the timber.

2 To ensure adequate service from Baltic redwood and other timbers of low decay resistance, insist on preservative treatment.

3 If durable hardwood is to be used specify the timber by name and insist on the exclusion of sapwood.

4 Protect joinery from the weather during delivery to the site, and on the site before installation.

5 Refuse to accept low quality shop primers. Ensure an adequate painting system.

4 Services

Pipes and fittings for domestic water supply

This Digest deals with the plumbing installation for cold water supply for houses, but much of what is said here is valid also for larger buildings. Soil and waste plumbing is dealt with in Digest 80 and plumbing applications of plastics in Digest 69. The installation is considered in its logical order, from the mains supply to the various types of outlet. In the second part, experience with the 'Garston' ball valve is reviewed and remedies for some early defects are described.

Imperial/metric units

Some of the dimensions quoted in this Digest are statutory requirements for which rationalised metric equivalents would not be appropriate, e.g. minimum depth of external pipes—2 ft 6 in., overflow pipes (Scottish) $1\frac{1}{4}$ in. diameter; others are nominal pipe bore sizes, still retained in metric standards. Imperial units have therefore been used throughout the text, with precise metric equivalents.

For domestic supply, water is not sold by measure; it is provided as a service, the cost of which is recovered by means of the water rate. As there is no incentive for the consumer to limit his consumption, the suppliers need to exercise some control. This they do through their byelaws, which are generally based on the Model Water Byelaws (1966 Edition) of the Ministry of Housing and Local Government and make provision against waste, undue consumption, misuse and contamination of the water supplied. The byelaws lay down in some detail the kind of materials and fittings to be used, the protection to be provided, etc., the emphasis being on avoiding waste while maintaining the amenity. Nevertheless, they afford considerable latitude in interpretation; this sometimes results in a wide variation between different suppliers' specific requirements and consequently leads to difficulties for designers and manufacturers.

Besides byelaw requirements there are other considerations, mainly of interest to the designer and consumer, affecting the design and construction of a water system. Durability, ease of maintenance, good appearance and quiet operation are treated extensively in the BS Codes of Practice for Water Supply (CP.310:1965), for Frost Precautions (CP.99: 1965) and for Sanitary Appliances (CP.305: 1952). The notes that follow cover various other factors, not mentioned in the byelaws and codes and commonly disregarded in traditional practice, that can make all the difference between an installation that causes repeated annoyance and an efficient one.

Design

It is common practice to provide the plumbing contractor with copies of drawings prepared in compliance with the local authority's requirements for approval under general building byelaws, and on them merely to indicate the positions of sink, bath, basin, etc. These drawings (which need not be to a scale larger than 1:100 or in some cases 1:200) are not intended to determine the system in all its technical details, and the resulting installation, governed mainly by costs and by the need to comply with the water authority's requirements, may not be wholly satisfactory to the user. It cannot be emphasised too strongly that an installation, to be free of faults, and dependable, must be functionally designed in relation to the building it is to serve, and that this calls for considerable understanding of the design principles involved. The builder or plumber should be provided with working drawings showing clearly, on an appropriately large scale, the position and full description of appliances, pipe runs, valves and other fittings, methods of fixing, protection and all other information which may affect the functioning of the system.

Distribution system

Water is delivered to the building from the main by way of a service pipe, from which branches may be taken to the various supply points or to the storage cistern, if any. Byelaws require one such branch at least to supply drinking water direct to the tap over the sink, and in some districts all other cold water supply points are required to be fed from a storage cistern in the roof space (or at least as high as possible above the topmost tap). The boiler for a hot water system is fed either from the storage cistern or from its own feed cistern.

Service pipes

Byelaws generally require underground service pipes outside buildings to be laid at a minimum depth of 2 ft 6 in. (0.762 m) as a precaution against frost. There have been many instances of frost damage, however, where pipes, although at the required depth as far as the footings, have been bent up to take them through the wall above the footings. This should not be permitted; the service pipe should enter the house at a depth of at least 2 ft 6 in. (0.762 m) and it should not rise until it has reached a point at least 2 ft (0.61 m) away from the inner face of any external wall. Where the pipe, on emerging, passes through the ventilated air space under a suspended floor, it should be protected with a 2 in (50 mm) lagging secured by galvanised wire netting or copper wire.

Within the building the service pipe should be placed on an internal wall and it should run straight to the storage cistern, with the drinking-tap branch taken from it where needed. This keeps the pipe away from the eaves, where it would be more likely to freeze up than anywhere else in the loft. All water byelaws require the service pipe to have a stop-valve of the 'screw-down' type where it enters the house, and it is advisable to have immediately above this a draw-off tap (with a detachable key) for emptying the pipe if the house is to be left unheated in the winter. The stop-valve is a very important fitting; its use in an emergency may avert much damage, and it should, therefore, be placed where it is easily accessible and where it is not liable to be cluttered up with household articles—when water is dripping through the ceiling, time becomes a very important factor. At least once a year the valve should be closed and opened to ensure that it does not become too stiff to operate. To avoid possible waterhammer it should have a fixed washer plate.

Materials for pipes

The composition of water varies between different areas, and some waters tend to corrode certain metals, used alone or in combination with other metals. The characteristics of the water in a particular locality are known by the local water engineer and, in the absence of past experience, he should be consulted on the choice of materials before any new work is put in hand. In general it is advisable to keep to the same metal throughout the system, as far as possible (see Digest 98).

Recently, tubes made of polythene under various trade names (e.g. Alkathene, Telcothene, Vulcathene) have come to be used for conveying water, especially on farms and in other developments where this material, when used in long lengths, has certain advantages over metal pipe. When polythene is used for internal plumbing, certain points should be borne in mind. Experience with the material is required for the making of good joints of either the fusion or the compression type; the former, when well made, seem to be the more reliable. If compression type joints are used, no jointing compound should be used; it may lead to cracking of the polythene tube. Tubes must be supported at short intervals (every 8 in. (200 mm) for ½-in. (nominal) tube on horizontal runs). For this reason, and also because the material does not readily take paint, it is preferable to place the pipework out of sight. Because of the slight permeability of polythene to gases, including coal gas, particular care should be taken when siting polythene tubing.

Polythene has a very high coefficient of thermal expansion; in the past, this has caused tubes to pull out at joints on cooling. As a precaution, long lengths of tube in unheated spaces should be 'snaked'. Because polythene tube is less resistant to physical damage than metal pipes, it should not be left exposed in places where it is liable to be damaged through accident or mischief. It resists damage by frost better than metal tube, but when frozen it must not be thawed out by means of a blow-lamp as the flame would damage it.

The above remarks apply primarily to low-density polythene tube (BS.1972: 1967). A new, more rigid type of polythene pipe (type 710) is covered by BS.3284: 1967) which has an Appendix giving notes on its use. For use of polythene and PVC pipework, Digest 69 should be consulted.

Although pipework of any kind is usually concealed as far as possible, the need for ready access to the pipe runs for repair should not be overlooked.

Storage cisterns

From the water supplier's point of view, the purpose of the storage cistern is to provide a reserve of water and to reduce the peak hour demand on the mains. To the user, the cistern gives the advantage of supplying all cold water draw-off fittings (except the drinking-water tap mentioned earlier) with water at a pressure much lower than that in the mains. This is very desirable, because the mains pressure in pipes and fittings causes noise and damages the seatings of taps and valves, in so far as these are still made to the traditional designs, developed at the time when mains pressures were much lower.

The life of a galvanised steel cistern may be considerably extended by an inside coating of a non-toxic bituminous composition that does not impart any taste to the water. Before a new galvanised cistern is put into use it should be carefully cleared of any metallic filings and scraps of metal; if these are allowed to remain they may set up rapid local corrosion through electrolytic action and cause a leak within a matter of months. Cisterns made of non-metallic materials, such as asbestos cement or glass-fibre reinforced plastics, though more expensive, have their obvious advantages. In some areas, because of the properties of the water, their use is compulsory.

Glass-fibre reinforced plastics and polythene cisterns are discussed in more detail in Digest 69.

It is sometimes practicable to place the cistern below the top floor ceiling, to give it full protection from frost and make it easily accessible. If the cistern is placed in the roof space, it should be located centrally and cased in timber or rigid sheet material, leaving a 50 mm gap for a layer of insulating material. Instead of casing in the cistern, pre-formed insulating slabs, made to fit cisterns of different sizes, are available. Finally the cistern should be provided with a well-fitting cover, similarly insulated. Trap doors to lofts should be large enough to pass the cistern in case it has to be replaced. For further details of frost precautions, see CP.99 : 1965.

The ball valve

Ball valves, which control the supply to the storage and flushing cisterns, can cause more trouble and annoyance than any other part of the water system, through failure of their moving parts. A ball valve may either fail to close, causing an overflow or flooding, or, less commonly, it may 'stick' in the closed position, cutting off the supply.

A valve may fail to close for any of the following reasons : perforated float, eroded seating, defective washer, or the presence of grit or lime deposit. Copper floats, especially when soldered, are likely to become corroded; sometimes they simply drop off the boss attaching them to the valve arm, or they become perforated and filled with water. Floats made of plastics—solid cellular or hollow—will not fail in this way.

High-velocity discharge of water from a ball valve may erode the seating, producing radial channels which cause the valve to leak. The remedy here is either a new seating, preferably made of nylon (if the valve is of the British Standard pattern), or re-seating the valve by means of a special tool sold by builders' merchants.

Worn washers should be replaced. It is advisable to inspect the seating at the same time, because damage to the washer is often caused by an eroded seating.

In hard water districts the combined effect of corrosion and lime deposition on the piston and the valve body can cause the piston to stick in the open position, causing an overflow or flooding. In areas where the trouble is known to recur, the valve should be periodically dismantled and cleaned, and the piston greased. Grit in the water is a similar source of trouble, especially in newly-built houses if the water system has not been thoroughly flushed, as it should be, after installation; it also occurs in a few districts where solid matter is formed in galvanised pipes by the action of certain types of water.

Sticking of the valve in the closed position tends to occur when the house has been unoccupied for some time, and lime and dirt have dried out on the working parts; it can be remedied by working the float arm up and down a few times or, better still, by taking the valve to pieces and cleaning it thoroughly.

Where the supply pressure is high, say about 350,000 N/m², ball valves of traditional construction make a high-pitched noise for which there is no cure. The splashing noise can, however, be reduced by fitting a silencing tube to the valve.

The 'Garston' ball valve, developed at the Building Research Station, was designed to overcome some of the troubles mentioned above. The experience gained in its field use is reviewed in the second part of this digest.

Overflow pipes

As a precaution against overflow in the event of failure of the ball valve, the cistern is provided near the top edge with a pipe led outside the building. In byelaws, this pipe is termed 'the warning pipe', emphasising its primary purpose. In England, the bore of this pipe when a $\frac{1}{2}$-in. ball valve feeds the cistern must be not less than $\frac{3}{4}$ in. (19 mm), and this is the usual size. Flushing cisterns for wcs are normally made to take this size of overflow pipe. If the ball valve leaks only slightly this safeguard may be sufficient; if the valve becomes stuck in the fully open position, however, the capacity of the warning pipe will be quite inadequate and water will overflow into the house. Scottish byelaws treat this 'warning pipe' as an overflow pipe in the full sense of the term and, for storage cisterns, require it to have a bore of not less than $1\frac{1}{4}$ in. (32 mm) or twice the diameter of the inlet pipe. A pipe of this size, costing perhaps £1 more than a $\frac{3}{4}$-in. (19 mm) pipe, can under similar conditions carry away three times as much water and thus give much greater protection. Whatever the size of pipe used—and for greater safety the larger size is advisable on a storage cistern—it can take away water more quickly the greater its fall.

Stop valves

When a fitting needs repair it is necessary to be able to stop the flow of water to it. Each pipe carrying water from the storage cistern should therefore be separately controlled by means of a stop valve. In the part of the system fed from a storage cistern, valves of the 'full-way' type should be used because 'screw-down' stop valves offer too much resistance to flow. The traditional practice is to place these valves as near as possible to the cistern, to bring the greatest length of piping under control. However, if the cistern is in the roof space, such an arrangement makes it difficult to reach the valve quickly in an emergency, while the control over a short additional length of pipe is of little practical value. It is better to fit the valves at a height at which they can be reached from the floor, but out of reach of children. If they are fitted in an airing cupboard, they should be positioned so as to be easily accessible without removing the contents of the cupboard. A label on each stop valve indicating the outlet it controls may be of great help in an emergency.

Water closets

It is often not realised that noise and inefficient flushing of wc suites are avoidable. Most annoyance is caused by the high-pitched hissing of the ball valve as the flushing cistern fills. There will be less noise if the ball valve is fed from a storage cistern or, if the supply has to be under mains pressure, if a 'Garston' valve is fitted.

A flushing cistern should fill reasonably quickly, say, within 2 minutes, and, to ensure this, the size of valve orifice should be chosen to suit the supply pressure. As a rule a $\frac{1}{8}$-in. (3 mm) orifice is used on mains supply where the pressure is above, say, 40 lb/in.^{2} (276,000 N/m^2), and a $\frac{3}{16}$-in. (5 mm), or $\frac{1}{4}$-in. (6 mm) orifice, depending on the available head, where the supply is taken from a storage tank. With a very small head, a $\frac{3}{8}$-in. (10 mm) orifice may be found to be necessary to give the required flow. Persistent slow filling may also be due to partial blockage of the valve by foreign matter, which should, in that case, be removed and cleaned.

There are several reasons why an apparently good wc suite may not consistently clear the pan at one flush. First, the cistern may be delivering less than the statutory 2 gallons; accordingly, the water level in the cistern should be checked, when the ball valve shuts off, against the water line marked on the inside back wall. If the level is below this line, the ball valve arm should be carefully bent upwards until the cistern fills to the designed level. The 'Garston' valve has a special screw adjustment for this purpose.

Some cisterns, particularly cast-iron ones, are operated by means of a cast-iron bell which is lifted by the chain pull and then allowed to drop with a clanging noise. These in time become corroded and deliver a slow ineffectual flush. Only too often they are replaced by one of the same type for no better reason than to avoid altering the position of the supporting brackets to fit the dimensions of a better cistern. If a change has to be made, this small amount of extra work should not prevent the installation of a better type of cistern with a piston-actuated syphon. Cisterns of this type work with much less noise, require less force to operate and are more reliable. For greater quietness, a thick-walled cistern is to be preferred.

Inefficient flushing may also be due to a fault in the joint between the flush pipe and pan. The waterway may be obstructed by putty which is still sometimes used as a jointing material, or the pipe may enter the pan socket at an angle. In both cases the rate of flow is reduced, and in the latter case the designed flow distribution in the pan may be disturbed as well. The remedies here are obvious but they may be difficult to apply if, through lack of space between pan and wall, the flush pipe has been forced into the pan socket at an angle and needs to be shortened. Experiments have shown that, other things being equal, low-level cisterns with flush pipes larger than the common $1\frac{3}{8}$-in. (35 mm) bore give a more efficient flush. A bad joint between the flush pipe and flushing cistern may reduce the flushing efficiency of a suite very considerably. Such a joint is difficult to detect because high velocity flow inside the pipe will cause air to be sucked in *without* water leaking out.

Finally, the trouble may lie with the pan itself. The action of the more common 'wash-down' (as against syphonic) type of pan depends on the weight and velocity of the flush water pushing the contents into the soil pipe, and its efficiency depends largely on the extent to which the shape of the pan usefully employs the available momentum of the two gallons of water flowing into the pan. It is not easy to tell its efficiency from the looks of the pan, but the way in which water flows into it during flushing may give some guidance. In a good 'wash-down' pan a strong jet of water at the back of the pan should discharge into the well of the pan near its back wall. The stream of water coming from the front and formed by the joining of the flow in both sides of the rim should be central and also directed into the well of the pan.

Pans with syphonic discharge are more positive in their action because the contents are pulled out by the suction created behind the trap. In some syphonic pans, particularly those with a single trap, the syphonic action is initiated by means of a slight constriction in the waterway. In normal use this causes no trouble, but an obstruction will cause a blockage more readily than would occur in a 'wash-down' pan, and it may be more difficult to clear. When a syphonic pan is installed it is even more important than with others that the flushing cistern made for the particular type of pan should be used. For maximum quietness and efficiency, a close-coupled double-trap syphonic suite fitted with a 'Garston' ball valve is recommended. Its cost may, however, be £10 above that of the cheapest suite.

Wash-basins

Wash-basins and wc suites for domestic use are made of vitreous china.

The present British Standard for ceramic basins (BS1188:1965) provides for only two sizes, namely 25 in. × 18 in. (635 mm × 457 mm) and 22 in. × 16 in. (550 mm × 406 mm). Although basins of other sizes do not comply with these requirements, this certainly does not mean that they are necessarily of a lower quality. British Standard basins will be found, however, to be priced lower than others.

The Standard requires basins to be provided with an overflow to prevent flooding, so designed that it can be easily cleaned. In practice this is very difficult to achieve, and it is virtually impossible to clean the overflow on most basins; when the waste plug is opened, the dirty water rises in the overflow passage leaving behind a coating of scum, which produces an unpleasant smell, particularly in warm weather when various bacteria and fungi thrive in the damp and dark environment. Moreover, an overflow of the specified dimensions cannot take away the full discharge of a tap in a plugged basin, and its effectiveness on the whole is doubtful. These considerations have led manufacturers in U.S.A. and on the Continent to make basins and baths without overflows, a practice which is slowly gaining ground in this country also; one large housing authority specifies basins, as well as baths and sinks, without overflows for its multi-storey housing schemes.

Taps

Leaking taps waste a lot of water, besides being a nuisance, particularly on baths, where the drip often makes a stain which is difficult to remove. Taps leak when the washer is worn out, or when the usual metal seating on which the washer bears has become eroded. As with ball valves, erosion produces radial channels through which the water leaks; the channelled metal also tends to damage the washer, making matters worse. Whenever a washer is replaced, therefore, the seating should also be examined; if necessary, it can be re-faced by means of a special tap reseating tool sold by builders' merchants.

Of the many types of washer available, not all give satisfactory service. Some are suitable for cold water taps, but not for hot and vice versa. Black synthetic rubber washers, as used by some of the largest water suppliers, are suitable for either cold or hot taps, and last a long time.

The 'Garston' ball valve in use

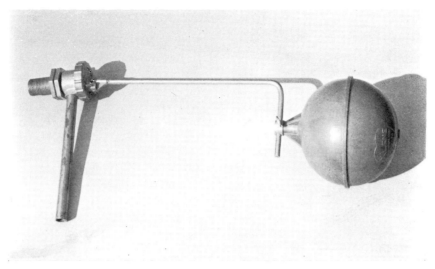

The 'Garston' ball valve

The 'Garston' ball valve developed at the Building Research Station has now been on the market for over ten years and about half a million valves of this type are in use in various parts of the country.

They are sold under the following trade names:

'Chem-Garston'—C. H. Edwards Ltd., Millfield, Wolverhampton, Staffs.

'Kingley—B.R.S.'—Kings Langley Engineering Co. Ltd., Kings Langley, Herts.

The 'Garston' valve was designed to overcome three disadvantages of other types of valve in common use: (a) early damage to the seating caused by cavitation, (b) 'sticking' of the piston, and (c) excessive noise. The main features of the valve are a nylon nozzle, shaped to reduce cavitation, and a rubber diaphragm which stops the flow of water when pressed against the nozzle by a plunger. The diaphragm keeps the moving parts of the valve dry and free from corrosion and incrustation. Movement of the plunger is con-

trolled by the usual float on a hinged arm which, at its free end, is bent down at a right-angle. By means of a thumbscrew the float can be clamped on to this part of the arm at any height depending on the water level required in the cistern.

Reports on the performance of the valves in field use show that in general they are proving satisfactory. Experience in the installation and assembly of any new type of fitting often leads to minor changes in procedure and the 'Garston' valve is no exception. Three different causes of defects have been identified and the following review of these should help present and future users of the valve to obtain the full benefit of the performance it is designed to give.

Leakage past the nozzle thread

In the early days of manufacture, loosening of the nylon nozzle in the tapped hole of the valve body, due to creep of the material, allowed water to leak past the nozzle thread. Experiments showed that this

Exploded view

138

tended to occur a few days after the nozzle had been screwed home, and that the nozzle could then be screwed in by another quarter of a turn. After the second tightening there was no further movement and the valve remained watertight indefinitely.

After this defect was first reported and investigated, the manufacturers modified their method of assembly which now ensures a permanently watertight joint at the nozzle, and they have replaced the faulty valves. They report no complaints of leakage from this cause in valves made since that time.

Valves failing to close

Failure of valves to close has been found to occur mainly in newly built houses. There, when the valves were taken apart, brick and mortar grit and large grains of sand were always found embedded in the diaphragms. All ball valves are liable to leak when grit lodges on the rubber washer or diaphragm, but the 'Garston' valve is more easily affected than the 'Portsmouth' type valve because of the small clearance between nozzle and diaphragm, which is one of the design features ensuring quiet operation.

The flushing of water supply systems in newly completed houses, a normal practice on a well-managed site, is particularly important where 'Garston' valves are fitted. The valves should be thoroughly flushed with the diaphragms removed and all grit adhering to the diaphragm and inside the valve cleaned off. If much grit has been allowed to enter the system a second flushing may be necessary later on. Reports from a large building scheme where several thousands of 'Garston' valves are in use have confirmed that once the water system has been cleaned of grit the valves need no further attention.

In this country there are three or four areas where grit is inherent in the water supply. It may be carried in the mains or it sometimes forms in the pipework in houses owing to the action of a particular type of water on the material of the pipes. In these areas all types of ball valves are liable to leak, but for the reasons already given, the 'Garston' valve is more likely to do so unless protected by a filter at the valve inlet.

Faulty fitting and assembly

In a number of instances, leakage was found to be due to faulty fitting and assembly of the valve, including, in a few cases, valves fitted at an angle or even with diaphragms missing. A more common fault is failure to ensure engagement between the locating lug on the end plate and the slot in the rim of the valve body, when assembling the valve. When this happens a gap is formed between the end plate and diaphragm and the plunger cannot reach the diaphragm to stop the flow. For the benefit of plumbers not yet familiar with the construction of the 'Garston' valve it may be worth while pointing out that the easiest way to assemble the valve is, with the cap nut placed over the end plate to start the cap nut on the valve body thread without trying to locate correctly the end plate. The cap nut is screwed up until a resistance is felt and then the arm, hinged to the end plate, is slowly twisted towards its correct position until the end plate lug is felt to click into the slot. A gentle twist is then given to the arm to make sure of the correct engagement, and, if it does not move, the cap nut is screwed up hand tight. *Grips or pipe wrenches must not be used.*

Although noise in operation has not been the subject of complaint, it has been noticed that occasionally the valves are fitted without silencing tubes. One of the main advantages of the 'Garston' valve is its quiet operation, and while it is true that most of the noise is eliminated by the shape of the nozzle, the full effect of its performance cannot be obtained unless it is fitted with a proper silencing tube. It is essential that there should be a small hole either in the body of the valve or at the upper end of the silencing tube. The absence of this hole may be responsible for a humming noise.

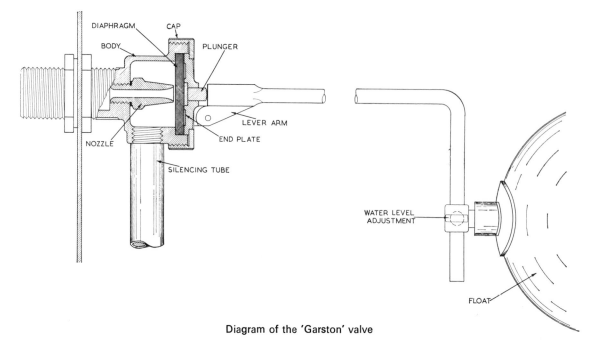

Diagram of the 'Garston' valve

Soil and waste pipe systems
for housing *Withdrawn See Nº 248 April 1981*

This digest describes briefly the problem of maintaining under all conditions the seals of traps to sanitary appliances in dwellings and makes detailed recommendations for the design of single-stack soil and waste pipe systems to meet this requirement in low-rise and multi-storey dwellings.

Importance of sealing

For any plumbing system to operate satisfactorily, the traps to the various appliances must remain sealed in all conditions of use; otherwise there is a risk of odours contaminating rooms in different parts of the dwelling. A seal will be broken if the pressure changes in the branch pipe are of sufficient size and duration to overcome the head of water in the trap itself. Such pressure changes can be brought about by:

(a) Induced siphonage: water flow down main stack; e.g. WC discharge; also water flow from other appliances through combined branches.

(b) Back pressure: water flow down main stack in conjunction with sharp bend at foot of main stack.

(c) Self-siphonage: liquid flow in waste branch pipe to main stack.

Both the old two-pipe system and the fully vented one-pipe system virtually eliminated the risk of seal breakage, the first by interrupting the continuity of the system at hopper head and gulley, the second by ensuring with the help of vent pipes that the pressure in branch pipes never deviated appreciably from atmospheric.

The single-stack system relies on the soil stack alone for venting and experience has shown that given good design and workmanship the scope of such a system is considerable. Using this as a basis, the usefulness can be extended by providing partial additional venting to either the stack or its branches, or both. The early recommendations have been steadily extended to multi-storey installations of increasing load.

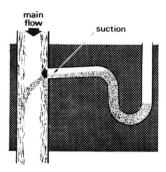

(a) Induced siphonage

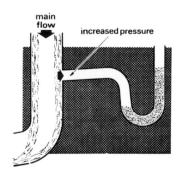

(b) Back pressure

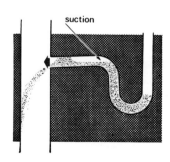

(c) Self-siphonage

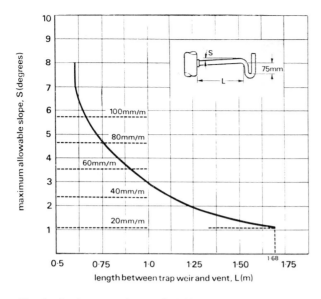

Fig. 1. Design curve for nominal 30 mm wastes and 75 mm seal P-traps connected to single BS lavatory basins. The minimum desirable slope is 20 mm/m—approx. $1\frac{1}{4}°$. (The slopes recommended are allowable maxima, but the pipes need not be fixed at exactly the gradients read off the graph.)

Fig. 2. Design of single-stack system—main features.

Branch pipes to lavatory basins

For lavatory basins the risk of self-siphonage is much more closely dependent on the design of the branch connection to the stack than it is for other appliances. Research has shown that the bore, length and fall of the waste pipe are all important factors. Basin branches of the usual nominal 30 mm bore normally run full and so cause suction on the trap at the end of the discharge. One remedy is to limit the length and, if necessary, the slope of the pipe. Fig. 1 gives maximum allowable slopes for varying lengths of

30 mm nominal bore waste pipe, used in conjunction with a 75 mm seal P-trap. When the basin is more than 1·68 m from the stack, a 30 mm nominal bore trap, with a short 30 mm tail pipe can be discharged into a 40 mm or 50 mm waste pipe. This should prevent the waste pipe from running full (which is sometimes noisy) and thus reduce the suction on the trap. It also reduces the risk of blockage by the deposit of sediment from the waste water. Any bends in the waste pipe should be of large radius.

Table 1. Design of single branches and fittings

Component	Action to be guarded against	Design recommendations
Lavatory basin waste	Self-siphonage	75 mm seal P-traps to be used. The maximum slope of a nominal 30 mm waste pipe to be determined from Fig. 1. Any bends to be not less than 75 mm radius to centre-line.
		Waste pipes longer than the recommended maximum length of 1·68 m should be vented, or a larger diameter waste pipe or suitable resealing trap should be used.
Bath and sink wastes nominal 40 mm trap and 40 mm waste pipe	Self-siphonage	75 mm seal traps to be used. Self-siphonage problems unlikely. Length and slope of waste branch not critical, but sediment may accumulate in long waste pipes and access for cleaning should be provided.
	Backing up of discharge from WC branch into bath branch	Position of entry of bath waste into stack to be as in Fig. 2.
Soil branch connection to stack	Induced siphonage lower in the stack when WC is discharged	WC connections should be swept in the direction of flow. Fittings should have a minimum sweep of at least 50 mm radius (but see also note on straight WC inlets in text). WC branches up to 6 m long have been used successfully.
Bend at foot of stack (Fig. 2)	Back pressure at lowest branch. Build-up of detergent foam	Bend to be of large radius. Two large radius bends (similar to the long one-eighth bends shown in Fig. 5, BS 65 and 540: Pt 1: 1971) should be used for 150 mm and also preferably for 100 mm. The minimum recommended bend radius for 100 mm pipes is 200 mm. Vertical distance between the lowest branch connection and invert of drain to be at least 760 mm (460 mm for up to three-storey houses with a 100 mm stack).
Offsets in stack	Back pressure above offset	There should be no offsets in stacks below the topmost appliances unless venting is provided to relieve any back pressure. Offsets above the topmost appliances are of no significance.

Another means of avoiding self-siphonage in long waste branches is the use of special re-sealing traps, but these may require periodic cleaning to perform well. Designs vary, and each must be judged on its merits.

S-traps produce particularly severe self-siphonage conditions, and venting or a special resealing trap is normally needed.

Combined lavatory basin and bath wastes

Some arrangements perform satisfactorily, but it is not possible to set down limits on design. Tests are needed to assess the behaviour of particular arrangements.

Branch pipes to WCs

Water closet branches do not run full and so there is no risk of self-siphonage whatever their lengths. However, the shape of the WC branch connection to the stack is important because it influences the amount of induced siphonage acting upon branches to other appliances lower in the stack. Thus the recommendations of Tables 1 and 2 assume that WC branch connections are swept in the direction of flow (Fig. 2).

If straight-inlet WC branches are used, more venting or a larger diameter stack may be necessary (see footnote to Table 2).

Design of main pipework

Back pressure and detergent foam

A sharp bend at the base of the stack can cause back pressure to affect the seals of the lowest branch connections. It can also cause a build-up of detergent foam. These difficulties can best be avoided by ensuring that this bend is of large radius (as described in Table 1). A further precaution is to connect ground-floor appliances directly to the drain or manhole or to use a bend at the base of the stack which is one size larger than the stack itself.

Venting

Induced siphonage can be reduced by providing cross vent connections between the soil and vent stacks, either at every floor or at alternate floors. To prevent cross-flow, the vent connection should slope upwards from the drainage stack at an angle not less than 135°. Table 2 shows the vents required for various loads on 90 mm to 150 mm stacks.

Offsets

An offset in the stack above the topmost connection to the stack has little effect on the performance of the system. Offsets below the topmost connection should be avoided, or extra vent pipes may be required to prevent large pressure fluctuations in the stack.

Table 2. Minimum stack sizes and vents required for various loading conditions

Type	Stack diameter mm	Requirements	
Houses (one-family)			
Up to 3 storeys	90	Single-stack	
Flats			
		Stack serving one group* on each floor	**Stack serving two groups* on each floor**
Up to 10 storeys	100	Single-stack	Single-stack.
11 to 15	100	50 mm vent stack with one connection on alternate floors	50 mm vent stack with one connection on each floor.
16 to 20	100	65 mm vent stack with one connection on alternate floors	65 mm vent stack with one connection on each floor.
Up to 12 storeys	125	Single-stack	Single-stack.
12 to 15	125	Single-stack	50 mm vent stack with one connection on alternate floors.
Up to 25 storeys	150	Single-stack	Single-stack.
Maisonettes			
		Stack serving one group on alternate floors	**Stack serving two groups on alternate floors**
Up to 10 storeys	100	Single-stack	Single-stack.
11 to 15	100	Single-stack	50 mm vent stack with one connection on alternate (bathroom) floors.
16 to 20	100	50 mm vent stack with one connection on alternate (bathroom) floors	65 mm vent stack with one connection on alternate (bathroom) floors.

* Each group consists of a WC, bath, basin and sink. Where dwellings contain more appliances, it may be necessary to provide more vents.

N.B. The above recommendations apply to systems with swept-inlet WC branches. With straight-inlet branches, a 100 mm stack with no vents has been found satisfactory up to 4 storeys; a 150 mm stack with no vents has been found satisfactory up to 15 storeys.

Surcharging of the drain

If the drain to which a stack is connected is sur-charged, the normal flow of air down the stack during discharge can be interrupted and very high back pressures can result. If this condition is likely, a vent pipe should be connected to the base of the stack above the likely flood level. The vent pipe bore should be at least 75 mm for a 100 mm bore stack, or 100 mm for a 150 mm bore stack; it should be as short as possible.

Drains with intercepting traps

An intercepting trap fitted in a drain serving a dis-charge stack can restrict the flow of air down the stack and cause high back pressures unless the base of the stack is vented. The vent pipe should be of the size described above for drain surcharging conditions.

Removal of rainwater

The highest likely rainwater flow from the roof of a small house or flat (with an area of approx. 40 m²) is equivalent to the maximum discharge from a lavatory basin. For this size of roof the rainwater can normally be ignored in the calculation of hydraulic loading on a soil stack. Where easy access to the roof exists, the roof gulley linking the roof to the stack should be trapped.

Wind effects

Suction caused by wind blowing across the tops of stacks on tall buildings has been known to result in loss of water from seals. Normal trap venting is no remedy but a protective cowl at the top of the stack is of some help. Suction is greatest nearer the corners of roofs and the edges of parapets and if possible the tops of stacks should be sited away from these positions.

Further reading

British Standard Code of Practice CP304
Sanitary pipework above ground

Hospital sanitary services: some design and maintenance problems

Some of the lessons to be learned from a preliminary study by the Building Research Station of hospital sanitary services are instructive in showing how critically the design and use of these installations determine subsequent maintenance needs and the ease with which these needs can be met. The main observations contained in this digest are directed principally to those involved in the design and maintenance of hospital services, but they have a wider relevance for the design of complex installations in general.

The advantages of single-stack plumbing for housing, the subject of the previous digest, are best realised when there is a close grouping of sanitary appliances round a vertical service duct. When appliances are more widely spaced apart, as they often are in hospital wards, it may be impracticable or even impossible to use a single-stack method.

In wards it is common practice for a drain to be run at a gradual slope beneath the floor and to receive the discharge from many appliances on its way to a stack. While this more or less horizontal arrangement may be economic and may fit in with architectural requirements, it has disadvantages in that the risk of blockage is likely to be greater than in vertical pipes, particularly if the drain has bends and junctions in addition to a shallow slope. There is a lack of information about the performance of these systems and of their anti-siphonage requirements. For these reasons the Station, with the encouragement of the Ministry of Health, began to study sanitary services in hospitals. The first stage of this work, involving the examination of several existing and proposed schemes, is reported below.

Pipework in existing hospitals

In several important respects the design of drainage systems in modern hospitals shows little advance over that of a hundred years ago. Admittedly, most

piping is now installed internally rather than externally, and there is greater provision for anti-siphonage devices, but there are still many different drainage layouts, including vertical and horizontal main drains within the building, and pipe systems which take tortuous paths through the structure (*see* Fig. 1). The main reason for this seems to be lack of co-ordinated planning of the different services, both with each other and with the main structure. The result is a network of piping which is spread throughout hospital buildings and which reveals how little thought has been given to the need for adequate access to the pipework.

Fig. 1. . . . tortuous path through the structure. . .

Fig. 2. Three short-radius bends close together

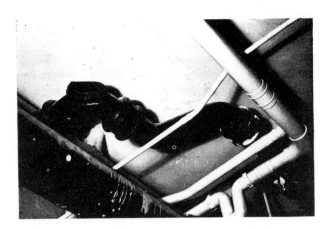

Fig. 3. An unnecessary offset

Layout of pipework in relation to stoppages

The complexity of pipe layout directly affects the number of stoppages which have to be cleared—expensive and often troublesome operations. Not only do they disrupt the work of the hospital, they may be a possible cause of cross-infection. Most stoppages seem to occur where the pipework is complicated by knuckle bends and sharp offsets and $92\frac{1}{2}°$ junctions. None was reported where straight lengths of 100 and 150 mm pipes sloped gradually. The kind of problem is well illustrated by Figs. 2 and 3. No excuse is offered for saying again that better design, planning and overall integration are called for.

Misuse of system during construction

Stoppages may result also from misuse of the building while under construction. Builders' rubbish was frequently found in the drainage system above and below ground. The open ends of soil branch connections are often to be seen on site stuffed with sacks or cement bags to keep out rubbish (*see* Fig. 4)—an unreliable method if these materials have to be removed as rubbish themselves from the completed system after handover.

While this kind of misuse occurs with all types of buildings, in hospitals it seems to have been particularly prevalent, and is of course particularly unfortunate in its effects. Plastic caps have been recommended for closing the ends of heating pipes during installation and there is much to be said for using this type of protective cover on soil and waste pipes also. In general, improved site supervision of the contract could help a lot in preventing the carelessness which causes trouble later.

Misuse of system during occupation

Special appliances such as sluices, slop hoppers and cleaners' sinks are available to ward staff for the disposal of materials unsuited to removal by conventional drainage systems. However, some misuse of these appliances was reported and dressings, sanitary towels, floor cloths, mop heads, syringes, spatulas and rubber gloves are known to have been among articles removed from the systems surveyed; cases were also reported of a blanket, a stainless steel bowl, false teeth and tea cloths contributing to stoppages. In addition, traps are readily blocked by match sticks and cigarette filter tips.

There is a special problem concerning goods such as plastic syringes and spatulas. Sometimes it is not appreciated by hospital staff that these 'disposables' should be incinerated rather than put into the normal drainage system. In other cases it appears that ward incinerators are much less efficient than they need to be and this leads to the misuse of drainage systems as the first alternative to hand.

Kitchen refuse also causes stoppages, and the misuse of kitchen appliances such as grease traps can lead to the accumulation of grease in the

Fig. 4. Floor access point blocked with polythene sheeting

drainage system. Regular cleaning of grease traps is essential, yet only one of the fifteen hospitals visited had arranged for this.

While it is important not to get the incidence of misuse out of perspective, there is no doubt that improved staff training in these matters would help, as would better refuse disposal facilities.

Access to drainage pipework

While much could be done to improve the layout and prevent misuse of drainage systems, some risk of stoppages will always remain. It is important, therefore, and particularly in hospitals, that adequate provision be made for access to the pipework. Many complaints were made of lack of access into ducts—it was either too small, blocked by other services, or in the wrong place. On the pipework itself cleaning eyes often could not be used effectively; some were partly embedded in concrete or turned towards the wall or ceiling, as in Figs. 5 and 6. Access to others was blocked by other services. In many cases it was not possible to use 0.6 m drain rods. Permanent lighting was absent from some ducts; a torch does not give a plumber adequate light to work by.

Some vertical and horizontal pipes with cleaning eyes were encased in brick or hollow pot ducts without access doors. In one example, a stoppage occurred in the enclosed pipe, no drawings were available and holes had to be knocked in the duct to locate the access point; eight hours were needed to clear the blockage which had occurred at a knuckle bend as a result of a build-up of kitchen waste on top of builders' rubbish.

Some horizontal pipes are enclosed within false ceilings, with removable panels providing access. This means that when a stoppage occurs by misuse of an appliance say, on the third floor, it has to be cleared from the second floor since this provides access to the drain above. The routine of two floors is therefore affected, whereas better design might

limit the disruption to one floor. Several medical authorities were concerned at the need to clear blockages within the clinical area. In one check test reported by a hospital pathologist, infectious bacteria were found in sewage that had discharged into a clinical area. As well as this risk there is the possible hazard of carrying dirty tools and wearing infected overalls in clinical areas.

Cases were also reported of electrical services being disrupted as a result of sewage leaking round lighting fittings.

Recommendations

While the internal drainage pipework is not normally among the most costly of hospital service systems, the foregoing notes will have indicated the serious consequences of poor design and misuse. Improvements are needed at every stage, from the preliminary sketch plans to the work of the subcontractor and site supervision, and finally to the use and maintenance of the services. Broad recommendations for each stage can be made as follows:
1. Adequate service space is fundamental to the design of a hospital. The services must be planned within the service area and installed in accordance with the plan. Service inlets and outlets should not be neglected at this stage; the position of sanitary appliances on the sketch plan, and the position and amount of piping needed beneath the floors, must be considered together. The service space should be well lit and capable of being easily cleaned.
2. Bends of large rather than small radius are always to be recommended but are particularly important beneath a ward floor. Similarly, oblique junctions are preferred to T-junctions since they allow loads to flow more readily from branches to main drains.
3. Access doors are advised for all changes of direction except the most gradual. They are also needed at all junctions on horizontal drains. Access doors should of course be easily accessible within

Fig. 5. Access door turned towards wall

Fig. 6. Two access doors turned towards ceiling

the service space. Flexible connectors between soil appliances and piping allow their ready removal if this should be necessary for rodding.

4. Planned maintenance is a necessity and thought must be given to the arrangements for maintenance staff to do their work with minimum interruption of ward routines or threat to hygiene. Drawings must be available to them showing the drainage layout and access points. Washing facilities should be provided for them.

5. The education of staff in the properties of sanitary equipment and services is essential.

Single-stack drainage

There are many cases in hospital buildings of various types where a stack serves several appliances close to it on different floors. This is a situation in which single-stack principles are likely to be applicable, and a study of the literature will show the possibilities in this direction.

Further reading

1. AFE Wise, Drainage pipework in dwellings: hydraulic design and performance. HMSO (London, 1957).

2. BRS Digest 80. Soil and waste pipe systems for housing.

3. BRS Digest 115. Soil and waste pipe systems for office buildings.

4. AFE Wise and R Payne. Sanitary services for hospitals: a review of current faults. Architects Journal, 1965, 142 (21st July), pp. 153-6. (Building Research Current Papers, Design Series 39.)

5. Institution of Heating and Ventilating Engineers. Hospital Engineering Services: Present and Future, Symposium held on 12th January, 1966.

Durability of metals in natural waters

This digest deals with: nature and concentration of impurities in water—hardness—types of scale formed—prediction of scale formation—resistance to corrosion of commonly used metals—effect of scale formation on corrosion resistance—hot water systems, the risk of using a mixture of metals—protective measures—loss of zinc from brass components—heating installations, means of avoiding corrosion and 'air' locking—protection of pipes against their external environment.

The properties of water that affect the durability of plumbing installations are:

1 nature and concentration of impurities
2 ability to form a protective scale

Varied compositions of waters from several sources are shown in Table 1. Of the mineral impurities, the chlorides and sulphates are the most aggressive to metals. Natural waters also contain dissolved oxygen and carbon dioxide which influence their corrosive behaviour.

The hardness of water is given in terms of the calcium carbonate content; water with the equivalent of 50 ppm is classed as soft, over 350 ppm as very hard. Hardness removed by boiling is 'temporary' hardness; that remaining after boiling is 'permanent' or 'non-carbonate' hardness, usually due to the presence of calcium and magnesium sulphates.

The composition of natural waters is governed by the nature of the ground from which they originate. Surface waters from lakes, rivers or reservoirs are maintained by rainfall in which the main dissolved constituent is carbon dioxide—up to 5 ppm. If the ground within the catchment area is relatively insoluble, the water will be soft and its acidity (low pH) will be controlled by the amount of decayed vegetation or peat within the area. Alternatively, if the water drains over or through chalk, it is likely to be very hard. The composition and temperature of deep well waters are much more constant than for surface supplies.

The ability of a water to lay down an inert scale is of prime importance in predicting its action on metals. Fortunately, many natural waters deposit calcium carbonate on any metallic surface. The combination of corrosion product and calcium carbonate can

Table 1. Varied composition of natural waters (parts per million)

Source of sample	Total dissolved solids	Chloride	Sulphate	Calcium	Magnesium	Hardness		pH
						Total	Temporary	
Reservoir, Scotland	37	Trace	17	3	<1	—	—	6·2
Deep well, Reading	511	117	39	42	29	233	216	—
Borehole, Harwich	2577	1132	136	—	—	602	305	7·8
Sea (average)	34,800	19,500	2380	380	1250	—	—	8·2

form a protective layer capable of reducing the rate of corrosive attack to a low value or even to zero. The type of scale produced by waters of the same chemical composition can vary in an unpredictable manner depending on factors which are not understood, although it seems established that small amounts of organic matter in the water are beneficial. Thin eggshell scales have the greatest effect in reducing corrosion, whereas thick nodular scales have far less effect. Excessive scale reduces the flow capacity of pipes, reduces their heat transfer characteristics and may produce almost complete blockage of heating pipes.

Metals for water services

The choice of materials for water distribution is governed by their mechanical properties, resistance to corrosion, appearance, ease of installation, and cost.

Iron and steel Galvanising gives effective protection against almost all hard waters but not against acid waters or soft waters with a free carbon dioxide content of 30 μg/cm^3 or more.

Lead The corrosion resistance of lead is excellent, but waters of low temporary hardness (incapable of putting down a protective film) and containing organic acids or free carbon dioxide are plumbo-solvent. A danger to health exists if drinking water contains more than 0·1 μg/cm^3 of lead.

Lead pipes may fail by creep and horizontal pipes should therefore be supported at intervals of not more than 0·5 m. Alloying lead with only very small additions of silver and copper (BS 1085) confers a degree of creep resistance which permits a one-third reduction in wall thickness, without detriment to corrosion resistance.

Fatigue failure due to repeated reversals of stress by vibration or alternate rapid heating and cooling can happen where pipes are rigidly held either by their fixings or by surrounding materials. They should therefore be isolated from excessive vibration and provision must be made for thermal movement.

Copper Above ground, copper tubing to BS 2871 : Part 1, Tables X and Z, is suitable; copper to Table Y of the same Standard is generally used for underground work. Almost all waters react with copper but the action ceases as a protective scale forms on the metal. A cuprosolvent action takes place in water with a high free carbon dioxide content. The amount of corrosion is too slight to have any harmful effect on durability and, from the health point of view, amounts up to 1·5 g/cm^3 can be tolerated. Amounts in excess of this react with soap, producing green staining on bathroom fittings. Lower concentrations greatly accelerate pitting corrosion of galvanised steel tanks, aluminium components and utensils.

Under certain conditions, copper tube may suffer intense localised pitting corrosion. This has occured when the tube contains an almost continuous film that is cathodic to the underlying metal in the supply water. Corrosion takes place at breaks or fissures in the film. On tubes manufactured many years ago, such films consisted of carbon, produced from the lubricant used during manufacture. The most rapid corrosive action took place in deep well waters; even here, pitting occurred only when both a film and a suitable electrolyte existed together. Since 1960, mechanical cleaning of tubes after manufacture has dramatically reduced, though not entirely eliminated, the incidence of attack. Visual inspection of the bore will not reveal the presence of a deleterious film. Laboratory investigation is needed. It is essential, therefore, if pitting corrosion is to be avoided, that the tubing should meet the requirements of the appropriate British Standard in all respects; for imported supplies, confirmation of this should be obtained.

In soft moorland waters containing manganese salts, a cathodic scale has been found to be deposited slowly in the hotter parts of the system, giving rise to pitting corrosion.

Stainless steel Thin-walled stainless steel tubing is a successful alternative to copper for conveying potable water and for closed circuit central heating systems. It is more difficult to bend and to cut than copper and jointing by capillary fittings requires a different technique. A special flux is needed to achieve a satisfactory soft-solder joint. When first introduced, such fluxes were chloride-bearing and found to be excessively corrosive, but subsequent formulations, based on phosphoric acid or acid phosphates, are far superior.

Further information about this tubing is contained in Digest 83.

Hot water systems

The metals most commonly used in hot water systems are galvanised steel or copper for storage tanks or cylinders, lead, copper, stainless steel or galvanised steel pipework, and cast iron, steel, copper or bronze for the boiler or back boiler.

In hard or moderately hard waters, galvanised steel cisterns and tanks have been used for many years with galvanised pipework and cast iron boilers, without any serious defects. Occasionally, pitting is experienced which may be due simply to iron swarf or rubbish left at the bottom of the tank, impeding the formation of a protective scale or, with hot water cylinders, excessively high temperatures during the early life of the system. Above 70°C, the polarity between the zinc and the steel of the tank is reversed and the galvanising layer no longer protects steel exposed at the base of cracks or by faults in the galvanising. Corrosion is localised at these defects and, with prolonged overheating, pitting can perforate the wall of the tank. The water temperature in a galvanised tank should be kept below 70°C until a protective scale has formed. Once a rust nodule has formed, the carbonate scale put down by the water cannot stifle further pitting.

A magnesium anode suspended inside a galvanised hot water tank and in electrical connection with it affords cathodic protection at any temperature. The anode will be consumed but not before a protective scale has formed, so that replacement will not normally be necessary. To protect the whole surface of the cylinder or tank, the current must be distributed evenly and this can only be achieved in waters of fairly high conductivity. In soft waters, where protection is more necessary, anodes are less effective because of the low conductivity of the water.

Pitting corrosion of galvanised components may also result from deposition of copper from the water on to the walls of the tank. Most waters will pick up a sufficient quantity of copper (0·1 ppm) for this from new pipework but continued pitting of a cold water cistern is more likely to occur by backflow of copper-bearing hot water through the feed pipe or drips from the vent pipe. Magnesium anodes provide effective protection; bitumen-coated galvanised cisterns are also available and should behave satisfactorily with copper pipework in soft water areas.

Bimetallic corrosion of galvanised components occurs in waters of low or moderate hardness at junctions with brass or other copper-bearing alloys. This can be eliminated by fitting plastics connectors or by using a short length of copper pipe between the steel pipe and copper cylinder; these treatments will not, however, protect against the pitting corrosion produced by copper-bearing waters. Galvanised steel and copper should not be used in the same hot water supply system unless experience in the area has shown that it is safe to do so. There is no evidence of failure with lead or stainless steel pipework used with copper cylinders.

In most waters, copper tanks and cylinders develop a thin oxide film which is protective, but, occasionally, with hard or moderately hard deep well waters, a film is produced which will break down and allow pitting to occur after a comparatively short period of service. If an aluminium rod is fitted inside the storage vessel and connected to it, the rod will slowly corrode but it will control the electrochemical potential of the copper whilst the film is forming and will assist the formation of a protective type of film. Copper cylinders and combination tanks fitted with aluminium protector rods are available.

Dezincification

Many components used in water services are of hot-pressed (alpha-beta) brass. This is satisfactory in very many waters but zinc may be lost from the alloy in acidic waters or in alkaline waters of high chloride content, so producing a porous copper layer which may extend throughout the wall of the fitting and cause water seepage. When this occurs, the zinc dissolved out of the brass forms a bulky corrosion product and eventually blocks the fittings. The pH and the ratio of temporary hardness/chloride content of the water largely controls the incidence of this form of dezincification. High tensile (alpha) brasses can be made immune by incorporating 0·03 per cent arsenic, but there is no simple treatment for hot-pressed brass. In some areas it is possible to treat the water so as to increase its temporary hardness, but where this is not done alternative copper or gunmetal fittings must be used.

Heating systems

Most heating installations now use pressed steel radiators and thin gauge copper tubing in combination with cast iron boilers. Defects sometimes develop after comparatively short periods of use; two problems are found to be most prevalent:

'Air' locking occurs either by entrainment of air through faulty design or by the generation of gas within the system. Air may be drawn in through the vent pipe if this is not sufficiently high above the topmost section of the circulation system to balance the suction developed by the circulation pump; it may also be taken into the system by circulation of hot water through the vent pipe and expansion tank due to the use of a pump of excessive pressure head. 'Air' locks caused by corrosion within the system are due primarily to hydrogen generation, although some forms of bacteria may produce nitrogen within the system. In a closed heating system, the initial dissolved oxygen content of the water is reduced fairly rapidly to 0·1 ppm or lower. When iron reacts with de-aerated hot water, ferrous hydroxide is formed. This is dissolved until an equilibrium is attained and the reaction ceases unless the ferrous hydroxide is removed. One process by which this occurs converts the ferrous hydroxide to the more insoluble magnetite with the release of hydrogen gas. This probably occurs at a very low rate in an all-steel system but the rate of the reaction is increased by the presence of copper. These corrosive reactions can be controlled by inhibitors. Inhibitors based on sodium benzoate and sodium nitrite and other additives including biocides, antifreezes and wetting agents are available commercially. Care should be taken to prevent the inhibited water from contaminating the domestic water supply.

Perforation of steel radiators by pitting corrosion of the internal face is very often due to entrained air taken into the system. However, sulphate-reducing bacteria have been identified within failed systems, associated with the production of hydrogen sulphide. Such bacteria are widely distributed in clay subsoils and gain easy access to the system; the risk of attack is small and can be eliminated by treatment with a biocide. Tests with acriflavine, at a concentration of 5 ppm or with dichlorophen, at a concentration of about 30 ppm, have been effective. The system should be flushed with the biocide when first filled, emptied and refilled with mains water; this is preferable to dosing the system, which might establish a resistant strain of bacteria.

External attack on water service components

Any material used to convey or store water must be able to resist the action of the external environment.

Soils Light sandy soils and chalk are not generally aggressive. Ground which contains large amounts of cinders and builder's rubble can be very corrosive to steel, copper and aluminium, which therefore require highly resistant and protective coatings. Heavy, anaerobic clays provide a favourable environment for sulphate-reducing bacteria and may be corrosive to ferrous metals. Saline environments cause severe corrosion of aluminium and galvanised steel; they have little effect on copper or lead but the latter can be severely corroded if it is connected, in this environment, to copper. In aggressive soils, backfills of chalk or sand (not sea sand) may prove beneficial but care should be taken to prevent the backfill becoming a land drain. Faults in buried pipework might not be detected until it is too late to apply remedial action and replacement may be costly.

Humid environments In kitchens and bathrooms, heavy condensation occurs on exposed cold water pipes. Even if these are unpainted little deterioration is likely unless the condensed moisture is heavily contaminated by contact with building materials adjacent to the pipework. Staining of copper and of stainless steel is possible in such conditions. Under severe conditions, the condensate on copper may produce green staining on adjacent materials or may attack nearby aluminium components. In humid conditions, stressed copper components such as ballvalve floats and WC thimbles may suffer stress corrosion failures, particularly in an atmosphere loaded with ammonia, for example from household cleansers. Lead cold water pipes passing through oak or sweet chestnut beams or panelling in humid conditions are also subject to continued and severe attack. All metal pipes laid in contact with chloride-bearing brickwork or concrete are susceptible to attack through leaching of chloride; contact should therefore be avoided by the insertion of an impervious felt or by keeping the pipes clear of contact with the material.

Concrete and plaster Dry concrete or plaster will not attack metals. In wet conditions, galvanised steel and lead will be attacked by cement mortar or concrete unless deeply embedded but copper will remain immune from attack. Wet acid plasters and magnesium oxychloride flooring are liable to corrode all metals with which they are in contact; protection should therefore be provided in one of the following ways:

1 A substantial coating of bitumen or coal tar composition
2 Wrapping tapes
3 Sheathing with protective metal or plastics sleeves

The last gives the most reliable protection and does not restrain thermal movement of the metal.

The action of the environment on stressed copper pipes in floor screeds surfaced with ammonia-stabilised latex adhesives has caused stress corrosion cracking. It is safer to avoid all contact between copper and ammonia-bearing materials unless the ammonia can evaporate freely from the vicinity.

5 Painted Surfaces

Painting walls
Part 1: Choice of paint

Whilst some walls are inherently weatherproof and aesthetically acceptable, others are painted for a variety of reasons: to provide colour or surface texture, to waterproof them, to reflect or absorb light, to facilitate cleaning or for hygiene.

This two-part digest gives, in Part 1, guidance on the choice of paints and other coatings for internal and external walls according to the appearance and life required and the type of substrate. It discusses plasters, cement and concrete, bricks and stone, but excludes metal, wood and plastics. Part 2 gives information on the adverse factors which affect paint on wall surfaces and ways of identifying and remedying defects. The two digests together replace Digests 55, 56 and 57 which are now withdrawn.

It is recognised that users have difficulty in relating the types of paint described to commercial products but there are too many different makes of each type of paint for trade names to be quoted; in case of doubt the manufacturer should be contacted to verify that a particular paint is of the correct type required.

Characteristics of wall surfaces

Lime plasters

Non-hydraulic Now rarely used except in restoration work, they have a rather absorptive, mechanically weak surface when new and harden slowly on aging, sometimes with development of shrinkage cracks. When made with high purity lime and clean sand, they are free of soluble salts or caustic alkali and do not themselves saponify oil paints. They may react with salts (principally of sodium and potassium derived from a brick background for example) to form caustic alkali which could attack oil paints and some emulsion paints. Lime may be gauged with gypsum plaster to increase the hardness.

Limewash has been the traditional treatment but matt emulsion paints can be used provided that painting is delayed as long as possible (preferably at least a year) to permit drying, carbonation and development of strength. The porosity of these plasters is usually high and if well aged a penetrating sealer may be found helpful. Tough modern paints are generally unsuitable.

Hydraulic These are not often used as interior finishing plasters but may be used in exterior plasters or stucco. They have a variable caustic alkali content and can attack paints severely.

Gypsum (calcium sulphate) plasters

BS 1191 Part 1 *Gypsum building plasters,* distinguishes four classes of gypsum plasters and CP 211 *Internal plastering,* gives information on their use. Used neat, in the fully set, dry state they can be painted without difficulty using almost any type of paint. The porosity decreases and hardness increases from Class A to Class D. Adhesion of paint is usually good even on the denser plasters unless they are trowelled to a glazed surface but is seriously reduced by dampness, particularly on the denser type. Added lime (or cement in the backing coats) may cause development of alkalinity and necessitate the use of alkali-resistant primers or non-saponifiable paints.

Class A Plaster of Paris This is not normally used for plastering but is sometimes used in repairs and may be gauged with lime or lime and sand. For painting purposes it may be considered with Class B.

Class B Retarded hemi-hydrate plasters (eg 'Thistle') These have a smooth, hard but moderately porous surface to which paint adhesion is good but absorption of water-thinned paints is sometimes patchy. They contain small amounts of lime (greatest in metal lathing plasters) and are slightly alkaline but this is quickly reduced on aging. They do not usually affect paint unless there is an additional source of alkali behind them. Lime may be added but

---

Prepared at Building Research Station, Garston, Watford WD2 7JR
Technical enquiries arising from this Digest should be directed to Building Research Advisory Service at the above address.

accelerates the set and increases the alkalinity (metal lathing plasters contain lime to reduce metal corrosion). Over-wetting during application may produce a powdery surface and in damp conditions (eg from condensation or moisture penetration from the rear) Class B plasters suffer from 'sweat out' leading to softening and consequent paint failure.

Class C Anhydrous plasters (eg 'Sirapite') These are for finishing only. They are harder and less porous than Class B plasters. Over-trowelling can lead to a glazed surface with poor paint adhesion. They are slightly alkaline but the addition of lime (to improve workability) is common and this may react with the accelerating salts present making the plaster more likely to affect paint.

If allowed to dry out too quickly, anhydrous plasters may not hydrate fully, giving a powdery surface on which paint adhesion is poor; this may not always be visible at the time of painting. If moisture later gains access, delayed expansion can then cause severe blistering or breaking up of the plaster.

Class D Keene's plaster This is similar to Class C plasters and can be trowelled to a smooth level surface especially suitable for gloss finishes although this sometimes leads to poor adhesion for paint. It may be alkaline or slightly acid in reaction; in either state it is itself unlikely to affect paint. It should not be gauged with lime, but in the presence of lime, (from the backing for example), it may become strongly alkaline. The traditional practice of 'following the trowel' with a sharp primer (one with a low oil content) is intended to ensure full hydration and improve paint adhesion, but it is becoming less common and should be used only on Keene's cement which shows an acid reaction on test.

Lightweight plasters

BS 1191 Part 2 *Premixed lightweight plasters* describes two types, (a) undercoat plasters and (b) finish plaster. They confer good fire-resistance and their good thermal insulation and ability to absorb some moisture help to reduce intermittent condensation although, if this property is needed, impervious paints should not be used. In one product ('Carlite'), both undercoat and finish are based on retarded hemi-hydrate gypsum plasters, with added lightweight aggregate such as perlite or vermiculite (or both in final coat plasters). Both contain small amounts of free lime (greater in the metal lathing and browning types) and are slightly alkaline. Being more porous than other gypsum plasters they hold more water initially and may take longer to dry out, particularly in winter; adequate drying out is essential if paints are not to be affected. On a background liable to produce stains or efflorescence, an aerated sand/cement backing coat is desirable. Patchy absorption of emulsion paint can result from uneven trowelling as with Class B, accentuated by the slower

drying out, and successive coats may 'pile up' on the more absorptive areas rather than even them out. A thin, non-aqueous paint or sealer is necessary to overcome this difficulty.

Another product ('Limelite') has an undercoat based on Portland cement and lime with lightweight aggregate. It resists movement of water and salts but is highly alkaline; precautions may need to be taken against alkali attack on paints.

Thin-wall plasters

These are based on organic binders and set only by evaporation of water; being used in thin layers they dry out rapidly. They should present no difficulty in painting if the background is dry but occasionally appear underbound and excessively absorptive even to the point of being softened by emulsion paints. A sealer coat may be necessary.

Dry lining

Dry finishing systems with paper-faced plasterboard and jointing compounds are usually finished with emulsion paint and give little trouble except for occasional excessive absorption by the jointing compound giving a patchy appearance or even severe cracking of the paint. Appropriate sealers should then be used. Spray painting is especially appropriate and some solvent-thinned paints, such as high-build chlorinated rubber or synthetic rubber types, may be used in cold weather.

Wallpaper This is a fairly common base for painting, usually with emulsion paints. It may give rise to 'bleeding' with a few colours or with 'gold' (bronze) pigments in the paper. Some paints weaken the adhesion of the wallpaper by their drying shrinkage, causing occasional failures, and in very dry weather the additional shrinkage of the wallpaper (especially heavily-embossed types) can cause widespread detachment. Vinyl wallcoverings seem to be readily coated with emulsion paint and less prone to such failures.

Portland cement rendering

The alkalinity of Portland cement is, with rare exception, so high that precautions against alkali attack of paints by new cement-based products should always be taken. Because of the caustic alkali present, carbonation of the lime content on aging is not always sufficient to prevent the saponification of oil-paints and even when the surface pH falls to about 9, there may be further alkali at a greater depth which will affect paints as moisture moves through. The free lime usually present in cement plasters is a cause of the lime bloom which is particularly noticeable on emulsion paints. If carbonation is allowed to occur before painting it can greatly reduce this effect and also reduce surface porosity.

Cement paints are suitable for very early decoration;

acrylic emulsion or other alkali-resistant porous paints can be used after about four weeks drying. For a glossy finish, a non-saponifiable paint (for example chlorinated rubber) is preferred; an alkali-resistant primer is essential under oil-based paints but the moisture content must be at a safe level. Chemically-resistant wall finishes require a hard base: cement rendering is normally suitable if dry but if a very smooth finish is needed, an anhydrous plaster can be used on top.

Concrete

Concrete is considered a durable, permanent material but long-term deterioration, especially in acid-polluted air, is possible; it may, therefore, require protection. Following deterioration and repairs, or even when new in the absence of sufficient cover to protect reinforcement, there is often a requirement to provide protection against penetration by water and salts. There is also an increasing need for decorative or colouring treatments to improve the quality of the surroundings where these contain large areas of concrete, or even for colourless water-proofing treatments to prevent accumulation of dirt and biological growths.

The general requirements for painting concrete are similar to those for cement renderings but the surface may be either hard and smooth with poor adhesion for paints (eg pre-cast components) or rough and porous with large voids, as in mass concrete. Residues of mould oil can seriously reduce paint adhesion; they are best removed by abrasion rather than solvents but detergents or emulsifying agents may be useful. The application of cement-based paints, or 'bagging' with a cement/sand mix, will reduce surface roughness. Larger voids may be filled with mortar or epoxy-resin mortars, or, *indoors in dry conditions only,* with gypsum plaster or water-mixed powder fillers. Alternatively, thin-wall plasters (indoors) or textured paints (either indoors or out) may be used to hide surface blemishes.

The coatings needed to provide additional protection must be impervious and should therefore be applied when conditions are as dry as possible but their effect in reducing the rate of corrosion of reinforcement is far from reliably established and no firm guidance is available on the acceptability of such a treatment in place of additional concrete; they will need periodic maintenance.

Stucco

New stucco, and repairs to cracks with Portland cement mixes, should be treated as an alkaline cement rendering. Problems also arise from the weak or friable condition of old stucco, the presence of hair cracks and of multiple coats of paint of doubtful adhesion. Many paint failures begin at cracks which re-open and allow water to enter. Cracks over 2 mm wide should be cut out to at least

20 mm and filled with a masonry cement or cement/lime/sand mortar. For finer cracks, an exterior grade of elastic oil-bound stopper (available from very few suppliers) is necessary; many water-mixed fillers are unsuitable but those based on emulsion binders, or made up from a cement/sand mix and emulsion paint, may be suitable under emulsion-bound coatings. Failures may also occur at a weak layer in the existing paint even when it appears sound, as a result of the drying shrinkage of the new paint; sealers are usually recommended but must not be expected to penetrate multiple layers of old paint and bind them down to the surface.

Suitable gloss paints are difficult to obtain: the possibilities are discussed in the section on gloss finishes for exterior use. Where a gloss finish or smooth surface is not essential, some fine-textured exterior emulsion paints or exterior masonry paints can be used on old, painted stucco and on new work. The old paint should be thoroughly cleaned by wet abrasion.*

Asbestos cement sheets

When new, asbestos cement sheets are strongly alkaline. They vary in porosity between different types and even over the area of single sheets. Emulsion paints are suitable if based on alkali-resistant polymers; the first coat should be well thinned to avoid patchiness on new sheets, and if this does not overcome the difficulties a solvent-thinned sealer should be used. If a glossy finish is required, chlorinated rubber paints would be preferred to the more complex system of alkali-resistant primer, undercoat and gloss. Asbestos cement should not be painted with an impervious finish on one side only since differential carbonation may result in warping or cracking; back painting with the same paint or a cheaper impermeable one is necessary. Asbestos insulation board is less dense and much more porous than asbestos cement, and also less alkaline. A coat of sealer is almost essential under any type of paint. For exterior use, conventional paint systems do not provide sufficient protection and manufacturers' recommendations should be sought.

Brick and stone

These vary considerably in porosity from almost non-porous granite, marble and engineering bricks, to the quite absorptive surfaces of sand lime bricks and (in parts) Flettons. If engineering bricks, glazed bricks or non-porous stone have to be painted, a strongly adherent paint is preferable such as chlorinated rubber, epoxy ester ('tile' paints) and the two-pack epoxy or polyurethane paints. There may be variation between adjacent areas of the more porous materials, necessitating thin, penetrating first coats. Emulsion paints differ in their

* Further information on stucco can be found in 'The maintenance and repair of regency painted stucco finishes', G E Bessey, RIBA Journal, Feb 1950, pp. 143–5.

adhesion to Fletton bricks, but the determining factors for this have not been investigated sufficiently to make recommendations. Solvent-thinned exterior masonry paints generally show poor filling qualities and fail by flaking. Adhesion of all paints is much better on sand-faced bricks. Soluble salts are present in some types of bricks and cause efflorescence.

New and repaired brick and stone work will require alkali-resistant paints because of the presence of Portland cement mortar.

Choice of paint system

Although colour and appearance are usually the prime considerations when choosing paint, the surface characteristics of the wall and the presence of moisture, alkali and salts must be taken into account. In addition, the overall cost in use, determined by the expected life and maintenance requirements, should play an important part except in the simplest situations. As well as paints with a total thickness of about 0.05 to 0.1 mm for two to three coats, a variety of thicker coatings is now available, sometimes described as 'organic' plasters or renderings, or 'textured' or 'plastic' coatings.

Many paints are applied over primers or sealers which may modify the properties, especially the permeability, of the finish. Although it is desirable to use sealers as directed by the manufacturer, some examples examined at BRS have proved unsuitable or even incompatible with their finishes. In particular, emulsion-based 'sealers' do not penetrate well into masonry and may lead to adhesion failures of finishes of low permeability.

Where Building Regulations require a specific fire performance for walls, coatings must be chosen from those specially modified and certified to have the necessary surface spread of flame classification. A list of these, on various substrates, has been prepared[1] by the Fire Research Station, Borehamwood, Herts WD6 2BL and manufacturers will supply copies of their certificates.

Interior use

Matt finishes These are most commonly used as they reduce the reflection of light sources and minimise the effect of surface irregularities. They are less suitable than gloss finishes when high wear resistance, ease of cleaning or maximum hygiene are desired. Matt paints in general are more permeable to water vapour than glossy ones (but a matt oil paint is less permeable than a matt emulsion paint) and mild condensation is generally less obvious than on glossy surfaces.

Emulsion paints are based on a variety of polymer binders; their general properties are dependent on many factors other than the nature of the binder. General purpose types may have a slight sheen but satin or silk emulsion paints are now available with the same advantages in ease of use (including water cleaning of brushes). Emulsion paints are moderately resistant to cleaning and this may increase with the degree of sheen. Because they are known to be permeable and usable when walls are not completely dry, they are often misused and applied within days of plastering. The glossier ones are least permeable and it is better not to use them for first decoration. Although relatively trouble free, emulsion paints occasionally give rise to difficulties with efflorescence or patchiness on plastered walls, in which case a penetrating sealer must be used first. A flat oil paint, or a sealer followed by more emulsion paint, can be used over the faulty paint film.

Better general dirt and wear resistance is achieved with oil-based (eg alkyd) matt finishes, but these are now rarely used; they require more skill in application and an alkali-resistant primer on most new surfaces. They are also more likely to yellow with age than emulsion paints. Types which are claimed to allow brush cleaning in water have recently been introduced.

Gloss finishes Alkyd gloss paints (used over undercoats and alkali-resisting primers where necessary) are suitable for moderately difficult conditions where good wear and washability are required; the one-pack polyurethane gloss paints are somewhat better. The latter may not need a special primer as they are fairly resistant to alkali. For industrial purposes (canteens, kitchens, food factories and in conditions of moderate chemical pollution) the chlorinated rubber paints would be preferred to oil-based paints; for the heaviest duty and specific chemical resistance two-pack epoxy and polyurethane paints are desirable but considerably more expensive in both materials and labour. They are best used on a hard rendering rather than, for example, lightweight plasters but are unsuitable over most types of existing paint system.

Water-thinned (emulsion) gloss paints continue to be developed but suffer from rather low opacity, low tolerance to poor application conditions (whether too damp or too dry) and are likely to be less resistant to wear than the oil-based paints.

Exterior use

Thorough surface preparation and a thick film, as well as the correct choice of coating, are essential for good performance.

Matt finishes Emulsion or solvent-thinned synthetic polymer paints (both often described as masonry paints) should be used; a life of up to 5 years is likely from both types. Oil based matt paints are not sufficiently durable outdoors.

Gloss finishes These are not often used on walls except of stucco. The lead-based gloss paints commonly specified for stucco are toxic and are considered by some to be undesirable; since BS 2525 was withdrawn they have not been generally

Table 1 Types of paint and coating for interior and exterior use
(durability is for average situations and sound surfaces)

Type	Durability outside (years)	Performance indoors	Other comments	Repainting	Stripping	Alkali resistance	Vapour permeability
Water-thinned							
Cement paints	5–7; soil quickly and erode rapidly in highly acid atmospheres; prone to algal growth in wet areas	Unsuitable on gypsum plaster Rough surface	Pastel shades may whiten outside; dark shades often become patchy	No special restrictions but if cement paint is used manufacturers' recommendations must be followed; may need a sealer with emulsion paints	No entirely satisfactory method; mechanical methods best	High	High but will reduce rain penetration of porous materials
Emulsion paint: general purpose good quality	Approx 3	Fairly good opacity washability, wear resistance	Various copolymers, not all of same properties; some types unsuitable in kitchens and bathrooms	Emulsion paint or oil-based paint		Low	High
Emulsion paint: matt or 'contract' lower quality	Unsuitable	High opacity at some loss of washability		As above		Medium	Very high
Emulsion paint: exterior, smooth	4–7		Acrylic, styrene/acrylic and pva/versatate copolymers	Same or textured	Thorough soaking softens many types (using detergent or wallpaper-removing paste may help); a few are removable with solvents or solvent paint removers; steam stripping for large areas; mechanical sanding if in bad condition	Should be high	Medium
Emulsion paint: exterior sand-textured or fibre filled	4–10, partly depending on film thickness; fibres not always beneficial		Thicker films than other emulsion paints, about 100 μm; fine texture; binders as above	Same		High	Medium
Emulsion paint: ('vinyl') silk, satin or gloss	Not normally used; some gloss types may be but experience limited	Opacity decreases as gloss increases; silk and satin claim good resistance to washing	'Vinyl' appears intended to relate to superior quality rather than composition	Emulsion paints and vinyl paints		Low or medium	Low or medium
Bituminous emulsions	1–10 depending on thickness and composition. May have decorative and protective top coat	The better ones are useful waterproofers and adhesives but few are decorative	Available in a few dark colours as well as black; decorative emulsion paints are available for covering	Bituminous emulsions	Possibly steam strippers	High	Low
Textured 'plastic' paint	Unsuitable	Adequate, may need top coat	Dry powders based on gypsum plaster. Ready mixed based on emulsion. Hand-worked or sprayed	Oil paint or emulsion	Soak with water and scrape. Do not abrade dry	Low	Medium
Textured or coarse mineral aggregate filled emulsion coatings (including 'organic renderings')	Over 10; some may show dirt in polluted areas	Useful for bold textured effects; some very rough others more rounded with smoother surface; opaque or translucent	Variety of textures; applied by brush, roller or trowel. Up to 2 mm thick, hence high material cost but low labour cost	Emulsion paint	Soaking or steam stripping	High	Medium

Solvent-thinned

Gloss paint and enamels (mainly alkyd resin based)	3–6 mainly on old painted walls including cladding; oil-based mas- onry paints preferred on stucco	Satisfactory; hard wearing and easily cleaned; gloss makes unevenness more conspicuous	Most good quality paints used outside and inside; also cheaper 'interior only' qualities. BS 2525–7, lead-based paints, withdrawn	Oil-based paints; possibly 'vinyl' silk, satin or gloss emulsion paints in dry conditions indoors	Solvent or alkaline paint removers Burning off possible on thick layers	Low	Low
Polyurethane (one-pack)	3–4 (usually too hard) for wood or stucco	Better wash and wear resistance than alkyds				Medium	Low
Flat oil paint	2–3; not generally suitable	Satisfactory; some may 'polish' on dry rubbing but resistance to washing usually good	Few examples now available	Oil-based paints; emulsion paint in dry conditions	Mechanical methods	Low	Medium
Imitation stone paints	5–10	Satisfactory but a rough finish	Formulations and properties vary; usually contain fine sand, stone or mica bound with varnish	Same type; oil paint and emulsion paint	Mechanical methods or solvent paint removers	Low	Medium or low
Exterior masonry paints (smooth, matt or semi-gloss)	4–7		Based on isomerised or synthetic rubber, vinyl or 'acrylic' resins	Same type	Some paint removers; consult maker if known	High	High
Chlorinated rubber (masonry) paints	4–7	For special purposes only, eg water, acid or alkali resistance (not resistant to oils and solvents); moderate gloss	Exterior and interior types may differ; high-build types preferred	Chlorinated rubber paint	Naphtha Consult maker for special strippers	Very high	Very low
Epoxy ester paints (one-pack)	3–5; not often used; sometimes as primers	For special purposes only, eg water, acid or alkali resistance; usually glossy finishes	Rather better water and chemical resistance than hard gloss paints	Same type	Solvent paint removers	High	Low
Textured coatings, sprayed or roller applied (not emulsion)	10 or more, some with guarantee; some claim 20 years without actual evidence of use	Rarely used	Mainly alkyd (polyester = alkyd); chlorinated rubber; some described as 'acrylic' or other polymer; thick films (0.6–1.0 mm); initial cost often very high, overall cost in long-term may be high but appearance very good	Emulsion; masonry paints but not chlorinated rubber; same type	Mechanical methods; solvent paint removers will attack but large quantities needed for thick films	Low	Medium
Mineral aggregate coatings (ready-mix or aggregate applied to an adhesive base coat)	10, best types may be more	Used for special effects; opaque or slightly translucent	Coarse grit, minerals or coloured glasses, premixed with a poly-urethane, epoxy or other binder (now rarely oil-based) or applied to tacky bitumen or other adhesive	Oil-based paints or emulsion	Mechanical methods	Medium	Medium
Chemically cured paints (epoxy and polyurethane based 'aliphatic' type for good colour retention)	3–10 depending on thickness; best types should exceed 10 years	For maximum water, chemical and solvent resistance and hard wear	Two components to be mixed just before use; special uses on concrete	Same type; adhesion of subsequent coatings may be poor	Solvent paint removers rarely effective; mechanical methods	High (some pu are low)	Very low
Multicolour paints (emulsion-based examples also available)	No experience; consult maker for suitability	Very hard-wearing	Helps to conceal uneven plaster and dirty marks; mainly spray application	Same type	May soften with solvent paint removers; possibly steam stripping	Medium	Low
Bitumen paints (solution type) Tar paints (solution type)	2–4 depending especially on exposure to sunlight	Useful waterproofers, especially below ground level, but not decorative	Bitumen paints give better outdoor life if final coat is pigmented with aluminium	Bitumen or tar paints	Solvent naphtha will soften and dissolve but mechanical methods often better	High	Very low

available. Oil-based masonry paints (with little or no lead pigment) are available from some manufacturers, but the ordinary alkyd gloss paints give thin films and last only three or four years. For concrete, glossy, two-pack polyurethane paints have been used; chlorinated rubber paints are also suitable where their semi-gloss finish is acceptable.

Textured finishes These are the most widely used exterior wall coatings and cover a wide range from the very fine sand or stone textures to those containing coarse aggregate or worked into patterns by rollers or hand tools. Although even the coarsest texture is not visible above two or three storeys, the greater durability of these coatings is a valid reason for their use. There is still considerable use of the old established stone-textured paints based on oleoresinous media, with sand or mica fillers, which have a useful life of around seven years, giving a reasonably economical balance between first cost and maintenance. About the same life is obtained from exterior emulsion based paints of similar texture.

Thick, textured, sprayed coatings (about 0.5 to 0.8 mm), usually based on 'polyester' (ie alkyd) resins with mica, perlite and sometimes fibres, have a life likely to exceed 10 years if correctly applied. Some are described rather incorrectly as 'plastic'. There are also somewhat similar types of coating based on oil-free polymers, chlorinated rubber or emulsions. Most sprayed textured coatings are offered with a 'guarantee' by specialist application contractors, which, although limited to the behaviour of the coating in specified ways, can be a useful feature if the operators or manufacturers are known to be of good standing and with several years background of successful applications. Nevertheless, at best, these expensive treatments may not show the lowest overall 'cost in use' over a long period on domestic buildings, for which the most economical treatment is probably with masonry paints at about half the cost of the textured coating and half the life. The longer life coatings have useful advantages on buildings where application costs are high or there is a requirement for a high standard of appearance or better resistance to rain penetration for which extra cost can be justified. Also, the possibility of eventually recoating the original textured coating with a thinner masonry paint would lower the calculated cost in use.

The thick, textured coatings can also contribute to the rain resistance of an external wall but are too thin to substantiate claims for acoustic and thermal insulation properties except that by reducing the moisture content of the wall they would prevent the reduction of its original thermal insulation value.

There will probably be an increasing use of recently-developed, coarse-textured, emulsion-bound treatments applied mainly by roller, widely used on the continent where they are described as 'organic renderings'. These produce films 1 to 2 mm thick and can be given a variety of textures by the method of working, including the 'scraped 'or 'scratched' type which contains particles of 2–3 mm but the film is often very thin in the scratched areas. Although expensive in materials they are low in labour costs. Their durability is not yet fully established in Britain but is likely to be in excess of 10 years; there could be excessive dirt pick-up in polluted atmospheres or softening in very wet situations, near the foot of walls for example. At a thickness of 1 to 2 mm they can barely hide normal joints in brick and blockwork, but it may be possible to use those with good resistance to rain penetration without a preliminary cement render coat, making them more economical. Other forms of emulsion-based thick coatings, applied by spray or trowel, contain mineral or glass particles in a clear binder with no pigment, giving a translucent or multi-coloured effect. These also have a life likely to exceed 10 years, with similar reservations as to dirt pick-up.

Surface water-proofing treatments These may be used where rain penetration has been established as the cause of dampness (rather than condensation or rising damp) but for extreme exposure and minimum maintenance some form of light cladding may be preferred. Coatings should be applied only after cracks and defects have been repaired.

Silicone and other colourless water-repellents are useful on exterior wall surfaces in good condition when the appearance of bricks or stone is required to be maintained rather than hidden by paint. When used in adequate strength (eg not less than a five per cent solution for silicones) they can be effective for up to 10 years. Much of the rain penetration of brick walls occurs at the mortar joints and water-repellents will not always seal these fine cracks, nor the larger visible cracks which may develop; water shed from treated parts tends to run into cracks and may make the situation worse. Clear solutions of acrylic resins may also be used for water-proofing and could be more effective where there are fine cracks but they tend to have more effect on the colour of the surface and slightly more restriction on the evaporation of water from the wall. The durability of such treatments is difficult to predict, being partly dependent on the depth of penetration, but the clear surface layer may last only a few years. Clear polyurethane water-proofers have not shown satisfactory durability.

Pigmented coatings form a better barrier to rain with, in general, a longer life. The thicker masonry coatings and especially the sprayed textured type are reasonably effective although some mineral-filled emulsion coatings may shed light rain but allow penetration by driving rain over long periods, as do water-repellents. One much-used system is a bituminous emulsion water-proofing coat followed by a specially-formulated decorative exterior emulsion paint. Another consists of a pigmented rubbery polymer, producing thick smooth decorative coatings (sometimes described as liquid plastics) with a life expectancy of over 10 years on walls and good crack sealing properties until they eventually embrittle. Some treatments include a reinforcing glass or synthetic fibre cloth to improve performance at cracks and joints.

Attempts to seal walls on the inside are usually less successful than external treatment, but the various proprietary compositions sold for this purpose can be useful against moderate or intermittent dampness. Some are based on a polyurethane formed by reaction with moisture in the wall but the amount of moisture they take up is very small; their performance has not been studied by BRE. If moisture in the wall cannot escape by another route, impervious coatings are liable to be disrupted; possibly the most useful application is where the dampness has brought out stains, on chimney breasts for example, which would effect other paints and have to be sealed.

Walls below ground should be sealed on the outside before backfilling; bituminous compounds and emulsions are effective, economic and durable. On the inside face most coatings are unsuitable when water has already penetrated; some proprietary treatments using rapid setting cements in conjunction with overall coatings are claimed to be effective. BRE has no experience of these materials but the makers should provide examples of use.

Reference

1 Results of surface spread of flame tests on building products; BRE Report; HMSO; £6.00

Further Reading

British Standards Institution, London

BS 1191 Gypsum building plasters:
Part 1: 1973: Excluding premixed lightweight plasters
Part 2: 1973: Premixed lightweight plasters
BS 5262: 1976 Code of practice for external rendered finishes
CP 211: 1966 Internal plastering
CP 231: 1966 Painting of buildings

BRE Digests

125 Colourless treatments for masonry
196 External rendered finishes

Other BRE Digests on painting

70 Painting: iron and steel
71 Painting: non-ferrous metals and coatings
106 Painting woodwork

Painting walls
Part 2: Failures and remedies

Painting the great majority of wall surfaces presents no special problems and the results are quite successful. Occasionally, however, defects or failures are experienced. This digest discusses the causes of paint failures on interior and exterior wall surfaces and suggests remedial treatments.

It is very often a combination of mildly adverse factors which causes a failure, factors which by themselves may not create problems.

Principal reasons for failure (see also Table 1)

Moisture The original construction water, water gaining access through defects in the structure or water produced by condensation.

Salts and alkali Present in the material of construction or gaining access, for example from rising damp, by deposition as salt spray or occasionally from operations within the building.

Unsuitable surfaces Plaster, rendering or concrete too fresh, friable or contaminated; weathered or deteriorated surfaces or paintwork.

Unsuitable conditions Very high or low temperatures and humidities during application can seriously affect most paints. Dust and dirt produce a 'bitty' finish.

Wrong choice of paint For a particular type of material, existing decoration, or climate. The occasions when the paint itself is not of its normal quality are quite few but some paints are less tolerant than others of adverse factors.

Prepared at Building Research Station, Garston, Watford WD2 7JR
Technical enquiries arising from this Digest should be directed to Building Research Advisory Service at the above address.

Moisture

The most important factor for satisfactory painting is the dryness of the wall. Excessive moisture affects the ability to apply most types of paint and affects the long-term performance. It can cause the deterioration of many materials and the movement of salts and promote the growth of moulds. Even in good conditions it may take several months to dry out a new building completely (a rough estimate being one week in drying weather for every 5 mm thickness of wet construction) and dampness often persists during the first year of occupation. Such long periods are usually unacceptable and there is a tendency to apply permanent decoration too soon. The surface of plaster or brickwork may dry quite quickly and can be decorated early provided that some restrictions on the type of decoration are acceptable, principally the inability to produce a glossy finish. Internally, on plaster, a coat of high-permeability emulsion paint is an economical temporary decoration which, unlike distemper, need not be removed later. Internally, ventilation and heat will speed up drying, and dehumidifiers can be used in very bad conditions. Ventilation is particularly important but is very often neglected, undue emphasis being placed on heating. Solid fuel appliances or other heaters vented to the outside will normally produce good ventilation but electric and central heating require extra ventilation by keeping windows open. Portable oil or gas heaters introduce additional water vapour and require maximum ventilation if they are to have any useful effect; without it they aggravate the problem and cause additional condensation on cold surfaces. Completing the painting of buildings on schedule is, of course, easier with dry forms of construction and factory-finished components.

On external work drying cannot be easily accelerated and all that can be done is to protect the surface from further wetting by such means as polyethylene screens arranged to allow ventilation. Rain falling on wet or barely dry paint may cause water spotting and loss of gloss. Even when paint has been applied to a dry or apparently dry surface, moisture may later cause blistering, loss of adhesion and eventual weakening and breakdown on the film.

Measuring moisture content The condition of the surface is not always a reliable guide to the moisture content of the wall. It is sometimes possible to estimate the suitability for painting from a knowledge of the weather conditions prevailing since the wall was constructed but when in doubt it is much better to measure the moisture content directly. There are several methods available.

Weighing The most accurate method is by direct weighing of the moisture loss during oven-drying of samples obtained by drilling under controlled conditions, using appropriate corrections[1]. A calcium carbide meter can also be used with drilled samples for on-site determinations to avoid heating. The drilling method can determine the moisture at different depths and the presence of soluble salts does not affect the results.

Hygrometer A fairly simple but reliable test is to determine the equilibrium humidity produced in an airspace in contact with the wall, using an accurate hygrometer. The space is best formed by a sealed and insulated box with a hygrometer mounted in the face opposite the wall but a simple alternative (more subject to condensation during temperature change) is to use a sheet of polyethylene fixed to the wall with adhesive tape, with the hygrometer inside. In both methods, several hours, preferably overnight, should be allowed for equilibrium to be reached.
The interpretation of the readings is given in Table 2. Coloured indicator papers which change colour according to the humidity at the surface have also been used in a similar way.

Conductivity meter Two needle probes are forced into the wall and the resistance between them is measured. The resistance is reduced by soluble salts as well as by moisture, so that apparent moisture readings can be misleadingly high and a fairly dry wall may appear unfit to paint. Areas of obvious efflorescence should not be tested. If the wall is believed to be damp but readings at a shallow depth indicate low moisture content, the area should be covered with a sheet of polyethylene and the readings checked again under the sheet next day. If there is woodwork nearby it is very useful to make a check of this; as there is less likelihood of soluble salts, the reading in the wood should be more reliable than in the adjacent plaster, especially if the readings are high in the plaster and low in the wood.

Capacitance meter This has two flat electrodes which are pressed to the surface of the wall. It registers moisture only in the upper 1 or 2 mm and is inaccurate on a rough surface; soluble salts introduce errors.

Microwave meter This projects a beam of high frequency radio waves through the wall to a receiver on the other side which measures the reduction in intensity caused by the presence of moisture. The readings are for the whole thickness of the wall and are affected by the presence of soluble salts. The meter needs access to both sides of the wall, with two operators, and is expensive for infrequent measurements.

162

Table 1 Painting walls—typical defects and their prevention

Defect	Cause	Undecorated — To prevent defect	Undecorated — To lessen the risk of defect	Decorated — To cure after the paint has failed
Loss of adhesion; blistering and flaking of paint	(1) Water behind paint film. Defect associated with alkali attack, efflorescence or friable plaster	Allow wall to dry before decorating. Prevent rain penetration or rising damp	If wall cannot be obtained in a dry condition, use porous alkali-resistant paints	Remedy cause of dampness, strip loose paint, allow to dry and redecorate
	(2) Repeated condensation causing swelling and shrinking of binder (especially found in distempers and fresh paint)	If heavy and repeated condensation cannot be avoided, use other forms of decoration	Hard gloss paints stand limited condensation well when dry. Anti-condensation paints make intermittent light condensation inconspicuous. Thermal insulation may help	Remedy for condensation is increased warmth with ventilation
	(3) Powdery or weak surfaces:			
	(a) Dry-out of gypsum plaster which loses mixing water before it has hydrated. Plaster in severe cases may be powdery or friable on the surface or throughout	Proper treatment of plaster by avoiding too rapid drying in early stages. Modern plasters rarely give trouble	If plaster is not too weak it might take a thin coat of emulsion paint alone or over a lining paper	Strip and replaster
	(b) Delayed expansion. If plaster suffering from dry-out later becomes wet, it may show slight rippling and softening or extensive rotting, expansion and blistering	As above	As above	As above
	(c) Sweat-out. If normally set gypsum plaster is wet for long periods, it loses strength	Gypsum plaster unsuitable. Conditions arise from sealing both sides of a new wet wall with impermeable finishes	As above	As above
	(d) If plasters, other than acid Keene's, are primed following the trowel, a thin powdery layer is formed immediately under the primer	Do not prime plaster other than acid Keene's until set and at least surface dry	As above	Surface is so rough it must be replastered
	(e) Poor preparation	Clean or strip powdery or dirty surfaces down to sound base	—	Strip, prepare thoroughly and repaint
	(4) Very smooth surfaces, eg glazed tiles	Degrease surfaces and use special primers. Often hard gloss paints without primers or undercoats adhere well	—	Strip and treat as new work
	(5) High suction, overall or in patches, partly due to backgrounds, trowelling and drying conditions. Lightweight plasters liable. So much of the binding medium may be removed that only under-bound pigments is left on the surface	Correct choice of plaster and good workmanship. Use an anti-suction or alkali-resisting primer	Special primers; thin coats of emulsion paint; oil-bound distemper thinned with petrifying liquid; use of 'clearcole' or size not advised	Use 'anti-suction' primers over existing paint or after its removal
Cracking of paint	(1) Weathering—with some paints this is their ultimate normal breakdown, eg some hard gloss paints crack and flake rather than chalk or wear away	Repaint while old paint film is firmly held and continuous. Interval between repainting will depend on the paint, its situation and exposure	—	Strip cracked paint and redecorate
	(2) Repeatedly recoating surfaces	—	Emulsion paints are least prone. Where several layers of old oil-bound distemper have been built up and it is desired to avoid stripping, use a binding-down primer. Avoid hard-drying paints and enamel paints	As above

	(3) Application of hard drying gloss over soft undercoat, or application before previous coat has hardened sufficiently; application over contaminated surfaces.	Ensure that finish is used with its own undercoat. Intervals between coats should relate to drying conditions. Do not apply thick coats. Avoid splashes of paste or size on surfaces to be painted	—	Strip and repaint. In some cases rubbing down will remove slight crazing when the work is not affected beneath the surface
	(4) Paint of unsuitable composition even when applied to sound, dry surfaces. Associated with paint which dries hard and shrinks	—	—	Strip and repaint. Consult manufacturer
	(5) Underlying surface shrinking and cracking	Use correct plaster and mortar mixes	Use 'elastic' paints	Use elastic stopper or filler before repainting
Soft sticky films with water blisters and brown or yellow oily runs. Some pigments are bleached or discoloured	Alkali attack on oil paints and oil-bound distempers, by lime in presence of sodium and potassium salts and moisture. Cement products, lime plasters and lime-gauged plasters may cause this. Also caused by residues from alkaline paint removers	Allow to dry before painting. A few weeks subsequent maturing lessens alkalinity. One, or better two, coats of alkali-resistant primer are a useful additional precaution under oil paints. 'Alkali-killing' washes neutralise alkali only in the surface	If decorating before drying is complete, use porous alkali-resistant paints such as emulsion paints. Oil-bound distemper and size-bound distempers satisfactory in mild cases. Alkali-resistant primers lessen risk if impermeable systems (oil-based) must be used	Strip and repaint. Treat as new work
Efflorescence—patchy, crystalline or fluffy deposits sometimes outlining bricks, etc, in the background. (Not to be confused with chalking, a defect of the paint itself.)	Salts from the structure carried to the surface by water and deposited on drying. They may push off the decoration or appear over it	Allow the wall to dry out fully then remove fluffy efflorescence with a dry brush or cloth. Remove residue with a damp cloth frequently wrung out in clean water. Hard bloom needs only sanding or scraping if glossy and offering no key. Avoid water-thinned paints if possible or use them over an alkali-resistant primer if surface is heavily contaminated with salts	If decorating before drying is complete, use thin coats of permeable paints over porous alkali-resistant primers and ensure that drying conditions are good (heat and ventilation). A few emulsion paints offer a better-than-average chance of fluffy efflorescence forming on the surface of the paint without disturbing it	Strip, allow to dry and redecorate, preferably either avoiding water-thinned paints or using them over primers if the surface is heavily contaminated with salts
Coloured spots, patches or stains, often grey, black, purple, red, green or pink (on wall surfaces or paint)	Moulds which are encouraged by damp conditions and can feed on the decoration indoors or outside. Algae need damp conditions but draw little or no food from the paint; usually on exterior especially on weather side. Lichens and moss may develop in time	Remedy damp conditions. Kill organism with a fungicidal wash before painting, allow to dry and remove the organism by scrubbing or scraping	If damp conditions cannot be remedied (eg on external decorations) and there is history of mould on similar buildings, use fungicidal washes and/or fungicidal paints. Less risk with hard-drying and chemically cured paints	In mild attacks the organism may be scrubbed off; otherwise strip off old decoration. Treat the wall with a fungicidal wash. Allow to dry and redecorate with special fungicidal paints
Popping and pitting: craters blown in the surface of the plaster	Expansion of reactive particles in the plaster, usually when wet		—	Cut out, make good with plaster. Apply thin coat of primer
Pattern staining: patterns are outlined by variation in thickness of dust deposited on the surface	Affected mainly by surface temperature—pattern often follows variation of thermal capacity or thermal conductivity	Increase insulation to minimise temperature differences	Frequent cleaning or use of darker colours or patterns will make the defects less conspicuous	Improve insulation and repaint
Faint brown or yellow patches, soon after first decoration	Salts and stains from hollow clay tiles, some types of brick (especially if under-fired) and clinker block where a gypsum plaster* and porous paint (eg emulsion) have been used. Highly pigmented emulsion paints especially prone to this defect	Use an 'anti-suction' or alkali-resistant primer with emulsion paints, or impervious (non-emulsion) paint (preferably alkali-resistant)	Use good quality emulsion paints with a slight sheen. (Not very reliable without special primer.) Use a cement-based undercoat to the plaster	Apply (on top of existing paint) an anti-suction or alkali-resisting primer plus further emulsion paint, or flat, eggshell or gloss paint
General patchiness of sheen or colour; variable density mortar joints visible; often occurs after further coats (usually emulsion paint)	Uneven trowelling of plaster*; variable density and suction causing varying penetration of paint binder	As above	As above	As above

*Although reported to be most frequent on lightweight plasters, this is probably only because of the predominance of these plasters in present use.

Table 2   Wall moisture content with choice of paint for early decoration

Relative humidity in equilibrium with surface %	Wall condition	Electrical meter indication (not microwave meter)	Recommendation	Suitable paint types	
				On alkaline surfaces	On neutral surfaces
100	Moisture visible	Red zone	Preferably postpone decoration and dry further; if treatment essential dry the surface before painting	Cement-based paint; possibly water-thinned epoxy paint; bituminous emulsion paint	Cement-based paint but not on gypsum plaster; possibly water-thinned epoxy paint; bituminous emulsion paint
90–100	Wet or damp patches, no obvious moisture on surface	Red zone	Preferably postpone; painting may be possible but with high risk of failure	As above; possibly emulsion-based paints	As above; emulsion paint internally
90–75	Drying, doubtful visual indication	Amber zone	Decoration possible with limitations and some risk at higher levels of moisture	Some emulsion paints; masonry paints (not chlorinated rubber); possibly epoxy paints	Most emulsion paints (except glossy); masonry paints; plaster primer; flat oil paints
Below 75	Dry	Green zone	No restriction	All oil paints on alkali-resisting primers; chlorinated rubber paint; epoxy and polyurethane paints; some emulsion paints; (alkali-resistance only as a precaution against future dampness)	Oil or emulsion paints (flat, semi-gloss and gloss); masonry paints; epoxy or polyurethane paints, one or two-pack types

Treating moist walls A permeable coating is essential if painting has to be started while appreciable moisture is present. Water-based coatings in general are more readily applicable to slightly moist walls but must not be expected to cope with really wet conditions.

Some water-thinned epoxy based paints are claimed to be applicable to moist surfaces, especially cement, but their permeability when dry is lower than that of emulsion paint; experience of them is limited.

Attempts to hold back excessive dampness by applied coatings are not usually successful, although a number of compositions are claimed to be effective. Their use may be justified if there is an alternative route for moisture to escape to the outside and if the further access of water is unlikely or can be prevented. Metal foils can also be effective sealers if the adhesive is not affected by dampness. But applications of impervious materials to damp patches or to complete walls will usually cause the moisture to reappear elsewhere and if the opposite surface of a solid wall is also impervious, eg tiled, the coating is unlikely to adhere for long. Polyurethane sealers which are claimed to react with the moisture in the wall have been introduced but results with them can be uncertain and they have a very limited capacity for reaction.

Salts and alkali

Many types of brick contain soluble salts which it is impracticable to remove. Salts may be introduced by the use of unwashed sand, especially sea sand, in mortars and plasters, or by the addition of 'frost-proofing' additives to mortar. Rising damp or penetration by sea spray are not likely in new work but may affect redecoration.

Efflorescence is the appearance of these salts at the surface after they have been carried there in solution and the water has evaporated. The salts may be fluffy and easily removed or hard and impossible to scrape or brush off completely. On new work, efflorescence should be allowed to continue, with occasional cleaning off until no more appears. The bulky crystalline type of efflorescence is likely to disrupt impermeable paint films but the very thin, hard films of lime bloom can usually be painted over without such risk if an alkali-resisting primer or a non-saponifiable paint is used. The crystalline type often comes through emulsion paint films without much disruption but it may reduce their adhesion and more may appear with subsequent moisture movement or condensation. A useful treatment for lime bloom (on cement-based surfaces) is the application of a dilute (10 per cent) phosphoric acid solution which converts the lime to an insoluble compound. Proprietary chemicals to 'neutralise' efflorescence on plasters appear variable in action and not always reliable. Prior application of a thin penetrating coat of plaster primer often prevents further development of crystalline efflorescence. Sea salts are hygroscopic and can cause the appearance of damp patches when humidity is high; small patches may be dealt with by poultices to draw out the salts but large areas may need replastering.

Alkalinity is likely to saponify (ie soften or even liquefy) oil paints and weaken or produce white patches in some emulsion paints. All walls containing lime or cement products should be treated as being liable to cause alkali attack and either non-saponifiable paints or alkali-resistant primers underneath oil paints should be used. The masonry paints based on synthetic rubber or some acrylic solution polymers are fairly resistant and more permeable than oil-based paints used with alkali-resistant primers and can be useful in the early decoration of walls. Chlorinated rubber paints and epoxy resin paints are fully resistant to alkalies in walls but are impermeable. Some pigments are attacked by alkalies and show severe fading but paints likely to be used on cement surfaces are usually formulated with suitable pigments.

Most alkali-resisting primers are based on oils which are not easily saponified; some are based on chlorinated rubber. They vary both in their effectiveness and in their permeability to moisture. In general, the glossier the film the less the permeability; chlorinated rubber paints are least permeable per unit film thickness, and are generally semi-glossy. Because it is difficult to ensure a continuous film without misses or pin-holes, a second coat of alkali-resisting primer is advised where the risk of attack is high. Emulsion paints are usually claimed to be unaffected by alkali, at least as found in wall surfaces, but this is a variable quality and some types may be affected by cement-based surfaces and develop a lime bloom or patchy colour. Even if unaffected themselves by alkali, emulsion paints will not act as a barrier coat under susceptible paints. In general, the exterior types, usually used on cement-based surfaces, are formulated with the more alkali-resistant polymers. It is possible to improve the performance of many emulsion paints on cement rendering by a coat of alkali-resisting primer but this should be thin and penetrate the surface, rather than produce a glossy film to which emulsion paints may not adhere well.

Brown stains with no appreciable surface deposit sometimes appear on emulsion paints and are usually derived from a background of certain types of brick, hollow clay pot or clinkerblock containing soluble salts and coloured materials, or from sands containing organic matter which reacts with alkali. The best defence against this is the use of a cement-based undercoat plaster, preferably air-entrained.

A coat of alkali-resisting primer is a further or alternative treatment which may also be used to correct the situation after the stains have appeared. Alternatively, flat oil paints are less susceptible to the defect.

Strong cleaning agents (washing soda, caustic soda, metal phosphates and silicates) or alkaline paint removers should not be used because they can cause saponification if not completely removed and they may be partly absorbed by porous surfaces. Neutral detergents and solvent paint removers are preferable.

Weak or unsuitable surfaces

Unsound, friable surfaces are produced by laitance on cement products or by incorrect hydration of plasters. Surfaces to be painted should be visibly sound and not powdery or crumbling. Excessively dusty and powdery surfaces provide little adhesion for paint films, particularly emulsion paints with their poor penetration, and cause a risk of peeling or flaking as well as a poor 'bitty' finish. New walls should be carefully dusted down before painting. A useful check for unsound surfaces is to apply transparent self-adhesive tape; if it shows little adhesion when pulled off and brings away loose dust and powder, the surface is unlikely to hold paint satisfactorily and should be treated. Most types of paint are affected by mould oil residues on concrete, which should be removed by solvent poultices, emulsion cleaners, neutral detergents or abrasion.

Variable or excessive porosity is often met in all types of plaster and can cause difficult or uneven application and variations in sheen, gloss or colour which persist through several coats of emulsion paint. It can often be overcome by the normal practice of thinning out the first coat with plenty of water and applying the second coat soon afterwards, but sometimes a sealer may be necessary. Alkali-resisting primers are generally suitable, but should be applied thinly so as to penetrate and not leave a glossy film. 'Plaster primers' (which are not necessarily alkali-resistant) can be used on dry, neutral walls. Oil-based paints are less affected by variable porosity, but should in any case be used over an alkali-resistant primer. Minor cracks and imperfections filled with a proprietary powder filler mixed with water may introduce areas of high suction. The difference in porosity may be evened out with a suitable sealer but it is desirable to mix the filler with diluted emulsion paint or with an oil-based undercoat.

Existing paintwork New films shrink on drying and the force exerted may be sufficient to detach existing paint which often has poor adhesion between coats. The adhesion may be tested by cutting through the film with a razor blade in a pattern of 2 mm squares, then firmly pressing transparent self-adhesive tape to the cut area and pulling it away. Sound paint should show very little detachment; old, brittle paints may break up during the cutting. If the original paint was water-based and not very water-resistant, gentle rubbing with a moist rag or the application of a new paint to a trial area will give some indication of any risk of trouble. Existing gloss paints should be lightly flatted or wet-abraded to ensure good adhesion of subsequent paint.

Areas of flaky paint should be thoroughly cleaned off; it may be found that paint is firmly adhering to other parts of the same wall but this also should be removed if possible because the application of fresh paint often accentuates weaknesses of adhesion. A sealer or binding-down primer is often a useful safeguard but too much reliance should not be placed on its ability to penetrate multiple layers of old paints. Paint films which have cracked deeply but are not flaking should preferably be removed because of the difficulty of obliterating the outline of the cracks. Fine hair-cracking or crazing may sometimes be filled by a knifing stopper or even an undercoat. Slightly blistered or wrinkled paint which has hardened may be left in place after rubbing down to a smooth surface. Sound paint films with a chalking surface should be thoroughly washed down or preferably cleaned with fine wet abrasive paper. Old cement-based paint is often powdery and should be washed down and treated with a penetrating sealer or adhesive primer if it is to be overpainted with a non-cement based coating.

Only a few paints are incompatible with others during application (eg epoxy or chlorinated rubber paints on oil paint) but the adhesion between very different types can be poor and it is always safer to continue the use of any paint of a type which has proved satisfactory. When the nature of the existing paint is not known or a change has to be made to achieve a different decorative effect, or for waterproofing or other reasons, a costly failure may be avoided either by painting a trial patch (which may require considerable time to show any defect) or by submitting a specimen of the existing finish for examination, which the BRE Advisory Service or any consultant would do for a fee.

Mould growth Consistently damp conditions indoors encourage growth of moulds (mildew) which creates an unsatisfactory surface for repainting. Good ventilation rather than fungicidal paints should be the first line of attack, especially at the source of humidity, with, for example, a kitchen fan or extract hood. Removal of mould is often difficult without completely removing the paint as well; it should be scrubbed off as far as possible with a detergent and the surface treated with a fungicidal wash. For a mild outbreak it may be possible to remove the growth and prevent its recurrence by curing the cause without recourse to special paints, but where there is a history of growth

or reason to expect it in spite of precautions special paints should be used. A few conventional paints (emulsion or gloss) are available with added fungicides; other manufacturers produce more active paints of different types, particularly for use in breweries, bakeries, etc. There is a risk that the latter will be incompatible not only with existing paint but also with other types that may be used in the future. If there is any likelihood of contamination of foodstuffs or if the paint can be licked by children, paint containing only non-toxic fungicides should be used. Sometimes it may be sufficient to use a paint which is relatively insensitive to water, eg a chlorinated rubber paint or an epoxy resin finish, without any fungicide present, but these should not be applied to existing paints.

Unsuitable conditions during painting

The drying of paints, whether water-thinned or oil-based, is retarded by low temperatures, high humidity and poor ventilation. It is the wall surface rather than the air temperature which is the deciding factor and it should be remembered that the wall surface may be cooler than the air in the morning and during a thaw, when condensation may also be present.

Emulsion paints, including emulsion gloss paints, may show very poor drying properties when the air is cold and damp; below $5\,°C$ they may fail to coalesce and thus not form a cohesive film; a rise in temperature after application may be unable to prevent a film failure. High humidity at low temperatures may lead to the paint running and separating on the wall. Paints based on solution polymers (eg chlorinated rubber and synthetic resins without drying oils) are rather better in cold, damp conditions. Oil-based primers, undercoats and gloss paints are usually slow to dry at low temperatures and pick up dirt and grit while they are tacky but will be sound when they eventually harden. Single-pack polyurethane gloss finishes are considerably better in cold, damp conditions than most ordinary (alkyd) gloss paints. Chemically cured finishes are slow to dry at low temperatures and must only be used according to the manufacturer's recommendations.

On porous surfaces in very hot or dry conditions, emulsion paint may be difficult to apply and may powder after drying. In these conditions, prewetting the wall is permissible.

Reference and further reading

1. Improvement of the drilling method for the determination of moisture content in building materials; BRE Current Paper CP22/75.

BRE Digest 139 Control of lichens, moulds and similar growths

Painting: Iron and steel

This Digest has been prepared as a short guide to the painting of iron and steel in buildings; for a fuller treatment of steel and protective schemes for bridges and other large structures BS CP 2008:1966 'Protection of iron and steel structures from corrosion' and DD24 'Recommendations for methods of protection against corrosion on light section steel used in buildings' should be consulted. BS CP 231:1966 'Painting of buildings' should also prove helpful.

Painting non-ferrous metals is discussed in Digest 71.

Protection and decoration

Metals in building are painted mainly for protection against corrosion and secondarily for decorative effect. But whatever its purpose, painting should never be skimped. Corrosion can quickly spoil appearance and incur high maintenance costs, even when the safety or life of the structure are not unduly affected. A rigorous preparation and painting schedule must be insisted on.

In the absence of known corrosion rates for a site, the corrosiveness of the local climate or microclimate can usually be judged by the appearance of metals in nearby structures. Environment may be the main factor influencing the choice of a protective system. The expected life of the structure and the frequency of maintenance are also important. If the indirect cost of maintenance, eg loss of production, is high, greater initial cost is justified to increase the intervals between maintenance.

In most situations the protection afforded by a correctly chosen and applied paint system will be adequate; in the most severe conditions, or where the least possible maintenance is required, coatings of non-ferrous metals or plastics will be necessary, and these may need painting, if only for the sake of appearance. Table 2 sets out the protective systems available for steel, grading them according to site, type of component and the conditions of exposure. On large jobs, inspection and control at all stages by independent consultants is a valuable method of ensuring satisfactory performance.

The adoption of factory painting to replace site painting is probably the best guarantee of durability that there is at present. The economics of factory painting are almost always more favourable; factory painting is more efficient and avoids delays from bad weather and other difficulties on site. But adequate cleaning and priming must be specified from the start; otherwise a single coat of cheap red oxide primer on uncleaned steel may well be applied leading to rapid paint failure and corrosion. Where possible it will be an advantage to apply all but the final coat before erection.

Corrosion—general precautions

Poor accessibility is the cause of a lot of corrosion. Designers should ensure that all surfaces of exposed metal that will need re-painting are fully accessible. Thus, metal surfaces should not be spaced small distances apart; they should either be treated with an anti-corrosive paste or very thick paint and butted together, or kept far enough apart to permit painting. Back-to-back angle-iron trusses are particularly susceptible. Outside pipework should be so spaced from walls as to be reached by a paint-brush.

Most paints tend to recede from sharp edges and from the crowns of corrugations or angles and rusting first appears at these places. An extra 'stripe' coat of primer should be given before the first full coat, even when economy prevents two full coats being applied overall.

Drainage of trough-sectioned members should be

ensured, eg by drilling holes, so that pools of rain-water cannot collect on them. This is especially important in salt-laden atmospheres.

Welds should be ground smooth or blast-cleaned (fluxes may be removed by washing with water before cleaning). Welds should be continuous and not leave gaps or crevices, but any that are present should be filled with an anti-corrosive composition.

Special care is needed when two dissimilar metals come in contact. Copper, brass and lead in contact with steel can accelerate its corrosion. Zinc and aluminium may corrode faster when in contact with steel but in some conditions aluminium may accelerate the corrosion of steel. However, as continuous coatings they are fully protective. Rainwater run-off from copper to steel can also cause corrosion.

Surface preparation

Mill scale and rust are not satisfactory foundations for paint and must be removed. Scale is often difficult to get off and it is sometimes held that if it adheres firmly it need not be removed. In practice, failure usually occurs over such areas. Oil, grease and dirt are also frequently present on steel and must be removed. The cleaning method used should be matched with the appropriate primer—see Table 1. For all important new structures, in either moderate or severe conditions, blast-cleaning is now considered essential.

Shot or grit-blasting

Blast-cleaning is the most effective method of cleaning—if done correctly. It is mainly a factory process though it is available on sites where conditions permit. Results depend on the rate of working and the coarseness of the grit. BS 4232:1967 'Surface finish of blast-cleaned steel for painting' defines three qualities of finish, the situations where each is appropriate and the sizes of grit required to achieve them. Instruments are also available for site use to measure surface cleanliness and roughness. (A photographic scale defining stages of rusting and treatment is available from the Paintmakers Association of Great Britain, Prudential House, Wellesley Road, Croydon CR9 2ET.) It is important to specify the kind of surface wanted: excessive roughness can lead to failure at peaks which are later not well enough covered by paint. Priming should follow blast-cleaning as quickly as possible and certainly within 4 hours. Thin film ('prefabrication') primers, including etch primers and zinc-rich epoxy paints, give immediate protection after cleaning and can be over-painted later.

Pickling and phosphating

Immersion in hot acid solutions will remove rust and scale. Many processes, some proprietary, do this and also form a surface film of metallic phosphates (see BS 3189:1959). Phosphate films, especially if treated subsequently in a chromate bath, provide a good surface for painting and improve the resistance to rusting under the paint film. The process is essentially one for the factory, as thorough drying is needed; painting should follow as soon as possible.

Chemical site processes

Hydrochloric or sulphuric acid is less suited to site cleaning of steel than washes or pastes based on phosphoric acid. The latter also facilitate removal of rust and scale by mechanical methods. There is a danger, however, of their leaving a brittle film, or on non-rusty areas, a sticky deposit, neither of which is a good foundation for paint. If drying is slow the steel may also become rusty again. Washing-off water must not be allowed to run over brickwork or stonework. Some solutions are said not to require washing-off; such claims should be confirmed with the manufacturer.

Degreasing

Not normally sufficient as the sole method of preparation; this is best done as a factory process, using organic solvents, or emulsions or hot alkali solutions followed by thorough washing. It is often followed by a phosphate treatment. On site all that is usually possible is to wipe over with white spirit and a succession of clean swabs, taking care to avoid merely spreading grease over the surface.

Table 1. Surface preparation: methods and primers for iron and steel

Factory	Site	Primer
Shot- or grit-blasting	Grit-blasting, open or closed circuit according to site conditions	Etch, 'prefabrication' (eg zinc-rich type) and/or inhibitive primers
Pickling	Pickling jellies or pastes, or acids generally: not recommended	Usually quick drying, zinc chromate types, but red lead, metallic lead etc. for heavy gauge
Flame cleaning	Flame cleaning	Inhibitive 'tolerant' primers
Phosphating	Phosphoric acid washes and chemical treatments (much less effective than factory processes)	Zinc chromate and other inhibitive (non-inhibitive in mild conditions)
Hand or power tools	Hand or power tools	Red lead, metallic lead (ie 'tolerant') inhibitive primers

Mechanical methods

Hand or power driven hammers, chisels, wire brushes, scrapers and grinding machines are available for site and factory use, but site working tends to be laborious, costly, and therefore skimped. Good supervision is essential. The surface obtained with these methods is not good enough for the newer anti-corrosive paint systems; in the absence of alternative cleaning methods a 'tolerant' primer such as red lead is normally specified.

Flame cleaning

An oxy-acetylene flame in conjunction with mechanical methods will remove rust and loosely adhering scale. The flame also drives off moisture, but, if the steel is not left warm, condensate from the flame may be left on the surface. It is best to prime while the steel is warm (not hot), using a more viscous primer than usual. Flame cleaning is also useful for removing old paint but if this contains lead, respirators must be worn. The method is not useful for thin sheet or sections less than 6 mm thick (because of the risk of buckling) or in confined spaces or near combustible materials.

Weathering

A traditional practice is to allow steel to weather to remove mill scale. This is not recommended because it cannot produce a uniform surface and leaves the difficulty of removing the resultant rust and contaminants.

Touching up factory-applied coats on site

Provision must be made for areas exposed by damage or corroded during prolonged exposure to be given further protection. If rust has spread under the primer the affected surface must be cleaned down as for unprimed metal. This must be as thorough as if for new work. In all but mild climates, if the primer is thin or badly weathered, a full coat of primer should be applied overall. A heavily chalked shop primer should first be washed and scrubbed down and allowed to dry.

Paints for protecting iron and steel

The choice of protective system, as indicated in Table 2, depends on the conditions of exposure and whether the system is to be site or factory-applied. For good protection a total film thickness of at least 125 μm and often up to 250 μm is necessary. With air drying paints this normally means at least 4 coats, including two priming coats; thixotropic and chemically cured paints may require fewer coats.

The paint system normally consists of primer, undercoats and finishing coats. These coats each have a special function and should be compatible. It is good practice to obtain all coats from one manufacturer, although oil-based primers are usually compatible with top coats from different sources. Certain systems, eg coal-tar/epoxy paints and some zinc-rich paints, are used alone without primers; the minimum thickness, whatever the number of coats needed to achieve it, is usually taken as 125 μm, but over twice this thickness is possible.

Lead-based paints: toxicity

Some of the most effective and tolerant primers are those based on lead compounds, eg red lead, metallic lead, calcium plumbate. These have always required precautions and cleanliness in working by the painter, and the requirements of the Lead Paint Regulations, 1927, must be observed when using them. More recently, doubts have been raised on the extent to which lead paints contribute, both in use and removal, to the level of lead in the environment, and to the possible dangers to casual users. Lead-based top coats are now rarely specified, but the same remarks apply. Unless the situation demands the tolerance and high performance of lead-based primers, and the conditions of use allow the necessary precautions, they can be avoided, particularly in domestic buildings. Alternatives include zinc phosphate, etch primers, zinc chromate, and zinc-rich primers (see p. 171). Of these zinc phosphate is probably the most suitable and convenient for general use in building.

Primers

The best primers contain pigments which chemically inhibit the corrosion of iron and steel. Examples of such pigments include red lead* (the oldest and still best known), zinc chromate, zinc dust, zinc phosphate. Their efficiency depends partly on the type of medium in which they are incorporated.

Other pigments (the majority) have no special inhibitive effects; they merely help exclude damp and aggressive agents.

Priming paints are intended for particular metals. For others they may be less effective or even stimulate corrosion. Thus red lead primer should not be used on aluminium. Where one primer is to be used for both steel and aluminium a zinc chromate primer is preferred. For zinc and steel together, calcium plumbate or zinc chromate is best. When primed steel is left exposed on site, the primer should be durable; red lead, zinc-rich (including 'prefabrication' primers) or metallic lead primers are best. For site use where metal preparation is by hand, a primer 'tolerant' of poor surfaces is preferred, eg red lead or metallic lead.

---

* The pigments red oxide and red lead are sometimes confused. Red oxide is an oxide of iron and has no specific corrosion-inhibiting properties. Certain types are used in the moderately effective oil primers, and also in many quick-drying primers which are not always satisfactory. Red lead is an oxide of lead and has valuable corrosion-inhibiting properties. It is sometimes mixed with red oxide or graphite. It is not advisable to use it in paints other than primers for iron and steel.

Table 2. Choice of protective system for steel

KEY

M — Metal coatings (see p. 6)

Primers (see pp. 3 and 5)

RL — Red lead

ML — Metallic lead

CP — Calcium plumbate

ZR — Zinc-rich

ZC — Zinc chromate

ZP — Zinc phosphate

RO — Red oxide

E — Etch or pretreatment

Finishes (see pp. 5–6)

Al — Exterior aluminium paint

MIO — Micaceous iron oxide paint (and u/coat)

Gloss — Exterior alkyd gloss paint

Conditions

Severe

Areas affected by direct salt spray from the shore (eg up to 3 km inland according to height and shelter); general heavy industrial pollution, or close proximity to chimneys and some industrial processes. Corrosion is rapid, very visible, disruptive of unsatisfactory paint films, and endangers the safety of structures.
Severe chemical attack by polluted atmosphere or liquid contact requires specialised coatings, usually chlorinated rubber, vinyl or epoxy resin based and specific advice should be sought

Moderate

Areas of high rainfall or continuous high humidity in industrial or urban conditions, or close to fresh water or calm sea water.
Interiors where condensation is heavy or there is a source of pollution (eg sulphur dioxide, sulphur, ammonia or weak acids). In moderate conditions corrosion is noticeable in a year or two and is a nuisance but not dangerous.

Mild

Inland areas of low rainfall and no special causes of corrosion; interiors of domestic buildings, schools, offices and factories not producing condensation or chemical pollution. Corrosion may be noticeable only over a period of several years.
Where maximum life without maintenance is important, the recommendations for conditions worse than those to be countered should be used.
Where a protective system is chosen as suitable for mild internal conditions (eg on steel frames of factory buildings) it may also have to withstand an agreed period of exposure during erection of the building. In winter, condensation and corrosion may be serious even under cover and a single coat of primer will be inadequate. Provision should be made for the application of an extra coat of primer or top coat if the building time exceeds the agreed period.

Iron and Steel	Conditions (see notes)		
	Severe	**Moderate**	**Mild**
Heavy structural	M+E+MIO or Al or CR; or 2 or 3 coats heavy duty bitumen, coal-tar or coal-tar/epoxy paints; or anti-corrosive wrappings	As severe; or 2 coats RL, ML, CP or ZP +2 coats, MIO or Al; or 2 coats ZR, +MIO	M with or without paint** 1 or 2 coats ZP, RL, ML or CP, +MIO, Al or gloss paint ZR with or without top coats
Light structural	As above	As above; or M and painted (MIO, Al or u/coat +gloss paint)	As above; or 2 coats ZP, ZC or RO, +u/coat+gloss paint
Sheet	Vitreous enamel or PVC coatings; M; or thick bitumen coatings (better if factory-applied) (May be necessary to substitute with plastics, asbestos-cement or aluminium)	M painted (MIO, Al or u/coat+gloss paint; or PVC coatings; 2 coats RL, ML, CP or ZP +2 coats MIO, Al or gloss paint)	PVC coatings; or M (painted if desired); or 1 or 2 coats RL, ML, CP, ZC or RO, + u/coat+gloss paint
Window frames,* doors and door frames	May be necessary to substitute with aluminium, or plastics	As severe; or galvanised and painted; or factory priming+ additional priming+ u/coat+gloss paint	Galvanised** and painted; or 1 or 2 coats stoved factory primer or RL, ML, CP or ZC, + u/coat+gloss paint
Railings	M or plastics coatings, or substitute with aluminium	M and painted; or 2 coats ZP, RL or ML, + 2 coats MIO or Al; or 2 coats RL or ML, + u/coat+gloss paint	M with or without paint 2 coats ZP, RL, ML, CP, ZC or RO, +u/coat+ gloss paint
'Wrought' ironwork (ie usually mild steel)	M or plastics coatings; or 2 coats RL or ML, + bitumen or MIO; or 2 coats RL or ML, + u/coat+gloss paint (Not entirely satisfactory)	2 coats ZP, RL or ML, + bitumen or MIO; or 2 coats RL or ML, + u/coat + gloss paint	1 or 2 coats ZP, RL, ML, CP, ZC, ZR or RO, + bitumen; or 1 or 2 coats RL, ML, CP, ZC, ZR or RO, +u/coat+ gloss paint
Rainwater goods (gutters, pipes and brackets) cast iron or mild steel	Consider substitutes for steel; or heavy duty bitumen, coal-tar or coal-tar/epoxy paints (2 or 3 coats)	Bitumen or tar coatings; or 2 coats RL, ML, CP or ZP+MIO or Al; or 2 coats RL, ML or CP+ u/coat+gloss paint; or galvanised and painted	2 coats RL, ML, CP, ZP, ZR or ZC+u/coat+ gloss paint; or bitumen or coal-tar; or galvanised and painted**
Gutters, internal surface	2 thick coats bitumen or coal-tar	Same as severe	Same as severe
Pipes (not buried)	M, bitumen or coal-tar; anti-corrosive wrappings	Same as severe; or 2 coats RL or ML, + bitumen or MIO; or 2 coats RL or ML, + u/coat+gloss paint	Same as moderate (though 1 coat of primer is permissible); or 2 coats ZR
Tanks,† external surface galvanised	Coal-tar/epoxy paints; or heavy duty bitumen or coal-tar paints	2 coats CP, or 1 coat etch primer+ZC, + 2 coats MIO or Al	1 coat CP or etch primer +u/coat+ gloss paint or 1 coat CP or etch primer+2 coats MIO or Al** Possibly ZP
Tanks, external surface not galvanised	As above	As for 'severe'; or 2 coats RL; ML or ZR+ 2 coats MIO or Al or u/coat+gloss paint	1 (preferably 2) coats RL, ML, CP, ZC, ZP or RO, +u/coat+ gloss paint; or 2 coats ZR or 1 coat ZR+u/coat+gloss paint

---

* Extra care or additional coats of paint are desirable for bottom members. Condensation can cause severe corrosion at the internal surface of metal windows even in moderate or mild climatic conditions.

† Internal surfaces may require special chemical-resistant finishes, but for fresh water, bitumen-based coatings are usual (eg BS 3416, Type I or, for drinking water, Type II).

** Painting of metal coatings in mild conditions is considered to be for decoration only as no further protection is needed.

The importance of applying two coats of primer in all but mild conditions is not stressed often enough. It is almost impossible to produce with one coat a continuous film of even thickness and free from pinholes—the points at which corrosion begins. A second coat of primer (rather than an extra top coat) can result in a much longer life for the whole paint system. It is much cheaper later to apply another top coat than to clean down, prime and apply a new system.

The dark-coloured primers such as red oxide and red lead tend to hide the appearance of the first pin-points of rust. For steelwork likely to remain in primer for some time it is preferable to specify a light-coloured primer so that additional protection can be given at the first signs of rusting.

Red lead These should comply with BS 2523: 1966 Types A, B or C. (Some commercial products contain less red lead than is specified in the Standard.) They are excellent for site use, fairly tolerant of poor surfaces, but unsuitable for spraying or dipping. These oil-based primers are slow drying; there are faster drying versions which do not conform to the Standard but they are usually less resistant to corrosion. However, in poor drying conditions their use could be beneficial.

Metallic lead Primers based on metallic lead are fairly tolerant of poor surfaces and have good corrosion resistance. There are quicker drying formulations with better flow than red lead. They should contain not less than 25% metallic lead pigment, and at least 40% for maximum resistance. They are preferred where resistance to chemicals is required.

Calcium plumbate Calcium plumbate primers are specified in BS 3698:1964 (Type A, 48%; Type B, 33% calcium plumbate). They are oil-based and fairly slow drying; quicker-drying primers are available and should have the same calcium plumbate content. Not all paints adhere well to these primers and it is important to specify a compatible undercoat and finish. The major use is on hot-dip galvanising rather than directly on steel.

Zinc phosphate This is a newly introduced anti-corrosive pigment of which experience is so far favourable. It is non-toxic and suitable for use in quick-drying primers. White and of low opacity, unlike most other anti-corrosive pigments, it can be used in white or light grey primers, which do not conceal the early appearance of points of rust which indicate that the primer is proving inadequate.

Until British Standard or other specifications become available there is little guidance on quality, but majority opinion favours a high zinc phosphate content (at least 70% of the total pigment). High-build versions are available and offer a better chance of adequate film thickness.

Zinc silicate Two-pack coatings in which zinc pigment reacts in situ with inorganic silicate solutions have shown useful properties in wet situations, such as immersed pipes, undersides of bridges, marine structures and for hot surfaces. They can be used as primers under various top coats or as multiple coats, but require a high standard of surface preparation.

Zinc (and other) chromates Not restricted on grounds of toxicity and media usually quick drying; they are therefore useful for spraying, dipping and stoving. They should contain not less than 15% of zinc chromate in the pigment and the better types not less than 40%. Often they contain red oxide. They produce thin films, are less tolerant of imperfectly cleaned steel and less corrosion resistant than lead-based primers.

Etch or wash primers Etch primers also contain zinc chromate pigments and have excellent adhesion to clean metal and to later coats. They are very rapid drying and are available in one- or two-pack versions. They are useful for the immediate protection of blast-cleaned steel, but should be followed by another primer coat. They are not suitable for hand-cleaned steel. They are especially useful on non-ferrous metal coatings on steel.

Metallic zinc This is a corrosion inhibiting pigment when used at a very high concentration (about 95% of the dry film, by weight) in 'zinc-rich' paints with non-saponifiable media such as chlorinated rubber or epoxy resins. They are often called cold galvanising paints, but their hardness and resistance to abrasion are not equal to that of zinc metal applied by hot dip galvanising or spray. The zinc-rich paints can be used either as primers or as the main protective system and can be rather expensive. Those based on epoxy resins are usually applied after grit-blasting as thin coats for short-term protection prior to final painting ('prefabrication' primers) and as such are much less expensive.

Welding primers These include some 'prefabrication' primers and are specially formulated to permit welding without weakening the joint or emitting toxic fumes. They are less effective than the fully inhibitive primers; the welded areas should be reprimed as soon as possible.

Other primers Primers claimed to penetrate and cover rust and mill scale, or to react with them, have been found to range from fairly successful to useless. With any primer designed to 'react' with rust, it is obviously difficult to ensure that there is neither too much nor too little rust on the surface treated. Where good preparation is deemed impossible, it is better to use a red lead primer.

Undercoats, finishes, and other paints

Undercoats and finishes provide additional film thickness, water resistance and possibly decorative appearance. In protective schemes undercoats and finishes are less differentiated than in normal decorative work, and the undercoat is often a version of the finishing coat, sometimes differently tinted to ensure that the subsequent coat covers it fully.

Ordinary undercoats for gloss paints should not be allowed to weather for more than a few days on site.

In the absence of any standard specifications, the quality of finishing paint varies widely. Finishes are described below in terms of either principal pigment or binder, but both are important to performance which varies considerably between commercial examples of each type.

Micaceous iron oxide These paints, with various binders, are very durable because their inert and flaky pigment gives a thick film. The colours are limited to grey and some dark shades of green and brown.

Stainless steel Stainless steel pigment, usually used in epoxy resin paints, is a recent introduction. It should provide an inert barrier; experience is limited.

Aluminium Aluminium paints, although giving thin films, are also very protective.

Alkyd gloss Alkyd gloss paints are protective in mild conditions and are useful where appearance is also

important. They may also be used, if the manufacturer approves, over micaceous iron oxide paint to improve the decorative appearance.

Chlorinated rubber paints These resist weather and moderate chemical attack; they are rather difficult to apply and the primer must be specially suited to them. The high-build modification gives thicker, more protective films and is easier to apply.

Bituminous and coal tar paints These if applied in thick films ('heavy duty' paints) give good, inexpensive protection against water, salt and some chemicals. In sunlight they chalk and craze and should be protected by a coat of bituminous aluminium paint. Thin coats of bitumen-based, so-called 'anti-corrosive' paints are inadequate. The solvents in some bituminous paints tend to lift oil-based coatings, or their own previous coats, producing unsatisfactory, thin films. Primers for use under them should have time enough to harden (up to one month) or be specially formulated.

Chemically cured paints Coal-tar/epoxy paints (two-pack, chemically cured) are valuable, highly resistant coatings, more expensive but more durable than the bituminous paints. They are especially useful in marine situations. Where white or coloured finishes of high resistance to chemicals are needed the cold-cured paints of the epoxy or polyurethane type are suitable, but require good surface preparation and greater care in use, and the colours tend to chalk on exterior exposure; alternatively, micaceous iron oxide and stainless steel pigments can be used for this purpose.

Heat-resisting paints Coatings to resist high temperatures are specialised and expensive; they are usually based on silicone/alkyd resin (up to 200°C) or silicone resins (up to 300°C), and are pigmented with aluminium or zinc dust. Zinc silicate paints are also used. Good exterior durability is difficult to achieve in coatings that reach high temperatures intermittently.

Metal coatings Zinc and aluminium may be applied by hot-dip, spray or electrolytic deposition processes as protective coatings for steel. The last gives thinner coatings and is used mainly on sheet, as is the hot-dip application of aluminium. Galvanising is limited to lengths up to about 27 m; spraying is used for structures larger than can be handled, or in situ. The choice between aluminium and zinc is not often critical and the cost does not differ greatly; aluminium is preferable in areas of salt spray or acid pollution and accepts a wider range of paint types. If zinc coatings are used in aggressive marine or acid polluted atmospheres, special care must be taken in the choice of paint system—micaceous iron oxide, chlorinated rubber or epoxy/coal tar paints being preferred. In mild or moderate conditions, the thicker metal coatings may be left unpainted for up to twenty years.

Table 3. Primers for metal coatings on steel

	Zinc	Aluminium
Hot-dipped	Weathered and washed: CP (possibly ML, ZC or RO). Some forms of ZP	E or ZC
	New, cleaned and degreased: CP or E Some forms of ZP	
	New, phosphated: ZC or omit primer Some forms of ZP	
Sprayed	E+ZC (E essential) ZC as second coat optional	E+ZC
	(Zinc silicate under water)	
	Do not allow to weather bare or in primer only	
Electrolytic	E	E or ZC

For Key, see Table 2.

Applying paints

Brush, spray or roller are all satisfactory on smooth surfaces, but a brush should be used on rough surfaces so that the paint is well worked in. It is accepted practice to spray some primers on grit-blasted surfaces; airless spray is a rapid and convenient process for all coats. Instruments are available for detecting pin-holes in the film.

Paints should never be applied to damp surfaces. This is especially important if application is by spray. (Some additives are claimed to permit painting on damp surfaces but their value is uncertain.) The air temperature should preferably be at least 5°C and the relative humidity not more than 80%. Shaded surfaces should be carefully checked to see that they are dry. Winter painting is very difficult; in the United Kingdom it has been shown that there is greater risk of corrosion following November site painting than at any other time.

Preparation for repainting

Repainting should not be delayed beyond the appearance of the first traces of rust. This avoids the more costly work later of removing all rust and paint.

The old paint surface may be merely rubbed down and finished with one or two suitable coats. Only wet abrasive hand processes should be used because of the risk of lead pigments in dust from the old paint. If open blast-cleaning is used gauze masks should be worn but vacuum blast methods are preferable. Any very small patches of rust can be removed and touched in with an inhibitive primer. Complete removal of the paint followed by suitable surface preparation are necessary if rust covers more than 0·5% of the area. Old paint may be difficult to remove. Solvent or alkaline paint strippers are reasonably effective but their residues must be removed by white spirit or lots of water, as appropriate; otherwise it is better to rely on a blow-lamp, scrapers and wire brushes. It is emphasised that angles or crevices, bolt heads and rivets, and similar features, must be cleaned with special care.

Severely rusted window frames must have all putty and glazing removed to permit thorough cleaning by brushing and scraping. Two coats of zinc-rich or zinc-phosphate primer for domestic situations (or red lead or metallic lead in severely corrosive industrial uses) should be applied before reglazing and puttying. The putty should be bevelled to shed water from the joint, and the exposed primer given undercoats and a finish of *exterior* quality paint—even indoors.

Painting in buildings: 2—Non-ferrous metals and coatings

Much of the discussion in Digest 70, dealing, for example, with preparing iron and steel surfaces for painting, applies equally to the non-ferrous metals and coatings dealt with here. The two digests should therefore be read in conjunction.

Preventing corrosion

General precautions

Non-ferrous metals are usually more resistant to corrosion than iron or steel. However, a non-ferrous metal which by itself is resistant to corrosion in mild conditions of exposure may nevertheless need protection in acid or marine conditions. As with iron and steel, satisfactory durability will depend on the primers being chosen for their inhibitive qualities, and the top coats for their protective and decorative properties. Many of the factors discussed under this heading in Digest 70 apply to non-ferrous metals also.

Avoiding contact with dissimilar metals

Because of the risk of electrolytic corrosion it is important to prevent the contact of dissimilar metals. In particular, contact of copper, nickel and their alloys (e.g. brass and bronzes) with aluminium or zinc, and of aluminium or zinc components with steel, should be avoided; there should be no electrically conducting path between them. Thick coats of bituminous paint or hot-applied bitumen, inhibitive primers, tapes or pastes, as well as bituminous felts and some sheet plastics are acceptable treatments.

Protecting against certain building materials

Non-ferrous metals may corrode in contact with alkaline concrete, cement or lime mortar, or with acidic gypsum plasters (e.g. Keene's). Water running off such materials may also be corrosive. Aluminium and lead must always be protected, zinc, cadmium and tin need protection in most conditions, copper rarely. Thick coats of bitumen give suitable protection. Alkali-resisting primers may be used on alkaline surfaces and will also suffice for the plaster contacts.

Wood, especially western red cedar, Douglas fir, oak and sweet chestnut, may affect metals. Bitumen, aluminium paint or zinc chromate primers may be used to prevent contact. Wood primers may not be suitable. Wood treated with copper-based preservatives should not be in contact with aluminium.

Preparing the surface for painting

Moisture, dirt, grease residues, corrosion products and old paint in poor condition can cause adhesive failure and should be removed. New surfaces, particularly if polished, can be roughened or etched on site or in the factory, without weathering. (Better adhesion is obtained for paints if wash- or etch-primers are used without other etching treatment.) Sprayed zinc and aluminium coatings require no special treatment before painting, apart from light abrasion to remove any nibs of metal.

Degreasing

Degreasing is particularly important for non-ferrous metals because they readily retain grease. In the factory, vapour degreasing or immersion in solvents or detergent solutions are used. On the site, it is usually only possible to wipe over with white spirit and a succession of clean swabs; there are also proprietary treatments which leave behind a powdery deposit to be wiped off.

Chemical pre-treatments

Processes similar to phosphating for iron and steel have been developed for zinc, aluminium and some other metals. For aluminium there are also acid chromate and alkali chromate processes. Treatments site-applied by brush are usually less satisfactory than factory processes but are better than none at all.

Some treatments formerly recommended were actually harmful, e.g. 'mordant' solutions containing copper salts could leave traces of copper on galvanised iron and thereby encourage corrosion. Simple acid treatments should be avoided.

Etch-primers (pre-treatment or wash-primers)

Etch-primers contain a resin medium, an inhibitive pigment such as zinc chromate, and phosphoric acid to etch the surface. They provide the best possible adhesion, but the film produced is usually thin and should be followed by a coat of normal chromate primer except in very mild conditions. Most are supplied in two parts, which are mixed in definite proportions immediately before use, and are applied preferably by spray. They remain workable for about eight hours. Instructions for use must be closely followed and subsequent coats of paint applied without delay. One-part etch-primers are now also available. Some etch-primers are water sensitive in their early life; if exposure to rain or dew is likely, a 'modified' type should be specified.

Weathering

Zinc and galvanised steel left exposed to the weather for a few months will acquire a good key for conventional paints, but weathering is not necessary if the correct primers are used. Loose dirt should be removed after exposure and, in industrial districts, the surface washed down and dried before painting.

Abrasion

Grit-blasting is not used on non-ferrous metals. Small areas to be painted on site can usually be prepared by abrasion with emery cloth and white spirit. Corrosion products on aluminium can be removed by a stiff bristle brush; brass, copper or steel wire-wool or pads should not be used, but stainless-steel wire-wool is permissible. Care should be taken not to abrade through the very thin films of pure aluminium on composite ('clad') sheets, and steel wool or hard abrasives should never be used on these.

Preparation for repainting

As with iron and steel, repainting is best done before the old coating begins to fail seriously. Normal cleaning down and removal of loose paint is then sufficient, bare metal being touched in with the appropriate primer before repainting. Any flaking usually means that the adhesion of all the old paint is suspect. The paint should therefore be stripped, preferably by solvent-type paint removers, and the metal treated as new. The original specification should also be checked and necessary changes made.

Painting

While the priming coat should be suited to the metal (or metal coating), as discussed below, the choice of protective coats depends on the external conditions. Since non-ferrous metals are more corrosion-resistant than steel the choice is less critical; the simpler paint systems such as ordinary alkyd undercoats and gloss finishes are usually adequate, but chlorinated rubber or epoxy paints may be employed in chemically contaminated environments. Adequate film thickness is important but may not need to be as great as for steel. In the absence of an accepted specification, paint purchases should be made on the basis of a positive statement of metal to be treated and external conditions to be met.

Aluminium and its alloys

Although aluminium and its alloys vary in their resistance to corrosion, similar paint treatments are used for most of them. Normally the priming paint should contain corrosion-inhibiting pigments such as zinc chromate or other chromates, which should constitute about 20% of the dry weight of the film. Red oxide primers with about 5% of chromate are, however, cheaper and can be used for dipping or spraying where the alloy is resistant to corrosion and the exposure is not severe. Etch-primers are particularly suitable for aluminium and its alloys; the two-pack type is superior to the single-pack, though the latter is more convenient for small jobs on site. A 'modified' type with improved water resistance can be used where exposure to rain or dew is likely before the later coats are applied.

Sprayed aluminium coatings may be painted as for zinc (see below), or simpler paint systems, usually with an etch-primer, can be used. Hot-dipped ('aluminised') steel should be painted as for aluminium sheet.

Aluminium intended for contact with alkaline materials such as concrete should be given alkali-resistant primers or protective coats; bitumen-base paints may be used. Priming paints for aluminium and its alloys should be free from graphite or lead pigments; because of the risk of incomplete cover, the same restrictions should also apply to other coats.

Zinc sheet, electroplated zinc, galvanised steel, sherardised steel

Zinc reacts with most oil-based paints, forming soluble salts under the film; this leads to embrittlement of the paint or loss of adhesion. Zinc primers must prevent these effects. Etch-primers, zinc-rich and zinc dust/zinc oxide primers can be used, and calcium plumbate primers are satisfactory if used with compatible top coats. Zinc chromate primers are recommended by some paint manufacturers, but they have proved variable and sometimes unreliable, and are best used over etch-primers. Red lead is not satisfactory, but metallic lead primers appear to be suitable although they are not yet used extensively.

Thorough cleaning with detergents or degreasing

Treatment of non-ferrous metals

| Metal | Preparation | | Suitable primers |
	Factory	Site	
Aluminium (smooth surface, e.g. sheet, extrusions, aluminised steel)	Phosphating Acid or alkali-chromate baths Anodising (mainly as alternative to painting)	Degreasing compounds Emery and white spirit (not wire wool) Phosphoric acid treatments	Etch-primer (not after phosphating); Zinc chromate (not lead-based primer)
Aluminium (rough surface, e.g. castings and sprayed metal)	Smooth off nibs with emery paper. Clean off dust and dirt	Smooth off nibs with emery paper. Clean off dust and dirt	Etch-primer; Zinc chromate (not lead-based primer)
Zinc (sheet, hot-dipped galvanised or electro-galvanised)	Degrease Phosphate and/or chromate treatments	Degrease with white spirit Weathering for at least several months, plus washing Phosphoric acid treatments (not as effective as factory processes)	Calcium plumbate; Etch-primer (not after phosphating); Zinc chromate primer, zinc dust/zinc oxide primer, or zinc rich paint
Zinc (sprayed or sheradised coatings)	'Denib' Clean off dust and dirt	'Denib' Clean off dust and dirt	Etch-primer (preferably plus zinc chromate primer)
Copper (also brass and bronze)	Special processes Electro-deposited tin coating	Emery and white spirit (Do not weather. Do not abrade dry) Phosphoric acid treatments	Etch-primer; Aluminium pigmented primer
Lead	Not usual	Weathering Emery and white spirit Phosphoric acid treatments (Do not abrade dry)	Etch-primer
Tin coatings	Degreasing	Light abrasion (do not abrade through coating) Degrease with white spirit	Etch-primer; Zinc chromate
Cadmium (coatings)	Phosphating	Emery and white spirit Phosphate treatments No weathering	Etch-primer
Chromium and nickel plating	Not usual	Emery and white spirit	Etch-primer

solvents is essential before priming, but acids or mordant washes should not be used.

Weathering of freshly galvanised surfaces makes them more receptive (after thorough cleaning) to paints, but need not be specified provided a suitable primer is used. The minimum period for effective weathering varies from a few months to over a year, and is difficult to specify.

All galvanised sheet produced in Britain by the continuous strip process (over 90 per cent of the total) is now chromate treated to prevent white corrosion during storage. This makes degreasing unnecessary and improves the performance of most paints, although etch-primers may not react fully with the zinc if the coating is thick. Calcium plumbate primers remain the best recommendation at present. Phosphate treatments may be incompatible with chromated surfaces.

Paints and PVC coatings (plastisols or laminates) may be applied in a continuous process, giving finishes of greater durability and allowing the sheet to be bent and formed without damage to the coating.

Electrolytic coatings are much thinner than hot-dipped galvanising and are used mainly on domestic appliances, not for exterior work. Etch-primers are recommended for coatings applied in the factory and for repainting base metal.

Sprayed zinc coatings

Although in mild conditions painting for protection may be unnecessary, the white corrosion products can become unsightly and are best avoided by painting. At present the best paint system appears to be a 'modified' (water-resistant) etch-primer plus a coat of zinc chromate primer (calcium plumbate primer should not be used). These may be followed by suitable alkyd gloss paint or other equally protective top coats; in the most severe conditions micaceous iron oxide paint is probably the best. Coal-tar epoxy paints can be used in very wet or immersed conditions, without a primer.

Copper and its alloys

These are painted mainly to make them match their surroundings; there is little need for protection except against specific chemicals. The chief difficulty in conventional painting arises from chemical reactions between the metal and the drying oil paints. Green stains or poor adhesion sometimes result. The surface can be roughened with fine abrasive paper before painting, preferably used wet or with white spirit. Aluminium pigmented primers and etch-primers are both satisfactory. Indoors it is possible to paint directly with one or two coats of an alkyd gloss paint. A special lacquer ('Incralac') has recently been produced to preserve the original appearance and prevent discolouration or a patina.

Lead

New lead surfaces should be abraded wet with water or white spirit or treated with phosphating solutions or phosphoric acid. Etch-primers are satisfactory, as are many ordinary metal primers, but any containing a graphite pigment should be avoided. Lead should be protected with bitumen against alkaline contacts.

Chromium, nickel, tin and cadmium

Painting chromium and nickel is rarely necessary when new, but if corroded they may need to be painted. Cleaning down with fine abrasive to remove corrosion products should precede an etch-primer and any decorative paint system.

Tin plate is relatively easy to paint; most paints adhere after light abrasion and degreasing.

Cadmium should not be weathered to produce a paintable surface; phosphate treatments are suitable, and an etch-primer will provide a key for decorative paints.

Further references

BSCP 231 : 1966. Painting of buildings.

Painting woodwork

Notes on the structure of wood as it affects the application and durability of paints and preservatives: cellular structure—moisture content and dimensional change—permeability—effects of sawing, planing, sanding—plywood.
External influences: water—sunlight—micro-organisms. Risk of decay.
Preservation and painting—preservative treatments—the paint system (knotting, primers, stopping, undercoats, finishes)—putty and glazing compounds. The painting process, including repainting.

Following increasing evidence of premature paint failure and wood decay, as noted in Digest 73 'Prevention of decay in external joinery', and with the traditional lead-based primer fallen into disfavour because of toxicity as well as cost, many alternative methods and materials have been introduced. Evaluation of protective systems has formed a part of extensive joint research by BRE and associated research organisations.* This digest embodies the findings in the form of recommendations for good practice, to serve as a guide until a revised version of BS CP 231 : 1966 *Painting of Buildings* is available.

Wood structure and properties

Cellular structure

Wood is a cellular material in which 90–95 per cent of the cells are aligned vertically in the tree, giving rise to the characteristic 'grain' of timber. The other cells lie in horizontal bands, known as rays, which run outwards in the tree.

In softwoods, coniferous trees, the vertical cells ('fibres' or tracheids) are about 3 mm long and contain an air space—the cell cavity. Adjacent cells overlap and the passage of liquids up the tree trunk is by way of the cavities and through openings (pits) in the walls of adjacent cells. The thickness of cell walls formed in the later part of the growing season is greater than in the early part, and the alternating bands of soft and hard tissue (early and late wood) give rise to the annual rings. Quarter or rift sawing (radial cut) produces a surface with close alternating bands of early and late wood, while flat or plain sawing (tangential cut) exposes large areas of early and late wood from each growth ring.

In hardwoods, broad-leaved trees, there is a greater variety of cell types. As well as the fibres, which are only about 1–2 mm long, there are cells of much greater diameter than those surrounding them,

*Building Research Station and Princes Risborough Laboratory, BRE; Paint Research Association; Timber Research and Development Association.

known as pores or vessels, and these are responsible for liquid movement. The size and distribution of these pores, together with the relative wall thicknesses of the supporting cells (fibres), determine the texture of hardwood. Liquid penetration is also affected by blockages in the pores by resin and other substances.

Moisture content and dimensional changes

Green timber contains both free water in the cell cavities and water absorbed into the substance of the cell walls. When the moisture content is reduced to about 25–30 per cent of the oven-dry weight, all the free water is removed from the cell cavities, but the fibres remain saturated ('fibre saturation point') and the wood is still in a fully swollen condition; it shrinks progressively as more moisture is removed by drying. This movement is greatest across the grain and is to a large extent reversible, even in seasoned timber, so that weather changes cause alternating movements. Wood should, therefore, be painted at a moisture content near to that at which it will stabilise in use, usually about 15–18 per cent for exterior woodwork and 10–12 per cent for interior work. Excessively dry timber will swell as it takes in moisture in order to reach equilibrium with the atmosphere, imposing tensile stresses on the paint film; very wet timber may, during drying, cause an impervious paint film to blister and joints to open, leading to rupture of the paint film and further points at which water may enter. The different amounts of swelling of the early and late wood bands also create differential strains in paint films.

Permeability of wood and penetration of liquids

Permeability is the property which governs the inward and outward movement of liquids. It affects not only moisture movement but also the ease of impregnation by preservative and to some extent the behaviour of paint. It depends on such factors as the size of the capillary paths, the intercommunication between cells by the pits in their walls, and the presence of resins and growths which may block the channels. Atmospheric moisture is taken up only by the cell walls, reaching an equilibrium with the relative humidity, but liquid water enters both by the cell walls and the capillary channels, and the total uptake can be much greater than the fibre saturation point, eg 100–200 per cent of the dry weight. Hydrocarbon liquids, such as paint and preservative solvents, enter by capillaries but are not absorbed by the cell walls; the speed and depth of penetration is greater with liquids of lower viscosity. The fastest and deepest penetration occurs through the end grain, but lateral penetration is more critical for preservative treatment. Heartwood is usually less permeable than sapwood, which for most species is readily penetrated, but spruce, hemlock, Douglas fir and larch are notable exceptions. There are also differences in permeability between the early and late woods in the annual growth rings and this can affect paint films; penetration is less in the early wood bands. The large pores in some hardwoods also cause rapid and deep penetration which is a cause of difficulty in painting.

Abnormal porosity

The wet storage of timber, particularly of Scandinavian softwood, can induce a form of bacterial attack which greatly increases the permeability of the sapwood. The affected parts are not readily visible and are not weakened mechanically, but they can take up excessive amounts of water or preservative liquids and thereby create difficulties with subsequent painting. Such areas may be detected by their rapid absorption of liquids such as iso-propyl alcohol, or by a special form of measurement of air permeability. Although much trouble of this kind has been experienced, its incidence is now very variable and has probably decreased.

Paint penetration

The ready penetration of paint into end grain is well known and demands the application of extra coats to keep out water; but paint is mainly applied to lateral cut surfaces where penetration is least, although these often contain cut cells at an angle to the surface which allow slight liquid entry. In hardwoods, the large pores absorb large amounts of paint and if thin films are left bridging them with an air space beneath, a weak point is formed which will lead to rapid breakdown. Hence it is common to use heavy consistency fillers so that the more liquid top coats do not penetrate excessively and a more uniform film is achieved.

Contrary to general belief, deep penetration is not necessary for good paint adhesion and it can be both wasteful and detrimental to performance. The cells may filter out pigment and leave an underbound film on the surface, or at the junctions of early and late wood the paint film thickness and even its composition may change, again creating strains in the film. The alternating bands of different sheen sometimes seen in primer coats on a flat-sawn surface are

a result of this. Good adhesion is best achieved by molecular attraction of the binder to the wood rather than by mechanical key. Thus emulsion wood primers penetrate very little, but the better kinds adhere well. Dry wood, say at 10–12 per cent moisture content, does not necessarily absorb paint or varnish more readily than moist wood at 25 per cent, since the paint enters the cell cavities whereas the water is held within the walls.

Effect of sawing, planing and sanding

A smooth surface is essential for good paint performance, and planing is necessary, but bad planing can leave a rough surface that is difficult to paint. Planing and sawing also cut and expose the cavities within the cell fibres, which can then be penetrated by paint. Sanding closes the wood vessels and rays by deformation of the cell walls and blockage by particles, thus reducing paint penetration and allowing more uniform spreading. This will produce a thicker and more uniform film than on unsanded timber, but if too high a pressure is used in sanding the damage to the wood fibres may be excessive and reduce paint performance. Sanding is beneficial to hardwoods with small pores but will not restrict larger pores sufficiently to reduce paint penetration.

Extractives

Many softwoods (pines, larches and, to a lesser extent, spruces and firs) contain resins which if present in large quantities exude and impair the painted surface. In pines, the exudation occurs from knots, pitch pockets and pitch streaks; in spruces and firs, the trouble arises from pockets. Some hardwoods, for example gurjun, keruing and, to a lesser extent, agba, may also exude resin. Kiln-drying is a useful method of lowering the resin content and activity of potentially troublesome timber. The exudation can be scraped off after drying and the remaining resin is hardened.

Other woods, such as teak and certain kinds of cedar, contain oil, which tends to interfere with the drying, hardening and adhesion of paint. They can, however, usually be painted successfully over special primers, particularly aluminium primers (see page 6). Interference with the chemical curing of some finishes has also been noted in some tropical hardwoods having a very high extractive content. Water-soluble extractives, such as tannin, when present in large quantities (for example in oak, chestnut and walnut), can also interfere with the drying and hardening of priming paints; they may discolour water-thinned paints but without necessarily affecting their durability.

Quality of timber supplies

The decreasing availability of softwoods has resulted in an increased use of smaller diameter logs which are less stable dimensionally, so that joinery is more difficult to paint effectively. Another factor in the overall performance of paint is the great variation in the extent of seasoning of timber.

Plywood

The form of construction of plywood imposes a restraint on only one surface of the outer veneer. Moisture movement results in the development of fine cracks (checks) on the surface which make painting difficult. The effect is more severe with thicker veneers but varies between species. On species not specially prone to checking, for example, African mahogany and gaboon, a four-coat paint system, or its equivalent in thick films or textured coatings, will give adequate performance. On species very liable to checking, for example, Douglas fir and Finnish birch, the life of paint is very much reduced ; a resin-treated paper overlay is a more effective base than primers. Plywood which has been purchased without such an overlay should be treated with two coats of a good waterproof primer as a minimum first step. Where checking has already occurred, an exterior grade filler should be used over a primer prior to further painting. Paint which has checked on plywood should be removed.

Plywood for exterior use is manufactured with a weatherproof adhesive, but not necessarily with durable species throughout. If it contains perishable species, preservative treatment is necessary to achieve a long service life.

External influences

Water

In the past, rain and dew have been the main sources of dampness in woodwork, but internal condensation has now assumed considerable importance. The absence of flues in many rooms and the closing of unused flues and airbricks, to avoid heat loss, have greatly reduced ventilation rates. Increased clothes washing and drying indoors produce more water vapour, most of which migrates to the colder rooms and condenses on windows, eventually penetrating the putty and the joint with the cill. Double glazing greatly reduces this source of moisture. The combination of external and internal moisture, with often a high moisture content at the time of installation of joinery, has led to a serious incidence of nearly saturated timber and consequent early decay and paint failure. Multiple coats of oil-based paint are effective barriers to the movement of liquid and vapour, but poor quality films are by no means impervious. In practice, however, breaks in continuity of the paint film, after relatively short exposure, form a more important means of entry ; the paint film will then act mainly as a barrier to its escape.

Water can enter at many points but the main ones are the bottom joints of window frames and doors, the joint between putty and glass or putty and wood, and the end grain of door frames and exterior boarding. Contact with masonry is a potential point of entry sufficient to merit attention to water barriers and double painting of contact surfaces ; nevertheless, decay is frequently found in opening lights not in contact with masonry.

Sunlight

Exposure to sunlight causes changes or loss of colour and degradation of the surface, although very durable timbers, such as teak, are affected mainly in colour. Painting is the most effective protection against sunlight ; clear finishes fail more rapidly because they do not filter out the damaging wavelengths in sunlight, which are able to attack the surface of the wood beneath.

Micro-organisms and decay

Rotting of timber and the growth of surface mould on wood and paint result from the deposition of fungal spores of many kinds which are widely distributed by air movement, and which will propagate when the moisture content of the wood exceeds about 22 per cent. The principal agents of decay in window and door joinery are the wet-rot fungi.

The heartwood of many timbers is resistant to decay, and some species, for example, teak and afrormosia, are so durable that their rate of decay is negligible. The sapwood of all species is regarded as perishable but it cannot be economically excluded from joinery grade timber. Since it cannot be ensured that the moisture content of joinery remains at a safe level, even when properly painted, preservative treatment is necessary.

Surface moulds and blue-stain fungi are objectionable in appearance and may disfigure paintwork, but they have little effect on the strength or durability of timbers. Preservative treatments have some effect on blue-stain fungi but less on the surface moulds. Where these are particularly common, a mould-resistant paint may be needed.

Preservation

Paint alone cannot prevent decay of susceptible timber when water is able to enter, as it almost invariably will at open joints and defective putty. Impermeable paints may even make matters worse by preventing the moisture from drying out. Hence window frames, door frames and softwood doors should be protected by paintable preservative treatment as described below ; non-durable cladding must be treated to satisfy the Building Regulations. The additional cost of preservative treatment is of the order of 5 per cent of the cost of the joinery, and this can produce very large savings in maintenance painting and replacement of timber. However, even when preservation has been carried out, excessive moisture in the timber will shorten the life of the paint film, and all necessary steps should be taken to exclude it.

Although paint is commonly used as the final decorative and protective treatment of joinery, some preservatives of the water-repellent type containing stains or pigments are also decorative and usable alone on certain timbers. Even with these, prior treatment with a joinery grade preservative, by immersion or double vacuum, is necessary on timbers of low durability.

Table of preservative and paint treatment

	Preservative	Primer	Paint finish and undercoats	Clear finish
Window joinery *except external cills*				
softwood eg *Baltic redwood* *Hemlock* *Whitewood* (*Norway Spruce*)	ESSENTIAL Vacuum/pressure—WB; diffusion—WB; vacuum—OS, WRP; dip—WRP	Oil-based (ie oleo-resinous or alkyd); emulsion (acrylic) *see text*	Externally: alkyd gloss (4–5) Internally: gloss, semi-gloss or flat (5 years or more)	Less satisfactory than paint but WRP usable on preservative-treated wood (other than dip treatment) (1–3)
Douglas fir (b)	OPTIONAL	Aluminium preferred		
hardwood eg *Teak* *Afrormosia* *Utile*	OPTIONAL— necessary if sapwood present	Aluminium preferred; oil-based possible; but not usually painted	Alkyd paints (5–6) —but not usually painted	Varnish if not fully exposed (1–3); externally—WRP (1–3). Not linseed oil
external cills **hardwood** eg *Oak* *Utile*	OPTIONAL— but necessary if sapwood is present	Oil-based (filler needed)	Gloss paint (3 years but longer with extra number of coats)	Not satisfactory
Doors and frames **external** **softwood**	DESIRABLE—as for window joinery	As for window joinery	As for window joinery	For softwood and plywood—varnishes not adequate
plywood	OPTIONAL (see text)	Oil-based or aluminium		Hardwood—as for window joinery
hardwood	OPTIONAL			
internal **plywood**	NONE	Low-lead oil-based or aluminium (filler desirable)	Gloss, semi-gloss or flat	
hardboard	NONE	Ditto or emulsion primers, but may be pre-primed		
hardwood	NONE	Aluminium	Gloss, semi-gloss or flat	Gloss or flat varnish; wax polish
Skirtings **softwood**	DESIRABLE; pressure, vacuum or dipping—WB, OS	As for window joinery— back-painting desirable	As for window joinery	As for window joinery
Cladding, barge-boards, fascias and soffits **softwood** eg *Pitch pine*	NONE	Not paintable		
Douglas fir (b) *Redwood* *Hemlock* (c) *Whitewood* *Spruce*	REQUIRED BY BUILDING REGULATIONS Vacuum/pressure, pressure or vacuum, dip or brush— WB, OS or WRP	Aluminium; lead-based or low lead (see Note (a)); acrylic emulsion. Back-priming desirable	Oil gloss or gloss (possibly emulsion for redwood and cedar (d)) (3–5); sand-textured oil paint (7–10)	
Western red cedar	NOT ESSENTIAL; unnecessary for painting. WRP	Any	As above but longer life; not necessary for protection	Not necessary for protection; WRP (3–5); not varnishes.
hardwood eg *Keruing*				Resin exudation limits treatment
Teak *Afrormosia*		Not painted		WRP
plywood	OPTIONAL (see text)	Aluminium or oil-based. Paper overlay desirable.	Oil gloss or gloss (3–5); sand-textured paint (7–10)	Not varnishes; WRP if preservative treated
Gates and fences **softwood**	ESSENTIAL—vacuum/ pressure, vacuum or steeping	Creosote—not painted		
		OS or WB—oil-based or aluminium	Oil gloss or gloss (3–5)	
hardwood eg *Chestnut*	DESIRABLE—ESSENTIAL if life is to exceed 20 years. OS or WB	Oil-based	Oil gloss or gloss (3–5)	

Notes: (a) Lead-based primers should not be used on internal surfaces and where accessible to children on external surfaces
(b) Douglas fir=Columbian pine, Oregon pine
(c) Balsam fir is often included and used as hemlock; it is even less durable
(d) There is little experience in this country of emulsion paint on external woodwork; oil-based primer is preferred as the first coat

Key: WRP = water-repellent preservative
WB = water-borne
OS = organic solvent

Figures in parentheses denote expected average life in years of treatment, varying with severity of exposure

Preservative treatments

1 Water-borne (copper, chromium and arsenic salts) BS 4072 Complete penetration of the sapwood of Baltic redwood and other timbers is achieved by vacuum/pressure impregnation. Some distortion may occur on re-drying, therefore the method is not much used for the treatment of completed joinery. After drying, these preservatives are no longer soluble and, provided that loose salts are wiped from the surface, have no effect on applied paints.

2 Diffusion treatment using water-soluble borates This process gives full penetration before seasoning, after which treated stock is cut and assembled exactly as if untreated. Because the salts remain soluble in water, adverse effects on paint, such as blistering, seem possible if the wood becomes wet, but there do not appear to have been any difficulties in practice.

3a Organic solvent These are mostly based on pentachlorophenol, tributyl tin oxide, zinc or copper naphthenates. Some proprietary formulations are listed in PRL Technical Note 24. A minimum treatment of 3 minutes immersion is considered necessary for redwood, but a more effective result is achieved by the double vacuum process. Application by brush or spray is not recommended except in situations where the other methods are not feasible, eg *in situ* and as remedial treatments. Quick-drying solvents may permit less than twenty-four hours' drying, but up to two days is normally needed to allow sufficient solvent to evaporate so as to avoid possible effects on paint. In the concentrations normally used, the preservatives are unlikely to harm paint.

3b Organic solvent, water-repellent These are similar to type 3a but with the addition of waxes and resins; the same methods of application are used. Properly applied, they improve the life of the paint, although some of the waxes can affect drying and gloss, especially on abnormally absorbent wood. Reducing the wax content to no more than 0·5 per cent, and the use of slack wax, can minimise trouble. The solvents can be very slow to dry but if drying is not almost complete, trouble can arise with subsequent painting; a drying time of at least 24 hours in a good current of air is therefore essential. The effects of retained solvents may not show until the finishing coat of paint is applied. A further defect, yellow stains after painting, has been found principally with preservatives based on pentachlorophenol. The compatibility of paints over preservative treatments should always be confirmed by a practical test, but when both preservative and primer are applied at the factory, compatibility should be determined by the suppliers of these materials.

Some emulsion primers are satisfactory over water-repellent treatments, but they should be used only if there is reliable evidence of their compatibility.

The paint system

On new wood, a four-coat system has been accepted as good practice. Although this has a potential life of at least five years, early failure at susceptible areas (cills and bottom rails) is common, partly as a result of timber movement. CP 231 permits a three-coat paint system for economy, but this has led to poor durability in many circumstances. Prior preservative treatment should now be considered normal good practice, and is generally specified by local authorities Some water-repellent types of preservative have been proposed as replacement for the first (primer) coat, but although those which contain resins can make a useful contribution to paint performance, it is not sufficient to warrant reducing the protection to only two paint coats; primer, undercoat and top coat are still necessary. A possible future system for exterior painting is a primer/undercoat, formulated for use over a resinous preservative, followed by two gloss coats.

Knotting

The traditional shellac knotting (BS 1336) and leafing aluminium primers remain the principal treatments for reducing staining by resins in knots or streaks, though paint adhesion on shellac is poor. It is a common complaint that in summer knots exude resin in spite of the use of knotting. This arises, if not from poor quality knotting, partly because of the wider use of low-quality timber with a greater proportion of knots, plus efforts to seal excessively large knots, and partly because of exposure to strong sunlight, which raises the temperature and lowers the viscosity of the resin; even the recommended two coats of good knotting may be inadequate. The only way to avoid trouble with cladding and fascias on the sunward side of buildings is to specify a higher grade of timber. Light-coloured paint reduces the solar heat gain in the wood and may therefore reduce exudation, but the resin is more easily seen (see also note under 'Emulsion primer').

Primers

A good priming coat is the essential foundation of a durable paint system. However, primers alone are often expected to protect the wood during a period of several months on site. Most primers, in the rather thin coats commonly used, will not survive this exposure, and if they do they may not exclude moisture to the extent normally expected; the high moisture content of the timber can cause blistering and peeling later. It is bad practice to leave primed or unprimed joinery exposed for long periods, and if it is stacked under cover but in contact with the ground, this is certain to keep its moisture content too high.

Primers should preferably be applied in a paint shop or factory. to ensure thorough treatment of all surfaces under good conditions; acceptable methods are brushing, dipping, spraying (including electrostatic spray), deluging or flood-coating, each having particular advantages, but, unfortunately, the use of excessively cheap and rapid-drying primers is all too common and can lead to early failure. For joinery that is to be delivered primed, the preservative treatment and primer should be specified.

Lead based-primers The traditional pink primer for softwood contains a high proportion of white lead and some red lead and has good filling properties, water-resistance and flexibility, giving sufficient durability to withstand some months of exposure on site. It is particularly useful on exterior oak cills. BS 2521 : 1966 was the accepted standard but is to be deleted since lead paint and primers have now been withdrawn from general sale by most paint manufacturers because of the objections to their use where children can lick or chew them. They can be obtained to special order if considered essential. Alternatives are described below.

Low-lead, oil-based primers BS 2522 is long obsolete and a replacement is being produced. Primers with an oleo-resinous or alkyd base, with a lead content of less than one per cent (BS 4310 requirements) range widely in quality. The worst are excessively brittle or of poor adhesion, and have been responsible for much premature failure of paintwork even with good quality top coats. The best of the slow-drying types used on site have been found at least equal to the lead-based primers, but others have been unsatisfactory; few of the quick-drying primers intended for factory application have even fair durability. For the present, specifiers of primed joinery should ensure that the primer is likely to meet the proposed requirements for a British Standard, or, for Government purposes, specification TS 10114. Prior use of resinous preservatives is of particular benefit with factory primers, and indeed may be necessary for them to achieve the requirements of the proposed specification.

Aluminium-based primers BS 4756 : 1971 *Ready mixed aluminium priming paints for woodwork*. The flaky nature of the pigments in these primers confers high water-resistance (about equal to that of white lead) and good durability, but it sometimes leads to poor adhesion of the later coats. The media employed are either fairly quick-drying phenolic resin/tung and linseed oil mixtures, or alkyd resins. They should not be of so low a viscosity as to penetrate deeply or their filling action will be insufficient. (Aluminium *paints* are unsuitable as wood primers.) Aluminium primers should be chosen where water exclusion is important. They are particularly suitable for use on timber such as Douglas fir (Columbian pine), where they help to even out the difference between the early and late wood, also on wood treated with metallic naphthenate preservatives. They may also have a greater resistance to exudation of resin from knots and streaks than other oleo-resinous types.

Where internal condensation on windows is likely, it might be a useful precaution to increase the water resistance by applying an extra coat of aluminium primer on the *internal* surface of window frames, especially the bottom rail and cill, whatever other primer is used first.

Emulsion primers BS 5082:1974 *Water-thinned priming paints for wood*. Primers of this type have many advantages, including non-flammable solvents and non-toxic pigments, ease of application and brush-cleaning, and rapid drying except in high humidity, allowing undercoats to be applied the same day if required. They have been found especially useful for factory priming. When correctly formulated with flexible (usually acrylic) polymers, they have adequate durability, about equal to that of lead-based primers, both in the finished job and also when exposed alone. They are usually permeable and will not exclude moisture if joinery is stacked in the open; their use could therefore lead to a high moisture content in joinery installed and painted during or after periods of wet weather.

Emulsion primers may be white or any colour specified, and there is no special merit in the use of pink; pale cream or grey primers may be used to permit easy identification of successive coats and to avoid skimping of the undercoat.

This type of primer seems less affected by resin exudation than others, though it is probably optimistic to regard them as 'self-knotting'.

Water-repellent/preservative primers

(a) Some penetrating water-repellent preservatives (type 3b) are described by their manufacturers as primers, specially when lightly pigmented pink. They do not have the film-forming characteristics of true primers and should not be described as such. For recommended methods of application, and other comments, see *Preservative treatments, 3b*.

(b) Primers of the film-forming type containing preservatives are also available. Penetration from these is only slight if they are brush-applied, but if used at low viscosity as dipping primers they may have some preservative action at the end grain in joints. A single-stage combined preservative and primer treatment is attractive economically, but it is too early to say if it can be as effective as successive treatments with preservative and primer.

Stopping and filling

Stopping and filling should follow priming, but decreasing attention to these processes, a result of cost-cutting, incentive payments and lowered standards generally, have reduced their use, even on high-priced buildings. Good stoppers and fillers have been difficult to obtain, and the water-mixed powder fillers based on soluble cellulose or gypsum plaster, which are useful indoors, have been used outdoors with disastrous results. They may, however, be mixed with primer or undercoat to produce a reasonable exterior filler. Linseed oil putty is not a satisfactory stopper although it can be improved by mixing with gold size; it usually shrinks and requires at least 48 hours to harden enough to take paint. Hard 'oil-stoppers' should be used (usually over primer) for filling holes and cracks of much depth; two-pack polyurethane or polyester fillers, such as are used for car body repairs, are also acceptable but should be applied directly to bare wood. Fillers for application by broad knife are used to fill flaws and fine cracks and can be sanded to a smooth surface with wet abrasive paper. Some newer types ('spachtel' or 'spackle') have recently appeared on the market. Oak cills normally need filling, and if lead paints and stopper have to be avoided, a properly formulated filler is desirable; otherwise, two coats of a heavy consistency primer may be used.

Undercoating

Before applying an undercoat, the primer film should be examined carefully. A shop primer which has been weathered should be thoroughly cleaned before recoating. If the primer film is thin or weak, a further coat of slow-drying primer should be applied; if it is cracked, flaking or heavily chalking, it should be removed as it would inevitably cause premature failure of the whole paint system.

Undercoats and finishing coats sometimes flake because the primer was excessively hard when they were applied, but it is not always possible for the painter to determine or allow for this.

Undercoats should be of the same brand as the finishing coat. Emulsion paints and 'primer/undercoats' are increasingly being used as undercoats because of their convenience but their outdoor performance is still doubtful.

There is still discussion as to whether a four-coat system should comprise primer, two undercoats and one top coat, or primer, undercoat and two top coats. In principle, better protection will be afforded to exterior woodwork by two finishing coats, but on interior work, if some rubbing down is specified, a smoother finish and better appearance will be obtained with two undercoats. Not all gloss finishes are suitable for use as consecutive coats, and manufacturers' specific instructions must be followed.

Finishes

Conventional alkyd gloss and flat paints with appropriate undercoats still form the major type of finish on wood, as they combine decorative and protective properties with the elasticity necessary to accommodate movement of the wood. Proprietary brands rarely separate interior and exterior qualities; any economies from the use of a lower quality indoors is doubtful, and in any case exterior quality paint is needed for window frames, surrounds and cills. Thixotropic varieties, with a structure ranging from slight 'body' to a full gel, permit easy brushing of thick coats and increased opacity, but with no better or even slightly lower durability.

White lead paints have traditionally offered good durability, although they darken in urban and industrial atmospheres, but because of their toxicity, which is now considered to prevent their use on domestic buildings, the British Standards are being withdrawn.

Polyurethane paints, of the single-pack type, are not necessarily more durable outdoors than the conventional alkyd types, and some have been found to chalk excessively; they are particularly useful indoors for hard wear and resistance to washing with soap, detergents or bleach.

Sanded and textured paints, based on emulsion, oleo-resinous or epoxy binders are available and have been used principally on panel products rather than on joinery. They vary considerably in durability and the high water permeability of some emulsion-based products has made them undesirable for use on wood. Smooth, high sheen or semi-gloss emulsion finishes for timber are also being marketed. Although their elasticity may be good, they tend to have high dirt retention. Their permeability allows a wider range of moisture movement in the timber than with less permeable types and this can lead to splitting and opening of joints even though the average moisture content may be lower.

For industrialised building, the complete finishing of timber before erection, especially window frames and door sets, is required. Among various systems, one specially formulated emulsion paint has been found reasonably satisfactory. Alternatively, finishes of the water-repellent stain type have been used, but their performance on window joinery can be unsatisfactory and they do not hide knots and other imperfections.

Putty and glazing compounds

Linseed oil putty (BS 544) is commonly used for glazing wooden windows; it should be applied on a primer and not to bare wood, and should be protected with the finishing coat carried up on to the glass. In time putty shrinks and cracks and allows water to enter if the paint is not well maintained. Some improvement in the durability of putty would be a useful contribution to the life of window joinery; butyl putties are available at some extra cost. Questions have been raised on the suitability of emulsion primers for use under putty, and complaints have suggested both too much and too little penetration by the oil from the putty. These complaints have not been substantiated for a range of commercial primers. The suggestion that metal casement putty should be used over emulsion primers is not confirmed.

Bedding mastics for use with glazing beads are also a source of water entry, if not of good enough quality and adequately applied. Wooden beads should always be back-primed to prevent absorption of binder from the glazing compound, or of rainwater which frequently leads to paint failure or decay; their small section tends to accelerate paint failure.

The painting process

Good appearance and durability cannot be obtained without good craftsmanship. Present painting costs rarely allow sufficient time for the proper sanding down of the wood and undercoats, or the use of fillers. Therefore a specification for joinery should include the necessary quality of finish and freedom from imperfections. Bad site organisation which allows other trades to be working at the same time as painters is a common cause of poor results.

Although most present-day paints brush easily (and can allow excessively thin films to be applied), too much thinning of paint still occurs on site, to ease the work of brushing and to speed up the job; this results in thin films and hence low durability and standard of finish.

The moisture content of joinery at the time of painting should not be more than about 18 per cent for exterior work and 12 per cent for interior work. The higher figure may be used for window joinery, which should be carefully checked by the use of an electrical moisture meter if it has been exposed to the weather. CP 231 recommends completion of the internal painting of timber in 'wet' construction before the outer, to minimise water uptake from the large quantities which have to dry out. Bare wood exposed to the weather during building, or by paint peeling, is best left unpainted during wet periods or in winter and painted when the moisture content falls. It should be protected meanwhile by a liberal brush application of a *paintable* water-repellent preservative.

Primers and undercoats which have been subject to rain or damp or foggy mornings should not be painted until they have had a good opportunity to dry off. Although work may be held up, premature failure may be avoided.

Repainting

It is neither necessary nor economic to strip paint which is adhering well, chalking only slightly and free from any other defects. It should be washed with a detergent solution or proprietary wash, and pre-ferably flatted all over with wet abrasive paper. Small areas of loose or defective paint must be scraped down either to the primer, if sound, or to bare wood and brought forward with primer and undercoat as appropriate before the rest of the work is continued. Thorough cleaning, preferably with wet abrasion, is the best method of ensuring good adhesion of the new paint. On sound existing paint, one undercoat and one finishing coat will normally suffice; a single gloss coat may show poor adhesion.

If the existing paint is soft, very chalky or eroded, cracked, blistered or peeling, or shows any adhesion weakness, it should be completely removed. Complete removal is also desirable if the paint has been affected by mould growth or by bleeding through of stains or preservatives, or if there is already an excessive number of coats present. Where neglect of repainting has permitted exposure of the wood to the weather and resulted in a friable or soft surface, this will require to be removed by planing, scraping or thorough sanding, and cannot be filled by any form of paint composition. Decayed timber should be cut out and replaced; both new and old timber should be treated with a brush application of preservative, all end grain being liberally treated before the new piece is inserted.

The blowlamp remains the quickest and most effective way of removing paint from wood, but where it cannot be used, for example, close to glass, paint-removers of the organic solvent type (BS 3761) not the alkaline type, are recommended. Care must be taken to remove all residues of paint-removers. The bare wood should be rubbed down with abrasive paper and the painting process continued as for new wood.

Further reading

Digest No. 73 *Prevention of decay in external joinery* London: HMSO. 6p (plus postage)

PRL Technical Note 24 : 1972 *Preservative treatments for external joinery timber* BRE*

PRL Technical Note 29 : 1973 *Ensuring good service life for window joinery* BRE*

CP 98 : 1964 *Preservative treatments for constructional timber* London: British Standards Institution

*Unpriced BRE publications available from:
    Distribution Unit
    Building Research Establishment
    Garston, Watford
    WD2 7JR

6 General

Durability and application of plastics

Few plastics products have been in use for as long as the expected lives of the buildings in which they might be used; to that extent predictions of durability must be based on less evidence than exists for more traditional materials. A sound prediction must take into account the intended conditions of use, all available details of chemical background, ie composition and method of manufacture, and the results of accelerated laboratory tests. The behaviour in service of products that have been exposed to similar conditions over extended periods offers the best guidance, if known.

All this information helps to make a broad assessment of durability possible, but performance in a particular situation will depend on the action of wear and tear, stress, dirt, chemical and other agencies, and weather. Because of climatic differences, the useful life of plastics products may be shorter in the tropics than in temperate conditions which are the concern of this digest.

Situations affecting durability

Sunlight, warmth and moisture are the major influences in exposure outside although atmospheric oxygen and pollutants also play a part. Indoor exposure offers partial protection but natural and artificial light, warmth and moisture may affect the material. The thermal environment both indoors and outside may be important because of the relatively low softening points of some plastics materials. Cleaning with abrasives or chemical agents may affect the long-term performance. The chemical environment has an effect although the chemical resistance of plastics is good and only in a minority of building applications are they likely to suffer from chemical action. The same applies to soil-burial conditions where plastics are not normally affected. The mechanical environment is important and plastics may suffer under the action of continuously applied stresses; mechanical failure, when it occurs, is often the result of sudden loading, by wind forces or direct impact.

Weathering influences

Sunlight Sunlight, particularly its ultra-violet component, is the most significant factor in the breakdown and colour change of plastics. Ultra-violet radiation initiates many of the chemical reactions by which plastics are oxidised and degraded. These are often chain reactions which are accelerated by a rise in temperature and which depend on the presence of atmospheric oxygen and moisture.

Heat Plastics absorb infra-red radiation from the solar spectrum, with consequent rise in temperature; this, together with warmth from the atmosphere and from artificial sources, plays a part in determining the rates of chemical reactions leading to breakdown. As a rough guide, an increase of 10 °C will double these rates. The mechanical and electrical properties of plastics are also significantly impaired by a rise in temperature. Usually, though, these changes are reversible and only in as much as heating affects rates of degradation or if the consequent softening results in mechanical failure, is a rise in temperature likely to affect the durability.

Moisture Most plastics, if not in cellular form, are impervious to water but some are sufficiently absorptive for water to play an appreciable part in weathering. The water may physically weaken the bond between a resin and its filler or reinforcement; it may cause small dimensional changes and may impair physical, electrical and mechanical properties; it may also play a part in the deterioration of pigments, leading to change in colour.

Chemical effects

Plastics are not affected by the inorganic materials found in most building environments, although moisture or alkali, from cement products etc, may interfere with the cure of some resins. Organic solvents, such as may occur in paints, paint strippers and jointing materials and in chemical plant or laboratories, may affect some plastics.

Soil burial

Buried plastics are protected from most of the harmful environmental factors but micro-biological action on some plasticisers has, in a few instances, been known to produce deterioration of the plastics; attack by rats, or in tropical climates by termites, may in some situations lead to failure.

Mechanical effects

In many cases mechanical action is likely to be the ultimate cause of failure of plastics components, although other physical agencies may be responsible for earlier loss of strength. Apart from damage that can occur on site during installation, continuous or intermittent stresses are likely to reduce the life of plastics. For example, sustained water pressure in PVC and polythene pipes will cause their eventual failure but, by extrapolating the results of short-term tests on these pipes, designs to withstand United Kingdom mains water pressures for upwards of 50 years have been evolved (BS 1972, 3284 and 3505). A similar basis for design can be applied to glass-fibre reinforced polyester (GRP) pipes, but as well as exerting pressure, the water weakens the bond between the glass-fibres and the resin, and this must be taken into account. Furthermore, the mechanical properties of plastics fall with long-term stressing. It may be necessary to design components on the basis of permissible stress levels that are only a small proportion of the short-term ultimate strength of the material. Impact or other mechanical forces may also produce failure of plastics components which have deteriorated under the action of other agencies, and the 'notch sensitivity' of some plastics profoundly affects their impact strength. Although building products should be designed to withstand a reasonable degree of rough handling, it is not possible to design for every contingency; as a consequence there are difficulties in predicting the long-term properties of plastics that may be subject to stress.

Orientation and location

In the northern hemisphere, a plastics panel on a south-facing roof slope will weather less well than one exposed vertically; a panel on the north side of a building may take longer to dry after rain but will suffer less from the effects of solar radiation. Degradation is much more rapid in clean, rural areas than in industrially polluted atmospheres which reduce the intensity of ultra-violet radiation and coat the plastics with a protective film of dirt. In coastal areas, the effect of moist atmosphere and high ultra-violet light intensity is likely to be even more severe. The dryness of indoor conditions improves durability. Window-glass filters out much of the ultra-violet from sunlight and may reduce polymer degradation; it will not prevent the fading of unstable colours but the rate of fading may be slower.

Weathering is less affected by regional differences in climate over the United Kingdom than by rural/industrial/marine differences. If any difference is detectable between performance in the north and south, it is that the climate in the north produces less polymer degradation, although where water plays a part in the breakdown, as for example with glass-fibre reinforced polyesters, this trend may be reversed. In the tropics, however, the combined effects of moisture, longer hours of sunshine and high indoor temperatures are much more drastic and exposure in the tropics is used as a form of accelerated weathering test to produce degradation as much as three or four times faster than in the UK.

Forms of breakdown

The most obvious breakdown is surface deterioration induced by weathering, eg fading, darkening, yellowing, chalking or erosion, sometimes with accumulation of dirt. Some of these effects may be due to changes in the additives, eg pigments. In translucent and transparent materials these effects may be characterised by reduced light transmission.

Loss of plasticisers or degradation of the basic material with breakdown of polymer chains may lead to embrittlement.

Mechanical failure can occur in a number of ways; impact may produce indentation or brittle fracture; continuously applied loading may produce collapse or rupture; thermal stresses accentuated by heat-softening may produce distortion; and stresses caused by poor moulding techniques may result in cracking, deformation, or delamination of surfaces. There is not necessarily any correlation between surface and mechanical changes.

Types of plastics
Acetal resins

Made by the polymerisation of formaldehyde, these resins can replace die-cast metals for some purposes. Many local authorities have accepted all-plastics taps based on acetal and a number of window manufacturers are using the material for their standard fittings. There is only a few years' experience of their use but no serious defect has so far been revealed. Loss of surface gloss and decline in mechanical properties may occur with age but on present evidence they should have a long, satisfactory life.

Acrylic resins

Polymethyl methacrylate has been used outdoors for upwards of 25 years and has shown excellent resistance to the weather. More recently it has been

Table 1 Typical properties of plastics used in building

Material	Density kg/m³	Linear expansion per °C Coefficient	mm/m	Max temperature recommended for continuous operation °C	Short-term tensile strength MN/m²	Behaviour in fire
Polythene* low density	910	20×10^{-5}	0·2	80	7–16	Melts and burns like
high density	945	14×10^{-5}	0·14	104	20–38	paraffin wax
Polypropylene	900	11×10^{-5}	0·11	120	34	Melts and burns like paraffin wax
Polymethyl methacrylate (acrylic)	1185	7×10^{-5}	0·07	80	70	Melts and burns readily
Rigid PVC (UPVC)	1395	5×10^{-5}	0·05	65	55	Melts but burns only with great difficulty
Post-chlorinated PVC (CPVC)	1300–1500	7×10^{-5}	0·07	100	55	Melts but burns only with great difficulty
Plasticised PVC	1280	7×10^{-5}	0·07	40–65	10–24	Melts, may burn, depending on plasticiser used
Acetal resin	1410	8×10^{-5}	0·08	80	62	Softens and burns fairly readily
ABS	1060	7×10^{-5}	0·07	90	40	Melts and burns readily
Nylon	1120	8×10^{-5}	0·08	80–120	50–80	Melts, burns with difficulty
Polycarbonate	1200	7×10^{-5}	0·07	110	55–70	Melts, burns with difficulty
Phenolic laminates	1410	3×10^{-5}	0·03	120	80	Highly resistant to ignition
GRP laminates	1600	2×10^{-5}	0·02	90–150	100	Usually inflammable. Relatively flame-retardant grades are available

Key: UPVC=unplasticised polyvinyl chloride GRP=glass-reinforced polyester PVC=polyvinyl chloride ABS=acrylonitrile/butadiene/styrene copolymer

* High density and low density polythene differ in their basic physical properties, the former being harder and more rigid than the latter. No distinction is drawn between them in terms of chemical properties or durability. The values shown are for typical materials but may vary considerably, depending on composition and method of manufacture.

introduced for various moulded fitments, in particular for taps. It is subject to loss of surface gloss by scratching although this may not be a serious problem.

Acrylonitrile butadiene styrene copolymer
Although ABS is widely used in other industries, the principal building use to date is in internal drainage. Experience of its weathering behaviour is that changes in surface appearance and loss of impact strength occur too rapidly for general use; developments in the United States of the use of ABS sheet laminated to weather-resistant facings may eventually lead to its use in vacuum-formed cladding panels, although it is too flexible to be used over long spans without reinforcement.

Nylon
Nylon has been widely used in door and window furniture and cold water fittings; on the basis of limited experience it seems durable enough for these applications. It has also been used with some success as coatings for railing and outdoor furniture.

Polycarbonates
Polycarbonates are unusually tough and resistant to impact. Their main use has been in vandal-resistant fittings and covers for lights and for electrical fittings for building site services. In the United States they have been used for glazing in schools but although durability indoors is good, experience to date is that on direct exposure they lose transparency and show a tendency to yellowing within a few years.

Polythene (or polyethylene)
Film, sheet or membrane, translucent polythene, as used for temporary glazing or protective sheeting to building works, has poor resistance to sunlight; it will last for only a year or so when directly exposed to it, or for three or four years in shaded situations. A grade incorporating UV stabiliser is claimed to have twice this life. The inclusion of $2\frac{1}{2}$ per cent finely divided carbon black greatly improves durability though the resultant opacity lessens its versatility; a life in excess of 10 years may be expected for black film even when directly exposed to sunlight. These estimates assume that the film is supported to

prevent undue stressing by the wind. As damp-proof courses or damp-proof membranes the black material is accepted as having a life expectancy adequate for 'permanent' building.

Polypropylene

In only a few applications do the advantages held by polypropylene over polythene justify its extra cost and experience of its behaviour in building use is limited. It resists higher temperatures than does polythene and has been suggested for hot water pipes, but because of its relatively high coefficient of thermal expansion it is used for this purpose to only a very limited extent. Considerable stress is placed on joints in polypropylene pipework subjected to large temperature fluctuations. It is used in fittings and couplings for pitch fibre pipes and should prove to be as durable as the other materials used. It is also used in domestic drainage, in waste pipes and sink traps, where pipe runs are short enough to avoid movement problems. It is used for header tanks in domestic hot water systems; temperature fluctuations occur less often with these, and in any case little difficulty is caused by the resulting thermal movement. The need for well-designed stress-free moulding applies equally to polypropylene as to polythene tanks. Polypropylene fibre is used to improve the impact-resistance of concrete, but as its main use so far has been in concrete piles where the need is only for resistance to hammer blows during driving, there is little experience of its long-term behaviour.

Plasticised (flexible) PVC

In the past the use of comparatively volatile plasticisers has led to some failures through embrittlement. More stable plasticisers are now available which make failure from this cause less likely, but there may still be a risk of thin films losing their flexibility when exposed to high temperatures and water.

Unplasticised (rigid) PVC

Experience of unplasticised PVC water and rainwater pipes dates from the late 1930s, but for most applications (roof-lighting and cladding sheets, water mains, drainage and soil systems) experience is no more than 15 years old. This experience, however, indicates that unplasticised PVC may be used in many applications with confidence.

Post-chlorinated PVC

The characteristics of this material are very similar to those of PVC except that it has an appreciably higher softening point. This complicates moulding techniques and its main building application is in blends with unplasticised PVC, for such applications as drainage stacks, to improve the performance when carrying hot wastes. It has been suggested for hot water supply systems but, although the material can be used at the temperatures reached, problems in design and installation to allow for thermal movement have so far prevented its use.

Polyvinyl fluoride

Polyvinyl fluoride film is available in a small range of colours for lamination to the surfaces of other materials, including aluminium, plywood and plastics. Experience of its weathering behaviour over more than 15 years is very encouraging. Provided that adhesion between the substrate and the film is not impaired and that the laminates are not damaged mechanically, the surface film is expected to retain its protective and decorative properties for considerably more than 20 years.

Phenolic resins

Phenolic resin-bonded laminates have been used as curtain-walling panels, wall linings and corrugated roofing sheets. Their weather-resistance is good, particularly if the laminates are heavily impregnated with resin, but their unattractive dark colour limits their use. They soon lose gloss on exposure to the weather and tend to fade, although they can be painted to improve their appearance. One of their principal building uses is in laminates surfaced with melamine films.

Melamine resins

Melamine resin-faced laminates are widely used for interior working surfaces and wall-linings and their indoor performance is good. The dyes and printing inks do not generally fade and the surfaces have good resistance to abrasion, water and household chemicals. One of their principal applications is where hygienic washable surfaces are required. Out of doors, performance for the first few years is likely to be determined as much by the moisture susceptibility of the backing as by the resins. The light-fastness of colours depends on the inks used. Trials have shown that even with a suitable backing, the surfaces of laminates show considerable deterioration in exposed situations over a period of about 10 years; the behaviour of exterior grades is not a great deal better.

Glass-fibre reinforced polyesters

Polyesters by themselves weather quite well but they are usually reinforced with glass fibres and contain additives to improve their fire resistance, two features which in practice largely determine their weathering properties. The bond between glass-fibres and resin is susceptible to attack by moisture and although the process is slow it can lead eventually to structural breakdown. Fire-retardant additives seriously reduce the resistance to solar degradation. In addition, poor control in manufacture can result in poor weathering, no matter how good the basic materials. BS 3532: 1962 gives a guide to quality control requirements for these materials. In addition to roof and wall lighting sheets and cladding, glass-fibre reinforced polyester materials have been used for service items such as inspection chambers, sewerage settlement tanks and gutter systems. Some of these have received Agrément certificates and are likely to give satisfactory performance. Circumferentially-wound glass-fibre reinforced plastics pipes have recently been introduced and experience of their use in drainage applications has so far been good.

The structural use of glass-fibre reinforced plastics is growing for specialised building types and they have also been used in more conventionally shaped structures, usually in conjunction with other materials which provide some of the necessary strengths. In exposed conditions the long-term strength of these plastics is considerably less than that measured by short-term tests. However, most applications are over-designed to provide rigidity as well as strength, and while this is so, the loss in strength is unlikely to be a significant factor in durability.

Applications

Damp-proof membranes and courses
Polythene Polythene of sufficient thickness to resist puncture can be expected to last the life of the building. When in position, the polythene is not exposed to solar radiation, but use of the black rather than the translucent form will prevent the degrading effect of sunshine before use.

Water pipes
Polythene BS 1972:1967 and BS 3284:1967. Polythene plumbing products are usually opaque; black is normally required if continuous exposure to light is intended. Polythene pipes to BS 1972 and 3284 for domestic cold water services must include $2\frac{1}{2}$ per cent carbon black, properly dispersed, to resist degradation and prevent algal growth. There is a similar requirement for pipes for industrial applications. In addition, the test requirements of the British Standards should ensure a service life of at least 50 years. Such failures as have been reported in pipes conforming to British Standards have been caused by mechanical damage or by incorrect jointing and fixing. Polythene is used mainly for small-bore plumbing particularly for buried connections from water mains to the buildings. In larger diameters, the greater wall thicknesses required for low-density polythene tend to make the pipes clumsier to handle and also less easy to extrude to close tolerances than PVC pipes of equivalent strength.

Unplasticised PVC BS 3505:1968. The British Standard includes hydraulic test requirements to ensure a satisfactory 50-year life under stress, provided the pipes are properly laid and jointed. Joints can be a source of weakness but both mechanical and solvent welded joint systems are the subject of BS 4346:Pt 1:1969 and Pt 2:1970, and these are likely to give good service for as long as the pipes. The greater strength of PVC makes it more suitable for this application than polythene.

Cold-water cisterns
Polythene BS 4213:1967. Many local authorities now approve the use of polythene cold water cisterns which eliminate the corrosion risk always present with galvansied iron products. Oil-based jointing compounds must not be used as they may lead to cracking failure by a form of chemical stress-deterioration. The British Standard aims to eliminate problems resulting from the tendency of plastics to creep under continued stresses. A platform should normally be used to support the cistern and eliminate any tendency to distortion where it bridges the joists. Provided that satisfactory design and moulding techniques minimise stresses in the material, there is every reason to expect polythene cisterns to last the life of the building. In normal use cisterns are not exposed to sunlight and deterioration is negligible, but where prolonged exposure to light is likely, whether in builders' yards or in subsequent use, black polythene should be used. The same considerations apply to polythene cistern floats.

Glass-fibre Both hot-press-moulded and cold-moulded tanks are available. With the use of suitable resins, which must be properly cured to avoid any possibility of tainting water, these should give very satisfactory performance. Some tanks of this type have been accepted by the British Waterworks Association.

Drains and sink wastes
Polythene Only badly moulded products or badly fitted drains are likely to prove at all vulnerable to chemicals used for domestic purposes, eg strong detergent solutions and fats. Apart from paint stripper, cleaning fluids and similar solvents (which should not, in any case, be poured down a domestic drain), normal effluents will not harm a good quality product. In laboratories or factories the durability of polythene drains and sink-wastes is threatened principally by certain organic chemical effluents. Designers should consult the laboratory or factory to ensure that the drainage system is suitable for the intended use.

ABS The higher softening point of ABS gives it an advantage over PVC for handling hot wastes. Because internal waste pipes are mostly short in length, the relatively large thermal movement is not likely to cause any problems. The good moulding characteristics of this material have made possible the fabrication of large drainage components such as inspection chambers, for which appraisal by the Agrément Board suggests that good durability may be expected.

Domestic soil and vent systems
Unplasticised PVC BS 4514:1969. PVC has a high coefficient of thermal expansion and joints and fittings must be properly connected to allow for movement. The British Standard requires that the

material should not soften below 79 °C for fittings and 81 °C for pipes and that it should cope with short-term hot water discharges from basins and sinks. Some types of washing machine discharge water at above 80 °C, with the risk of distorting PVC pipes. The risk is slight with discharges of up to two minutes, particularly if the pipe supports are closely spaced, but long full-bore flows at 80 °C or over could cause permanent damage. The manufacturer's recommendation should always be complied with.

The Building Regulations 1972 require such pipes to be placed within the external walls of a building, where the problem of weathering does not arise, but in external situations black, grey or white PVC pipes are recommended because these colours are least affected by sunlight, although in time it may be necessary to resort to painting to improve their appearance.

Underground drain pipes and fittings
Unplasticised PVC BS 4660:1971. Design requirements of the British Standard are based on the need to resist external soil loading and accommodate any thermal movement. Provided the installation makes allowance for thermal stressing and does not receive excessively hot effluents a long life is expected for properly manufactured systems, which are normally out of contact with the factors responsible for degradation.

Sinks and baths
Acrylic resins BS 4135:1967 and BS 4305:1968. Care is needed in using acrylic sinks and baths because they have less heat and impact resistance than those made in vitreous enamelled steel. Acrylic sinks will not withstand hot frying pans and burning cigarettes. The belief that they are easily damaged by cleaning powders has not yet been substantiated by experience; though the near-mirror initial gloss may soon be lost, the use of ordinary cleaning powders as recommended by manufacturers, followed by an application of metal polish, will soon restore the finish almost to its initial brilliance. Given reasonable treatment, good service is likely for many years.

Rainwater goods
Unplasticised PVC BS 4576:Part 1:1970. Unplasticised PVC is the only plastics material now commonly used for rainwater goods. Black, grey and white are the only colours normally available, although with modern experience other colours could be formulated which would offer reasonable stability. Even the more stable colours may change on appearance after long periods of exposure, though the change may be tolerable. If painting is considered necessary, surfaces should be washed, without the use of an abrasive, and no etch primer should be used. There is no evidence of incompatibility of normal alkyd paints with unplasticised PVC.

Whether or not painting is necessary, plastics rain-water systems have the advantage over metal that the supporting brackets, the most common point of failure in traditional systems, have the same freedom from corrosion as the rest. There is a slight loss of resistance to impact, for example by ladders, as weathering proceeds, but this is not serious. Demounting weathered PVC rainwater goods in cold weather can lead to fracture of brackets and junction clips. This can be avoided if sensitive parts are warmed gently, with a rag dipped in warm water. The indications are that PVC rainwater goods will give good service for 20 years or more, and there is every reason to expect that they will last as long as the buildings on which they are installed. Early problems in joints and fixings sealed with mastics or foamed synthetic rubber gaskets have been overcome by new designs of solid rubber gaskets which provide adequate water-tightness and provision for thermal movement.

Sarking felt
Plasticised PVC Plasticised PVC film is available as an alternative to sarking felt under pitched roofs, and a similar product is used on the Continent incorporating synthetic fibre reinforcement. For this purpose a plasticiser with low volatility is essential because of the high temperature reached in roof spaces in hot weather. Film of suitable thickness and composition is better able than bitumen paper to resist tearing during installation and is not damaged by high winds, when temperatures are low, even after long periods of use.

Roofing membranes
Plasticised PVC Agrément certificates have been issued for plasticised PVC membranes backed with asbestos paper for covering flat roofs. Because these are intended for single-skin use, particular care is required in installation and detailing. Hardening due to loss of plasticiser will in time increase the tendency to crack as a result of building movements and maintenance is likely to be necessary after about 10 years.

Pitch-polymer Membranes of pitch-polymer are likely to behave similarly although there is not much evidence of their performance.

Roof and wall-lighting sheets
Unplasticised PVC BS 4203:1967. Corrugated transparent and translucent PVC sheeting is widely used for roof-lighting and for cladding small structures such as building extensions. The sheets become increasingly opaque when exposed to the weather, sometimes rather suddenly after a long period with little change. Although some of the thinner sheets available on the 'do-it-yourself' market may deteriorate within five years, for most products made to the British Standard, a life of 10 or more years may be expected before reduced light

transmission justifies their replacement. Pressed flat PVC sheet has been used for glazing in schools and in situations where vandal resistance is necessary. Its durability is expected to be at least as good as that of corrugated PVC sheeting. The same is probably true of polycarbonate sheet.

Glass-fibre reinforced polyester A surface rich in resin weathers better than one in which fibres are very close to the surface. In practice such a surface may be obtained by the use of a gel-coat. Alternatively a protective surfacing tissue of glass filaments can be incorporated. Mechanically made sheets are usually of more uniform quality than those made by hand, though it is possible to produce excellent quality sheets manually. Sheets can be made with a life of about 30 years but most sheets normally available are likely to have a considerably shorter life. Poor quality sheets, particularly self-extinguishing grades, may last for less than 10 years before their light transmission becomes unacceptably low.

Acrylic resins Clear and translucent acrylic corrugated sheets have been found to show little change on weathering: a life of 40 or more years may be expected. Crazing, which may occur inside the material producing a spangled appearance, is the result of incorrect temperature control during manufacture. There has been some use of the material in fascia panels, and as shaped lighting panels in domes. Excellent durability is expected and stability of most of the materials is likely to be good.

Ventilation ducts
Unplasticised PVC Ducts are not normally exposed to the weather so that only when they are placed close to heat or are overstressed at joints is there any risk of failure.

Wall cladding
Unplasticised PVC White opaque PVC extrusions are becoming widely used as an alternative to painted timber shiplap weather boarding. Allowance must be made in installation for thermal movement particularly if the boards are backed with thermal insulation material and exposed to the sun. Properly formulated white PVC is likely to retain its colour very well and should remain mechanically sound for more than 20 years although it may be susceptible to impact damage.

Glass-fibre reinforced polyester One of the advantages of the technique used for moulding glass-fibre reinforced polyesters is that it permits the production of cladding panels with a wide variety of surface finishes and shapes. It is general practice with cladding panels to apply a surface gel-coat and, provided that this is well cured and well bonded to the glass-fibre reinforcement, mechanical breakdown

of the surface is unlikely. A pigmented panel is likely to be more durable than translucent sheets because of the protection afforded by the pigment to the resins, but there may be some surface deterioration. The appearance of a deliberately uneven finish is likely to remain acceptable for much longer than that of an even surface which rapidly shows up defects. For this reason such panels quite often have an exposed aggregate finish which also gives some protection to the resin. Stability of colour through pigmentation may not be easily achieved. As with melamine resin-faced laminates, the moisture susceptibility of the backing largely determines the weathering behaviour. A properly made glass-fibre reinforced polyester is likely to remain structurally sound for considerably more than 30 years. Closely controlled manufacture and suitable design and materials are essential for long-term satisfactory performance.

Water stops
Plasticised PVC Heavy gauge plasticised PVC is being increasingly used to provide waterproof joints between heavy concrete units. The material handles well and can be joined by solvent or heat-welding on site. Alkalies in the concrete are not likely to impair the waterproofing properties of the material by attacking the plasticiser, as has been suggested. Provided that the water stops are of sufficiently heavy section to permit site handling and that differential movements between the concrete units are not excessive, there is every indication that they will perform satisfactorily for as long as necessary.

Skirting and architraves
Unplasticised PVC PVC extrusions can be produced with hollow sections to carry electrical services. Little maintenance is expected, but if necessary they could be painted with a normal alkyd paint system.

Window frames
Unplasticised PVC PVC is the most widely used material (though GRP is also used), but lack of rigidity in the plastics materials has so far hindered this development and has required either that window members are of a relatively large section, or that the plastics are used in combination with metal or timber stiffeners. White or off-white grades are probably the most durable of those available and are likely to have a life in excess of 20 years. The chief problem in window frame design, whatever plastics are used, is to accommodate high thermal movement; the performance of joints and, in metal or timber reinforced frames, the continued ability of joints to exclude moisture, is likely to be critical in determining the durability of the product.

Plasticised PVC is also used as an alternative to synthetic rubber in weather stripping for window frames made of various materials, and is likely to retain its mechanical properties satisfactorily for many years, though it could, if necessary, be replaced. If required, PVC window frames could be repainted to restore the appearance, but weather-stripping, whether of plasticised PVC or other material, should, ideally, never be painted.

Architectural features

Glass-fibre reinforced polyesters Roof trim, window frames, church spires, gargoyles and other features have been moulded in glass-reinforced polyesters and, apart from slow changes in surface appearance, are likely to give satisfactory service. The same material is also used for roof trim, where it has the advantage of giving a very satisfactory bond with hot asphalt or bitumen. Window cills and window frames are also available, the latter produced by hot-pressing techniques; provided their low rigidity is acceptable they are likely to have adequate durability and substantially retain their appearance if cleaned regularly. Weathering is likely to be influenced by the factors already noted, with control of manufacture dominant among them.

Metal coatings

Plasticised PVC PVC in films of 0.1 to 0.2 mm provides a decorative and protective coating for steel and aluminium. It is applied either as a bonded film (laminate) or as a fluid composition (plasticol or organosol) and provides a warm, resilient surface, generally textured. A long life for such films is expected with little hardening resulting from loss of plasticiser. Colour stability, especially of brighter colours outdoors, has so far proved of a lower order than film durability, and differential colour changes of different batches of sheet on a single building may cause problems. The softness of the film causes dirt retention in polluted atmospheres, or indoors if likely to be handled. Cut edges and fixing holes in the metal must be protected from corrosion. Sheet metal must be galvanised to prevent both rust creep under the PVC film and corrosion of the reverse side if this is uncoated.

Air-supported buildings

Plasticised PVC The strength and composition of the plasticised PVC-coated fabric obviously control the performance but resistance to wind loading is expected to be maintained during several years of use.

Condensation

Principles involved in condensation; conditions producing condensation—atmospheric conditions and artificial influences. The behaviour of absorbent materials and surfaces. An explanation of interstitial condensation. Designing to avoid condensation—characteristics of the building fabric—characteristics of the environment. Estimating condensation risk—a worked example. Lightweight sheeted roofs.

Principles involved in condensation

The amount of water vapour that air can contain is limited and when this limit is reached the air is said to be saturated. The saturation point varies with temperature—the higher the temperature of the air, the greater the weight of water vapour it can contain. Water vapour is a gas, and in a mixture of gases, such as when present in the air, it contributes to the total vapour pressure exerted by the mixture. The ratio of the vapour pressure of any mixture of water vapour and air to the vapour pressure of a saturated mixture at the same temperature is the *relative humidity* (RH), which is expressed as a percentage. Alternatively, relative humidity can be regarded as the amount of water vapour in the air expressed as a percentage of the amount that would saturate it at the same temperature.

In conditions of, for example, 20°C and 80% RH, all the moisture can be held in the air. If more water vapour is introduced into the air and the temperature remains constant, the relative humidity will increase; saturation point (100% RH) may be reached and thereafter any further vapour will be deposited as condensation. If on the other hand the amount of water vapour remains constant but the temperature falls, because the colder air can support less moisture, the RH will rise until at about 15°C it is 100% and any further cooling will cause water to condense. This is the *dew-point* of that air which at 20°C had an RH of 80%.

Conditions producing condensation

It has shown that changes in temperature or in moisture content can cause condensation to occur. These changes can occur naturally—by changes in atmospheric conditions, or artificially—by living habits or industrial processes.

Atmospheric conditions When warm damp weather follows a period of cold, the fabric of a heavy structure which has not been fully heated will not warm up immediately but may remain comparatively cold for several hours or, if the walls are very thick, for a day or more. When the warm, moist, incoming air comes into contact with cold wall surfaces which are below its dew-point, water will condense upon them, but as the walls warm up and eventually exceed the dew-point, condensation ceases and the condensed moisture evaporates. A building of light construction will warm more rapidly and is less likely to suffer condensation from this cause.

A solid floor, with a non-insulating finish, has a surface that is slow to warm, and if there is a rise in temperature and humidity of the air above, it may suffer condensation for several hours. In general, the bigger the heat capacity of the structure, the longer will condensation persist on its surface in adverse conditions.

Artificial influences The humidity inside an occupied building is usually higher than outside. People themselves and many of their activities increase the amount of moisture in the air. Sedentary persons breathe out more than a litre of water, as vapour, in twenty-four hours; physical exertion may raise this to four times the rate. Moisture vapour is released by cooking, by clothes-washing and drying and by the combustion of oil or gas; a litre of oil burnt produces in vapour form the equivalent of about a litre of water and if burnt in a flueless appliance this vapour is emitted into the air within the building.

Many industrial processes require high humidities and temperatures and some release large quantities of steam. The risk of condensation is great when the

RH and temperature of the air remain above 60% and 20°C for long periods.

Condensation, particularly in dwellings, does not necessarily occur in the room where the water vapour is produced. A kitchen or bathroom in which vapour is produced may be warm enough to remain free from condensation except perhaps on cold, single-glazed windows, cold-water pipes and other cold surfaces. But if this water vapour is allowed to diffuse through the dwelling into cold parts such as the stair-well and unheated bedrooms, condensation will occur on the cold surfaces of those rooms, which may be remote from the source of the moisture. Soft furnishings, including bedding, and clothing may become damp because of this, especially as some of these materials are slightly hygroscopic.

Removal of the moisture-laden air from the building, from a point near to the source of the moisture, will greatly reduce the likelihood of condensation.

Water absorbed during construction During its early life, a building may be prone to condensation from the evaporation of water which entered the structure during construction, either as mixing water for the concrete, mortar and plaster or by exposure to the weather before the roof was completed. Much of this moisture evaporates into the internal air in the building and then condenses in the colder regions, usually at night. The amount of water can be as much as 4000 kg, the drying period may be as long as a year.

Some benefit can be gained by leaving all internal doors open and the upper storey windows ajar to facilitate the drying-out process; incoming occupants should be warned of the drying-out period.

Absorbent surfaces and materials

Temporary or intermittent condensation which is clearly visible on a non-absorbent surface may pass unnoticed on an absorbent surface or material. Condensed water can be absorbed and held until conditions change and allow it to dry out, but condensation can only be accommodated in this way if the periods of condensation are short enough and drying periods long enough to avoid complete saturation of the absorbent material. This is the principle on which anti-condensation paint works.

Fig 1 Temperature conditions in wall which may lead to interstitial condensation

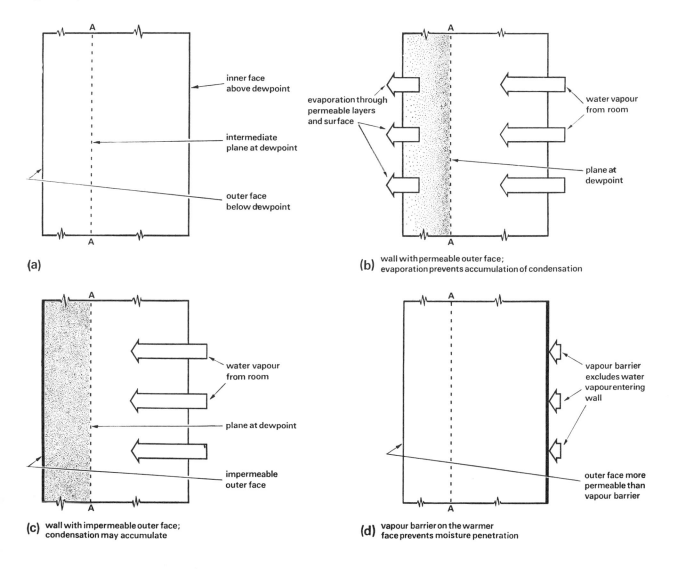

(a)

inner face above dewpoint

intermediate plane at dewpoint

outer face below dewpoint

(b) wall with permeable outer face; evaporation prevents accumulation of condensation

evaporation through permeable layers and surface

water vapour from room

plane at dewpoint

(c) wall with impermeable outer face; condensation may accumulate

water vapour from room

plane at dewpoint

impermeable outer face

(d) vapour barrier on the warmer face prevents moisture penetration

vapour barrier excludes water vapour entering wall

outer face more permeable than vapour barrier

Interstitial condensation

When the material of a wall, roof or similar building element is permeable to water vapour—and this applies to nearly all building materials—a dew-point temperature is associated with each point within the material. In the same way that a temperature gradient exists through a structure, depending on the thermal properties of the component materials, so a dew-point gradient depending on their water vapour diffusion properties exists also. If at any point the actual temperature is below the dew-point, then condensation will occur at that point within the material or structure. For example, the temperature through the thickness of a wall may vary from the inner face being above dew-point to the outer face being below dew-point; at some intermediate position the temperature will then be equal to the dew-point and condensation will begin at this plane (Fig 1a).

The exact processes taking place are complex and are further complicated by the fact that the condensed water changes both the thermal and vapour-transmission properties of porous materials, but the simple concept above is adequate for determining situations in which the risk of condensation trouble is unacceptably high.

If the outer portion of the wall is permeable to moisture, or if ventilation is provided behind impermeable wall or roof claddings, condensation will not be troublesome because the moisture can evaporate gradually to the outside air (Fig 1b).

If the outer surface is impermeable, the condensed moisture tends to accumulate in the wall and may ultimately saturate the material (Fig 1c). The situation will be most severe when the humidity of the indoor air is high.

A vapour barrier on the inner face of the wall (on the potentially warm side of any layer of insulating material) will prevent the passage of water vapour into the wall but only if it is undamaged and continuous. If the outer face of the wall is more permeable than the inner vapour barrier, any moisture contained in the wall can escape to the outside air (Fig 1d). If, however, the outer face of the wall has an impermeable cladding, or if the cladding is of organic material that would suffer in prolonged damp conditions, a ventilated cavity should be formed between the cladding and the wall so that any moisture evaporating from the wall surface is removed.

In some forms of construction, for example, behind timber cladding or tile hanging, a moisture barrier may be needed near to the cold outer face of the wall, to exclude wind-driven rain or snow: a 'breather' type of membrane, i.e. one that will bar the passage of liquids but will transmit vapour, is then required for this position. It should be used in conjunction with a vapour barrier on the warm side of the construction so that less vapour can enter the wall from the warm side than can escape by the breather membrane and there will be no accumulation of condensed moisture on the inner face of the breather membrane.

Designing to avoid condensation

The chart (Fig 2) shows the interdependence of relative humidity, on the left-hand vertical scale, dry-bulb temperature, on the horizontal scale, and the concentration of moisture in the gaseous mixture on the right-hand vertical scale, expressed for this purpose as mixing ratio, the mass of water vapour per unit mass of dry air.

An example of this relationship is shown by the reference points A–D, marked on the chart, which represent the following conditions:

At A, the outdoor dry-bulb temperature is 0°C, the mixing ratio of the air is 3·4 g/kg of dry air, which gives an RH of 90%.

If this air is warmed to 20°C and the mixing ratio remains the same at 3·4 g/kg, the RH will become 23% (point B).

If excess moisture amounting to 7 g/kg is now introduced as a result of activities within the building, at the same temperature the RH will increase to 70% (point C).

D shows the dew-point temperature of the resulting air/moisture mixture, from which it follows that condensation will not occur if the adjoining parts of the building fabric to which the air has access are kept above 15°C.

Two additional scales, not so far mentioned, have rather different uses. The scale of partial pressure of water vapour is directly related to that of mixing ratio, and it may be used, as explained later, to estimate the rate of diffusion of water vapour through the structural fabric. The scale of wet-bulb temperature denotes instrumental readings that are commonly taken with a sling psychrometer. Simultaneous wet-bulb and dry-bulb readings, when transferred to the charts, define the physical properties of an air sample at the conjunction of the respective oblique and vertical temperature lines.

Characteristics of the exposed building fabric

In all buildings heated and occupied during the winter, it may be assumed that the air temperature and water vapour pressure indoors will be in excess of those outside. As a result, heat and water vapour will attempt to flow outward through the fabric in an effort to restore the balance. Their progress is determined by the precise construction through which they must pass, and the result is a characteristic distribution of temperature and vapour pressure throughout the exposed structure.

The relationships governing this distribution are

depicted in Figs 3 and 4. The gradients shown are determined by the total differences of temperature and water vapour pressure across the structure and by the succession of resistances to flow that must be overcome. Table 1 gives a selection of typical values of thermal and water vapour resistance. The estimating procedure described later makes direct use of vapour *resistivity*, for which values may be obtained from the table, but other sources will be found to present figures for vapour permeability, or *diffusivity*, which is the reciprocal of the resistivity.

In Fig 3 it will be seen that the boundary surfaces of structures offer resistance to heat flow. Unless the structure is independently heated, the internal surface is at a temperature lower than that of the indoor air, and it will consequently cool the layer of air in contact with it. How far the local air temperature is

depressed depends on what proportion of the structure's total thermal resistance is contributed by the internal surface. Figure 5 shows the appropriate depressions for a range of temperature differences and comparative levels of structural insulation. It is

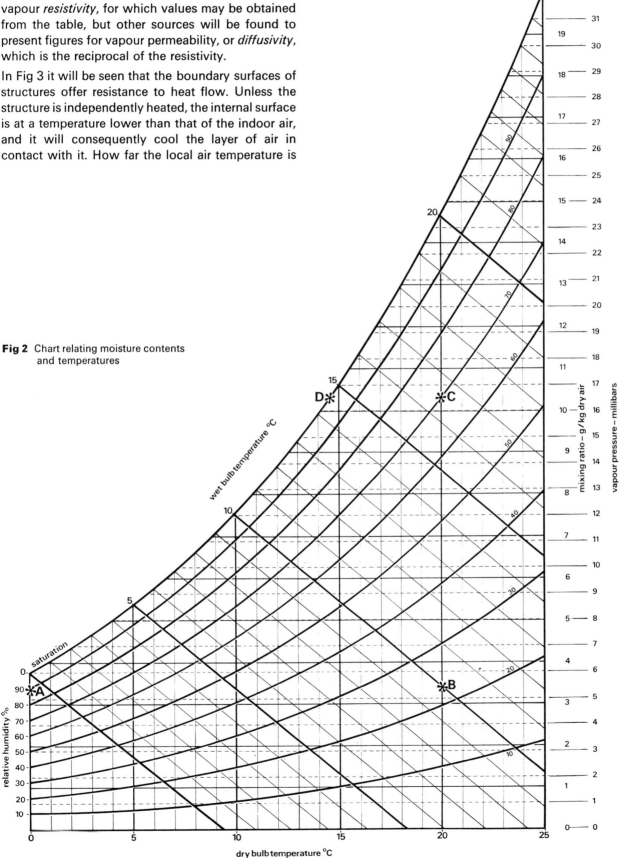

Fig 2 Chart relating moisture contents and temperatures

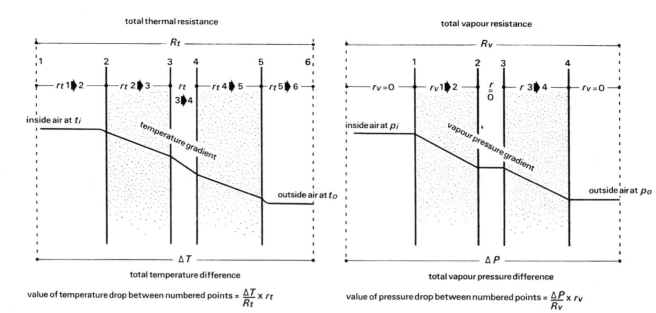

Fig 3 Temperature gradient through a structure

Fig 4 Vapour pressure gradient through a structure

applicable only to steady state conditions. In buildings of high thermal capacity construction, heated intermittently, the depression of temperature at the internal surface will often be greater, thus increasing the likelihood of condensation. Relating Fig 5 with the earlier example of outdoor air at 0°C, indoor air at 20°C and dew-point at 15°C, the maximum allowable drop of 5°C in the inside surface temperature will be seen to require a structural U-value not greater than 2·1 W/m² °C.

In the gradient of Fig 4, no vapour pressure drop occurs at the internal surface. Furthermore, it is practically possible to maintain the total indoor/outdoor pressure difference across the internal surface if the latter can be made impervious to water vapour. In this event the sole provision against condensation is that the surface should remain above the internal dew-point temperature. Not all surfaces can be so chosen to stop the passage of moisture vapour, and the more permeable they are, the greater is the chance that, at some internal part of the structure, a sufficiently low temperature will be

Fig 5

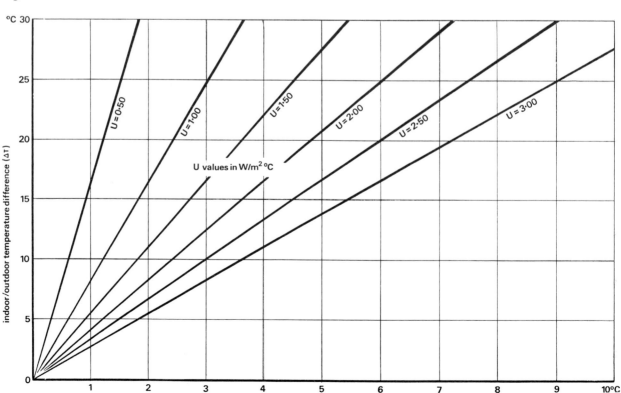

reached to cool the vapour below its dew-point. The respective temperature and pressure gradients, when charted, can be used to identify the point where condensation might occur in given circumstances, as demonstrated in the worked example later in this digest.

Characteristics of the environment

Except when a warm front brings moist air to follow a cold dry spell, the risk of condensation through natural ventilation in a heated building is slight. It is almost wholly dependent on the amount of excess moisture introduced by the occupants and their activities.

At normal ventilation rates, the gain by the air of body moisture from persons not engaged in physical exertion is roughly 45 g/person in one hour. This results in the indoor atmosphere having an excess moisture content over outdoor air of some 1·7 g of water vapour per kg of dry air. Provided the ventilation rates were properly controlled, this would be a suitable design assumption for shops, offices, classrooms, public meeting-places and dry industrial premises. For dwellings, taking account of the moisture produced by cooking and bathing and the likelihood of restricted ventilation in cold weather, a safer design value for moisture excess might be 34 g/kg. Catering establishments and industrial workshops requiring humid atmospheres or using wet processes may well contribute 68 g/kg or more to the internal air. In naturally ventilated premises such design values may be added to the assumed mixing ratio of the outdoor air.

Table 1. Typical values of heat and vapour resistance

	Thermal resistance (r_t) m² °C/W
Surfaces	
Wall surface—inside	0·12
—outside	0·05
Roof (or ceiling) surface—	
inside	0·11
outside	0·04
Internal airspace	0·18

	Vapour resistance (r_v) MN s/g
Membranes	
Average gloss paint film	7·5–40
Polythene sheet (0·06 mm)	110–120
Aluminium foil	4000

Materials	Thermal resistivity m °C/W	Vapour resistivity* MN s/g m
Brickwork	0·7–1·4	25–100
Concrete	0·7	30–100
Rendering	0·8	100
Plaster	2	60
Timber	7	45–75
Plywood	7	1500–6000
Fibre building board	15–19	15–60
Hardboard	7	450–750
Plasterboard	6	45–60
Compressed strawboard	10–12	45–75
Wood–wool slab	9	15–40
Expanded polystyrene	30	100–600
Foamed urea-formaldehyde	26	20–30
Foamed polyurethane (open or closed cell)	40–50	30–1000
Expanded ebonite	34	11,000–60,000

*Resistivity—1/diffusivity

Fig 6

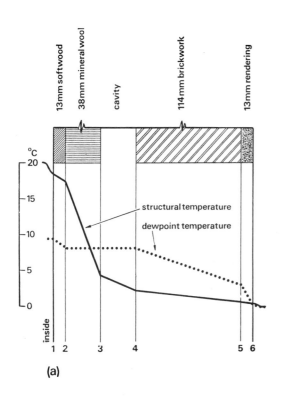

(a)

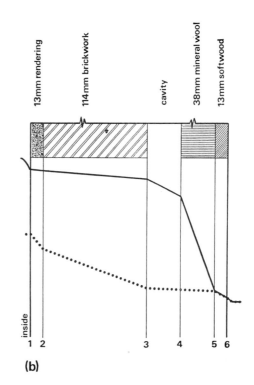

(b)

Estimating condensation risk

The principles used in this digest to predict the likelihood of condensation, and to design so as to avoid it, may be applied to wall, floor or roof constructions, but lightweight sheeted roofs present special problems, see page 203.

Figs 6a–6d show schematically some variations of a wall construction. The four illustrations are drawn with the thicknesses of the components to scale, the boundaries of the materials are numbered in sequence and the temperature difference across the structure is set up on an adjacent vertical scale. Using Fig 6a as an example, the design assumptions and the estimating procedures are then as follows:

1. Indoor/outdoor air temperature difference, ΔT, assumed to be:
$$20-0 = 20°C$$

2. Thermal resistance
(value from Table 1 × thickness of component):

Inside air to point 1		0·12
1–2	13 mm softwood 6·93×0·013	= 0·09
2–3	38 mm mineral wool 27·72×0·038	= 1·05
3–4	cavity	0·18
4–5	114 mm brickwork 0·9×0·114	= 0·10
5–6	13 mm rendering 0·83×0·013	= 0·01
6—outside air		0·05

$$R_t = 1·60$$

3. Temperature drop between points:
$$=\frac{\Delta T}{R_t} \times r_t = \frac{20}{1·6} \times r_t = 12·5 \times r_t \text{ (°C point to point)}$$

Inside air	=	20°C
Inside air—point 1	= 12·5×0·12 =	1·5
	drop to	18·5
1–2	= 12·5×0·09 =	1·12
	drop to =	17·38
2–3	= 12·5×1·05 =	13·12
	drop to	4·26
3–4	= 12·5×0·18 =	2·25
	drop to	2·01
4–5	= 12·5×0·10 =	1·25
	drop to	0·76
5–6	= 12·5×0·01 =	0·12
	drop to	0·64
6— outside air	= 12·5×0·05 ×	0·63
		0·01 *
Outside air		0°C

*Error due to approximation

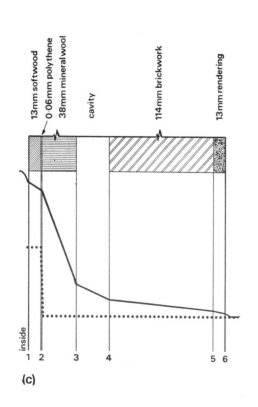

(c)

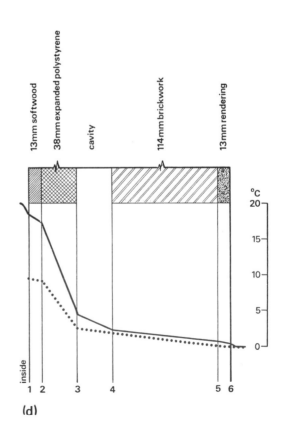

(d)

4. The profile of the temperature drop is plotted against the vertical scale.

5. From Fig 2, using the design assumption that the outside air is at 0°C and is saturated at a mixing ratio of 3·8 g/kg, the outdoor vapour pressure can be read (on the right-hand scale) as 6 mb; if a moisture vapour excess of 3·4 g/kg is contributed by activities indoors, inspection of the two right-hand scales of Fig 2 shows that the total moisture content of 7·2 g/kg gives an indoor vapour pressure of 11·4 mb. The indoor/outdoor vapour pressure difference, ΔP, is therefore 11·4−6·0 = 5·4 mb.

6. Vapour resistance
(value from Table 1 × thickness of component):

$$
\begin{aligned}
\text{point } 1\text{--}2 &= 60 \times 0\text{·}013 &&= 0\text{·}78 \\
2\text{--}3 \text{ (virtually nil)} & &&= 0\text{·}0 \\
3\text{--}4 \text{ (nil)} & &&= 0\text{·}0 \\
4\text{--}5 &= 25 \times 0\text{·}114 &&= 2\text{·}85 \\
5\text{--}6 &= 100 \times 0\text{·}013 &&= 1\text{·}3 \\
&&& \overline{} \\
& R^v &&= 4\text{·}93
\end{aligned}
$$

7. Pressure drop between points:

$$\frac{\Delta P}{R_v} \times r_v = \frac{5\text{·}4}{4\text{·}93} \times r_v = 1\text{·}10 r_v \text{ (mb point to point)}$$

				Corresponding dew-point temp. from Fig 2
Indoor vapour pressure		11·4		9·4°C
point 1–2	1·10×0·78 =	0·86		
	drop to	10·54		8·0°C
2–3		= 0·0		
		10·54		8·0°C
3–4		= 0·0		
		10·54		8·0C
4–5	1·10×2·85 =	3·13		
	drop to	7·41		3·0°C
5–6	1·10×1·30	1·43		
	drop to	5·98		0·0°C

8. Profile of dew-point temperature: Reference to Fig 2 will show the respective dew-point temperatures for the vapour pressures at points 1, 2, 5 and 6 from which the dew-point profile may be constructed.

9. Estimation of condensation risk: At any point where the computed temperature is lower than the computed dew-point temperature, condensation can occur in the conditions assumed. In the worked example, liquid may form in a position where, clearly, it can reduce the effectiveness of insulation and it is likely also to put the nearby timber at risk of rot. As an illustration of the effect that structural detailing may have, Fig. 6b shows the construction reversed and free from risk in the same surrounding conditions. Slight modifications, shown in 6c and 6d, are sufficient, however, to limit the potential risk by using materials that modify the vapour pressure gradient.

Some calculated risk may be accepted, as for example when condensed moisture can do no damage to the weather side of a structure and can be prevented from soaking back. In a great deal of masonry construction it is probable that condensate is soaked up harmlessly until it has an opportunity to distil outwards or evaporate from the surfaces during favourable periods.

Where there is an estimated likelihood of intrastructural condensation the greatest risks arise if vegetable-based materials are exposed to the consequent dampness, particularly where the weather side of the construction is highly resistant to vapour flow. Then, ventilated cavities may offer some help and their value increases as the vapour resistance of the warm-side materials is improved.

Lightweight sheeted roofs

The lowest temperature to which a roof cladding falls occurs in winter, on calm frosty nights when the sky is unclouded. The cooling effect of the low outside temperature is then intensified by the roof radiating heat to the sky, which in these conditions has an effective temperature of about −45°C for radiation from the earth.

With roof cladding of low thermal capacity, e.g. single-skin metal or asbestos-cement sheeting, the change in temperature of the inner surface as a result of a sudden drop in the effective outdoor temperature takes place rapidly, and the cladding may be about 5°C below the outdoor temperature for several hours. The use of vapour barriers, ventilation and insulation to combat the high risk of condensation is discussed in National Building Studies Research Paper 23, A. W. Pratt. *Condensation in sheeted roofs*. HMSO 1958 (*now out of print*).

Further reading

Digest 108, Standardised U-values.

BRS Current Papers Design Series 24, E. F. Ball. Condensation in large panel construction. BRS 1964.

Condensation in dwellings, Part 1: A design guide, £1.00; Part 2: Remedial measures, £1.25. HMSO.

Control of lichens, moulds and similar growths

Algae, lichens and mosses are to be found on external surfaces of buildings in rural districts. Their appearance is often regarded as desirable and they are rarely destructive although they may have undesirable effects. Means of encouraging their growth, and of destroying them, are set out in this digest.

Mould growths on internal surfaces are evidence of dampness which should be cured before the affected surface is treated with one of the toxic washes recommended. Moulds may also grow on external paintwork.

The growths discussed in this digest are those that are to be found on building materials, in conditions where their needs of moisture, food and light are met. Some of them need only moisture, minute quantities of mineral salts, and light; others require more elaborate food materials but do not need light.

Methods of dealing with wood-destroying organisms 'wet rot' and 'dry rot' are dealt with elsewhere.[1]

For the purpose of the digest it is not necessary to identify the organisms but some of their characteristics are set out in the table on p. 205. When established, they can exist under a wide range of moisture conditions and many can withstand drying out; for active growth they require a fairly high level of moisture in the building material or an atmospheric humidity of over 85 per cent. At lower relative humidities growth is slower and ceases below 70 per cent. In this country, moisture conditions are more generally favourable on northern than on southern aspects, though lichens often flourish on south-facing substrates.

External surfaces

Algae, lichens and mosses are commonly seen on roofs and outer walls in rural districts. The resulting appearance is often regarded as mellow and pleasing, and it may be desired to encourage rather than destroy them, particularly where there is a harsh contrast between old surfaces and new materials introduced in the course of repairs. A traditional method for encouraging growth is to apply a wash of cow dung and water; human urine or skimmed milk are also said to be effective. When rendering is to be patched, the porosity of the original work should be matched as nearly as possible, so that similar organisms may eventually grow.

Although organisms are rarely destructive, their acidic metabolic products can weaken asbestos-cement and eat into limestone. Lichens may obscure carvings and inscriptions; algae may produce disfiguring stains on masonry, brickwork or renderings; mould may attack paints and plastics. Moss may impede the shedding of water from roofs or lead to blockage of gutters and downpipes. Where it is desired to prevent or destroy such growths, one of the toxic washes discussed below may be used. These take a few days to become effective and, in wet weather, may be washed out before they have time to act. They should preferably be applied during a dry spell; the action is hastened if thick surface growths are partly removed or torn with a wire brush and the wash then well brushed in. The wash, repeated if necessary, kills the growth but the dead organism takes some time to disappear. If the wall is to be painted or rendered, the dead matter must be removed so as to obtain a good bond for the new finish; this may be done by scraping or wirebrushing and is often more effective when the dead organism is dry. A further toxic wash at this stage, whether or not the wall is to be painted or rendered, can delay re-establishment of the growth.

The effective life of the treatment depends on the porosity of the surface and on the extent to which it is washed by rain: on a porous sheltered surface, growth may be prevented for two or three years; a dense concrete or a cement paint finish may require retreatment at the beginning of each rainy season. The application of a colourless water-repellent after the toxic wash has dried will increase the effective life of the wash, but it should be remembered that the use of a water-repellent may not always be appropriate[2] and may interfere with subsequent redecoration, for example, with cement paint.

Organic growths on buildings

Organism	Food needed from surface	Light requirements	Appearance	Remarks
Algae	Mineral salts	Necessary	Green, red or brown powders or filaments which may or may not be slimy according to the moisture conditions	May occur on all types of building surfaces outdoors
Lichens (combinations of certain algae and fungi)	Mineral salts	Necessary	Leathery plates of tissue with crinkled edges and often with cup-shaped fruit bodies—usually orange or grey	May be found on stone and slate, on asbestos-cement roofs, concrete roofing tiles and renderings, and other concrete surfaces, where they often cause darkening
Liverworts and mosses	Mineral salts	Necessary	Some liverworts occur as leathery tissue with smooth edges, not unlike lichens in appearance; others resemble mosses	Usually found in angles, crevices and on surfaces where soil and dirt have accumulated
Fungi (moulds, mildew and yeasts)	Organic material	Unnecessary	Moulds appear as spots or patches which may spread to form a furry layer on the surface—grey green, black or brown. Mould may grow within a paint film causing a stain, usually pink or purple, but the mould itself may not be visible	May be found on paint, distemper, wallpaper or the paste used to fix it, and on dirt and dust when these contain suitable food; vinyl finishes may be stained. Yeasts have been found occasionally in places where appropriate nutrients were available
Bacteria	Various	Unnecessary	Not visible individually to the naked eye	May cause yellowing of cement paint containing casein or pink stains in size-bound distemper. Sulphate-reducing bacteria in gypsum plaster may cause dark stains in paints containing lead and may promote deterioration of limestone and corrosion of steel

Mould growth often occurs on paint surfaces outdoors, resembling a dirt deposit. In the early stages it can be washed off but, later, may become embedded. It can damage paint films, especially on wood. The main safeguard is in the inherent mould-resistance of the paint, augmented if necessary with fungicidal additives which, however, rarely have an adequate life in the film.

Internal surfaces

Mould growth on internal surfaces is evidence of dampness. This may be due to rain penetration, to deficiencies in damp-proof coursing, leakage from plumbing, defects in the rainwater disposal system, or to condensation. Moulds may also appear in a new building before the water used in construction has dried out; during this period, flueless gas, paraffin or oil heaters should not be used to accelerate drying because of the large amount of water vapour they produce.

The source of dampness should first be cured[3] and the walls allowed to dry thoroughly before any further step is taken. It may not always be practicable to achieve this completely but a partial cure is better than none at all. In breweries and bakehouses, conditions may be conducive to mould growth even if the ventilation is good.

Where the organism is growing on undecorated stone, brick or concrete, a toxic wash should be applied to the affected surface and its surroundings. After a suitable interval the area should be brushed down and rinsed with a small quantity of water if this is necessary to restore its appearance. The treatment should be repeated if any signs of new growth become apparent.

On decorated surfaces, the procedure will depend on the type of decoration and the extent to which it is affected. In general, decoration that has been attacked should be stripped; the surface should be sterilised by application of a toxic wash and kept under observation for a week or so, a further wash being applied if there are signs of renewed growth. When dry, the surface may be redecorated. If the area of attack is small, local stripping and sterilisation may be all that is required.

Where attack is slight and the existing decoration will withstand treatment with a toxic wash and is sufficiently absorptive to be impregnated by it, it may be sufficient to clean down without stripping and then to apply the toxic wash, allow to dry and redecorate. Oil-bound distemper, which may be difficult to strip, can sometimes be dealt with in this way. Size-bound distemper should always be stripped.

In food-processing and other rooms where condensation is prevalent, organisms may grow in dust deposited on the surfaces. Such surfaces should be kept clean by frequent washing. Where they are painted the use of a paint incorporating a toxic ingredient will prevent the growth of organisms in the paint film at least for some time; the protection afforded is particularly valuable during the early life of the paint film when it is most sensitive to attack.

Toxic washes

Some toxic washes are listed on page 207. Their efficiency will vary according to the circumstances. It is therefore best to make a preliminary trial of two or three and to use the most effective. Where time does not permit this, it is recommended that household bleach should be used, since this is effective with a wide range of organic growths and is readily available.

Although it is undesirable in principle to introduce soluble salts, particularly sodium salts, into porous building materials, there is no evidence that, in the concentrations mentioned, any of these washes will harm building materials.

Care in use

All of the toxic materials listed must be used with great care. Many of them are caustic in concentrated solutions but even solutions diluted ready for use should if splashed on the skin be washed off immediately with soap and water. Particular care should be taken to ensure that they are not splashed into the eyes. Formalin used in an enclosed space is a health hazard unless good ventilation is arranged.

If an area of skin larger than about 30 cm^2 is affected, do not delay in transporting the person concerned to the nearest hospital and tell the medical staff the nature of the material being used.

The instructions about care and safety issued by the suppliers should be followed meticulously.

Redecoration

Where there may be moisture in the backing, a fairly porous type of decoration—distemper, vinyl water paint, emulsion paint, flat oil paint—will permit drying to continue. It may be advantageous if the distemper or paint contains a fungicide. Digest 55, *Painting walls—1*, gives some recommendations based on the measured moisture contents of walls.

When the source of moisture is heavy condensation, an impermeable finish, for example high gloss paint, is likely to be the most durable. This will not permit condensed moisture to reach the backing but it has the disadvantage that condensed moisture may run or drip from the surface. Anti-condensation paints may prevent this but often these are less suitable where a readily cleaned finish is required. Some emulsion paints withstand scrubbing and may offer a useful compromise.

If condensation arises from a commercial process that can be interrupted for no more than a short time, if at all, the surface should be made as dry as possible before the decoration is applied; if necessary it should be dried out carefully with a blow-lamp or an electric heater. Asbestos-cement, however, is liable to shatter if it is strongly heated; it should not be dried with a blow-lamp and great care should be taken if an electric heater is used. Similar care is needed when drying gypsum plaster; overheating may decompose it.

Some manufacturers make special quick-drying paints for use in breweries, greenhouses, etc., and these are likely to be the most effective in these circumstances.

Mould-resistant paints Toxic ingredients incorporated in paint protect only the paint film itself; they do not sterilise an infected backing or prevent the growth of organisms in dirt deposited on the paint film.

Special types of mould-resistant paint are supplied by many manufacturers. These vary greatly in effectiveness and should be used mainly where control of the dampness is not possible, for example in cellars and breweries, and only as a secondary safeguard in dwellings.

Paints for external walls vary in susceptibility to algae and few, if any, additives seem successful. Paints with a cement base or emulsion binder tend to be rather more affected than those with a chlorinated rubber or other resin basis.

The addition of toxic ingredients to paint by the operative is not recommended because it is difficult to ensure thorough mixing and because the whole balance of the paint may be altered and its performance adversely affected.

Fungicides can be fairly readily incorporated in size-bound or oil-bound distempers by adding them with the thinning water. Distemper containing 20 g of sodium pentachlorophenate to 1 kg of paste has been used successfully and has given good service, with only the slight disadvantage that the distemper thickened a little during application. The manufacturer of the distemper should be consulted before this step is taken.

The addition of toxic substances has not been found effective in preventing organic growth on cement paint out of doors. Treatment after the cement paint has cured is usually more effective.

References

1 Forest Products Research Bulletin No 1 *Dry rot in wood* HMSO London 1960: 20p (22½p)
   Technical Note No 44 *Decay in buildings* Forest Products Research Laboratory, Princes Risborough, Bucks 1969 (free)
2 BRS Digest 125 *Colourless treatments for masonry*
3 *Protection from rain* Building Research Station, Watford 1971 50p
   BRS Digests: No 27 *Rising damp in walls*
   No 77 *Damp-proof courses*
   No 110 *Condensation*

Some toxic washes
Care in use—see text

Material	Strength for use	Form	Supplier	Notes
Household bleach	1 part to 4–5 parts water (by volume)	Liquid	Hardware stores, etc.	Effective against many organisms and will bleach the colour of dark ones; may change the colour of paints and some building materials. No active residue. Rinse off with cold water
Sodium ortho-phenylphenate *Brunosol*	2% solution in water	Concentrate	Preservation Developments Ltd, 99 Regent Street, London W1	
Sodium pentachlorophenate *Brunobrite*	2% solution in water	Liquid	Preservation Developments Ltd	
Cuprinol dry rot killer		Liquid	Cuprinol Ltd, Adderwell, Frome, Somerset	
Hepta-San		Prepared solution or powder	B J Ellis Ltd, Apollo Works, Epsom Road, Leyton, London E10 6ES	
Protim wall solution		Liquid	Protim Ltd, Fieldhouse Lane, Marlow, Bucks	
Santobrite		Prepared solution; dilute as required	Monsanto Chemicals, 10 Victoria Street, London SW1 (bulk supply only)	
Zinc or magnesium fluorosilicate (formerly described as 'silicofluoride')	4% solution in water (1 kg to 25 litres)	Crystals	Laporte Industries Ltd, General Chemicals Division, Moorfield Road, Widnes WA8 OHE Also available under various trade names as a concrete floor hardener	
Formalin (40% formaldehyde)	5% solution in water		Pharmacists	Evaporates, leaving no active residue
Copper carbonate Ammonia solution (sp. gr. 0·880) Water	30 g 300 cc 50 litres			Will destroy algae and lichens but may stain some materials; test on a small area
Nuodex 87	1–5% solution in water	Liquid concentrate	Durham Chemicals Ltd, Birtley, Co Durham	Effective against algae, lichens and fungi. Non-staining and does not need rinsing off; active residual film
Benzalkonium chloride BP	1% solution in water	50% concentrate	Pharmacists and manufacturing chemists	
Phenolic *Thaltox* Organo-tin quaternary ammonium compound *Thaltox Q*	As directed	Liquid	Richardson & Starling Limited, 21 Hyde Street, Winchester	
A quaternary ammonium compound *Gloquat C*	1% solution in water	50% concentrate	Glovers (Chemicals) Ltd, Wortley Low Mills, Whitehall Road, Leeds LS12 4RF	
Borate *Polybor*	5% solution in water	Powder	Borax Consolidated Ltd, Borax House, Carlisle Place, London SW1	

This list does not claim to be complete or to comment in any way on the relative merit of products; there is no significance in the order.

Colourless treatments for masonry

The first section of this digest deals with water-repellents for masonry (the term masonry is used here in the broad sense of walls built of bricks, concrete blocks or stone), and the second section discusses colourless preservative treatments for stone.

Colourless water-repellents for masonry

Colourless water-repellent liquids are intended to improve the resistance to rain penetration of masonry without appreciably changing its appearance. The treatment lines the pores with a water-repellent material which inhibits capillary absorption, so that water does not sink into the surface but stays in droplets and runs off. Although the treatment can reduce the water taken up in a shower to a negligible amount, appreciable quantities may still be absorbed during prolonged rainfall, even in mild exposures.

Treatment with a water-repellent may increase the degree of penetration through cracks or defective joints. Before application, therefore, the pointing should be examined carefully and any defects greater than haircracks made good. Although the treatments need renewal from time to time, they are valuable in improving a construction which has proved to be not quite satisfactory for its conditions of exposure.

Surface permeability

A surface treated with a water-repellent liquid remains permeable to water vapour; moisture that has penetrated the surface, by absorption or by defective detailing for example, can still escape by evaporation but at a much slower rate than from an untreated surface.

When a concentration of soluble salts is present in an untreated wall, the salts move in solution to the surface of the wall, the water evaporates from the wall face and leaves the salts deposited on the surface in the form of an unsightly but harmless efflorescence. Treatment with a water-repellent may be detrimental because the salts are prevented from moving in solution to the surface and are deposited within the pores at a depth dependent on the depth of penetration of the water-repellent. Spalling of the treated surface may then occur. It is advisable therefore to wait until the efflorescence has been washed away by rain or, if necessary, to hasten its removal by repeated washing, drying and brushing, before the treatment is applied. Where there are only slight traces of efflorescence, it may be enough to brush down the surface and to wipe it with a damp cloth or sponge.

Use

There are many situations in which the use of a colourless water-repellent liquid provides a comparatively inexpensive way of minimising rain-penetration, but it cannot be expected to remedy all deficiencies in the choice of materials or in the design and construction of a building. On rare occasions, it may suppress evaporation to so great an extent as to be harmful to the particular structure. Water-repellent liquids should be used with discrimination, having regard to the cause of the dampness and the suitability of the surface for treatment.

Composition

Early water-repellents were solutions or emulsions of waxes, oils, resins, fats or metallic soaps such as aluminium stearates. More recent introductions are based upon silicone resins in the form of solutions of silicones in organic solvents, aqueous solutions of siliconates and silicone emulsions.

The active ingredients for water-repellents are produced by relatively few manufacturers. They are supplied in concentrated form to the many firms that market water-repellent liquids in a form suitable for application.

BS 3826:1969, Silicone-based Water Repellents for Masonry, sets out performance standards and offers user guidance. There is no similar standard at present for water-repellents other than silicone-based, but at least one manufacturer claims that his products meet the performance requirements of BS 3826.

Preparation

Cracks wider than haircracks, and defective mortar joints, should be made good and dirty surfaces should be cleaned. Detergents must not be used as they nullify the water-repellent properties of the treatment.

Organisms such as lichens or algae should be removed by brushing, a process made easier if they are first killed with a suitable fungicide and allowed to dry. Slight contaminations of efflorescence can be cleaned with a bristle brush or air-blast, or by wiping with damp rags rinsed in clean water. This is best carried out in dry weather.

Selection and application

It is advisable to use materials which either are manufactured to BS 3826 or which meet its performance requirements. Care should be taken in the selection of repellents, as not all are universally applicable to all types of surface. Of the silicone-based materials covered by the standard, Class A should be used on sandstone, all fired clay, in-situ and precast hydraulic cement-based products, cement and cement-lime rendering and asbestos-cement; Class B on natural limestones, calcium silicate bricks and cast stone; and Class C as Class B but excluding calcium silicate brickwork. If in doubt, professional advice should be sought.

The treatment should be applied to a dry surface by brush or spray, preferably during a spell of dry weather. (If there is difficulty in drying the surface, Class C materials are recommended, either as a full treatment or as a preparatory treatment before using Class A or B.)

Application should be in accordance with the maker's instructions and any warning about the toxicity or inflammability of the solvent should be strictly observed. Firms which formulate water-repellent liquids can advise on application. As far as silicone-based water-repellents are concerned, BS 3826 contains a section entitled 'Notes on Use', with guidance on such important aspects as application, preparation of the surfaces for treatment and selection of the right class of product.

Renewal

Water-repellent treatments have to be renewed from time to time because of a gradual deterioration in their efficiency. The first effect is noticed when the surface no longer sheds the water that falls on it. This does not of itself indicate that the treatment has ceased to be effective; the pore surfaces behind the exposed face still retain an adequate degree of water-repellence for some considerable time.

Since the durability depends on the character of the surface and on the conditions of exposure, the frequency of renewal must be determined by experience with the selected water-repellents in the particular circumstances. Renewal is called for when signs of dampness begin to make an appearance, after first checking for structural defects. However, it will usually be advisable to renew a treatment that has served its purpose for a reasonably long time, say 10 years, without waiting for dampness to appear again.

Details other than walls

In addition to their use for the treatment of walls, colourless water-repellent liquids may also be useful for preventing rain-penetration through particular parts of a building. Stone mullions and window jambs, for example, often show deterioration of the inner face, particularly in buildings near the sea, because rainwater carrying salts in solution is absorbed through the outer face and evaporated from the inner face, where the salts are then deposited. Treatment of the salt-contaminated inner face may induce flaking, whereas an effective water-repellent on the outer face will reduce further contamination. The accumulated salts can then be removed from the inner face by repeated brushing and washing to minimise further deterioration. Similarly, moisture finding its way through permeable sills or copings that have not been properly provided with damp-proof courses may cause extensive damage to interior decorations. In these circumstances a metal covering may be considered unsightly or too expensive and the appearance of an oil-paint may be equally unacceptable. Provided it is recognised that the treatment will need renewal more frequently on a horizontal than on a vertical surface and that the joints in sills and copings must first be sealed by raking them out to an adequate depth and repointing, preferably with a mastic composition, some success can be obtained by the use of an efficient surface water-repellent. Attention should be given to the throatings, and the treatment must be carried far enough to ensure that the water discharged from the treated surface is not absorbed elsewhere.

Water-repellent treatments are not an effective substitute for sound materials and proper design in the first instance or as effective as the insertion of damp-proof courses or flashings, but they are useful when it is not practicable to adopt more radical measures.

Colourless preservative treatments for stone

When the stonework of a building decays sufficiently to cause concern but insufficiently to justify a drastic programme of redressing or refacing, the owner is naturally inclined to try to arrest the decay by applying one of the many colourless preservative solutions that have been advocated from time to time. The owners of new stone buildings, recently cleaned buildings or buildings in which new stone has been inserted in the course of repairs may also be inclined to try such treatments on the stonework in an attempt to prevent or postpone the onset of decay. Unfortunately, the indiscriminate application of colourless stone-preservatives has usually resulted in disappointment. This should not be taken to mean that all methods must necessarily fail, but sounds a warning against any undue optimism about methods that have not been given adequate trial.

Likely situations for effective treatment

Externally. As discussed in the previous section, when stonework near the coast is exposed to salt-bearing winds, the salt deposited on the external surfaces often finds its way to the internal surfaces where it can cause powdering and flaking. Mullions, transoms and door and window jambs are particularly vulnerable features. The application of a colourless water-repellent treatment to the outside of such stonework can reduce or even arrest the decay inside, but on no account should the treatment be applied to the inside, because this would almost certainly cause spalling. After treatment on the outside, powdering must be expected to continue for a time, particularly during dry weather, as the moisture content of the stone is reduced. The powder should be lightly brushed off and carefully removed to avoid contamination of other building materials. The treatment will need renewal periodically—see Colourless water-repellents for masonry, Renewal.

Internally. Interior stonework that has become heavily contaminated with moisture-absorbing salts, but is no longer exposed to liquid water can have the salts immobilised by impregnation of the stone with a molten colourless wax. White paraffin wax with a melting point of about 50°C has been used with success. Deep impregnation is essential to reduce the risk of spalling, and is achieved by warming the stone with radiant heat (over a long period, if the stone is thick) before applying the wax. Excess wax should be scraped off and the surface of the stone swabbed briefly with a suitable wax solvent, e.g. white spirit to BS 245:1956. Care must be exercised when using inflammable solvents. This treatment will darken the stone and may cause it to pick up dirt more readily than untreated stone.

Other circumstances

The Station is still obtaining information on the behaviour of treated stonework but the present data do not show that there are any other circumstances in which the application of a preservative treatment would be beneficial.

Prospective buyers are advised to ask to be shown examples of the use of such preservatives on stone similar to theirs, exposed under similar conditions, and in such a way that fair comparison can be made between treated and untreated surfaces. Stone decay usually takes place very slowly, so that even after a lapse of some years an untreated building might look no worse than a treated building. If comparative information is not available, the building owner might like to carry out a trial himself; the Station would always be interested to hear the results of such trials.

Choice of treatment materials

Any silicone-based masonry water-repellent used externally should meet the requirements of BS 3826, and be of the right class for the type of stone involved —see Colourless water-repellents for masonry, Selection and application. Reputable suppliers will give advice about methods of application and the resultant appearance.

Cleaning external surfaces of buildings

Considerations in planning the cleaning of a building.

*Descriptions of cleaning methods: water spray—dry grit-blasting—wet grit-blasting
—mechanical—chemical—steam. A comparative table of cleaning methods.*

Materials to be cleaned—suitable methods.

*Safety precautions for operatives for the general public, for the material to be
cleaned and adjacent work. Sources of advice. Giving notices.*

Deposits of dirt not only affect the appearance of buildings, they can act as a reservoir for harmful chemicals and can hide decay. The choice of cleaning method is important, for the use of an unsuitable one could result in damage. When selecting a method, therefore, the type and condition of the surface to be cleaned must be considered, in addition to the cost, speed and convenience of the operation. The aesthetic aspects of cleaning are not discussed in this digest.

Damage may result from the employment of operatives who lack the necessary skill and experience. The standard of supervision is important as the true condition of the fabric may become apparent only during cleaning.

Cleaning methods

Water spray Water is sprayed on to the surface only in sufficient quantity to keep the deposits of dirt moist until they soften. Larger quantities of water are no more effective and may inconvenience the public; they might also penetrate to the interior of the building. Cleaning should begin at the top of the building so that surplus water will run down and pre-soften the dirt below. The time taken to soften the dirt needs to be found by trial; it could be anything from a few minutes to several days. In some instances the softened deposits can then be removed by hosing but usually it will be necessary to assist their removal with brushes of bristle and non-ferrous or stainless steel wire. For cleaning string courses or below

Figs. 1 and 2 The effect of cleaning—nineteenth-century Portland stone.

cornices, abrasive stones may be needed. Heavy encrustations of dirt usually require careful use of mechanical or grit-blasting means to assist in their removal.

This method is effective when the dirt merely sits on the surface or is bound to the wall with water-soluble matter.

Dry grit-blasting Abrasive grit is blown under pressure at the surface to scour away the dirt. Some of the surface, particularly at arrisses, will also be removed if it is soft or decayed. Four sizes of nozzle may be used on the blasting gun; large, for large areas of plain walling; medium, for smaller areas; small or very small for enrichments. The smaller nozzles are better used in conjuction with a remote control valve, giving the operator control of the flow as well as of the direction.

Protection must be provided against dust and rebounding grit. Respirators of a high standard must be worn by the grit-blasting team and the gun operator must wear a well-fitting air line helmet in which a positive air pressure is maintained to prevent the ingress of dust. The air supplied to the helmet must be clean; unless this can be ensured by drawing it from some distance away, a high-efficiency in-line filter must be used. The helmet will protect the operator's eyes but other members of the team must wear suitable goggles or spectacles.

All dust is harmful but silica dust is particularly dangerous because free silica can cause long-term irreversible lung damage. HM Factory Inspectorate therefore advises that only non-siliceous grit be used, but when sandstone, granite or slate are being cleaned by this method, active silica dust may be generated from the building material, even though non-siliceous grit is used for blasting. Except on isolated sites, the work area must be close-sheeted to reduce the dust nuisance, but even with this precaution escaping dust can be troublesome to the general public and to neighbouring properties. Door, window and any other openings in the walls must be sealed with adhesive tape and protection given to windows, lead rainwater pipes, electrical leads, and paint if it is not to be renewed.

For best results, the building should be washed rapidly with water after dry-grit blasting to remove dust left lying on the surfaces. A high-pressure water lance is usually recommended for this operation.

Wet grit-blasting This method is very similar to dry grit-blasting except that water is introduced into the air/grit stream. The water reduces the visible dust but the smaller harmful particles remain a hazard to health and so the same standards of protection are needed as for dry grit-blasting, as is the use of non-siliceous grits. The method is particularly useful when it is important to avoid dust nuisance to the public and to keep the interior of the building free from dust.

It again involves an extra operation in rinsing down the surface after blasting, which tends to produce a mottled effect if the operatives are careless.

Many operatives do not like this method and there is a temptation to turn off the water if supervision is inadequate.

Mechanical cleaning The tools used include conical-shaped carborundum heads of various sizes and textures, grinding and buffing discs, and rotary brushes, all used with power tools. These spin off the dirt and weathered face in one operation. Hand tools such as chisels, brushes of bristle and non-ferrous or stainless steel wire and abrasive blocks (natural or synthetic) are used to supplement power tools, particularly for cleaning enrichments. Exhaust ventilation devices should be fitted to all power tools, or the operatives should wear high-efficiency breathing apparatus; eye protection is a statutory requirement. While cleaning siliceous masonry, the use of an air line helmet is recommended for complete protection.

Great skill is needed to avoid damage to surfaces being cleaned and to adjacent areas. Since the surface is reduced to some extent, the method is more suitable for plain areas than for mouldings.

Chemical cleaning Most chemical cleaning agents either contain soluble salts or react with stone to form soluble salts. Every precaution should be taken to avoid contamination of building materials with soluble salts as this is likely to cause damage to the fabric: the effects can be continuous and progressive and the removal of salts is a lengthy and tedious operation. The only chemical cleaner known to leave no soluble salts in masonry is hydrofluoric acid,

Fig 3 Dry grit-blasting

which is used as a dilute solution either alone or mixed with phosphoric acid. Proprietary mixes of this kind are said to reduce the risk of iron staining which very occasionally occurs with hydrofluoric acid alone. The acid is brushed or sprayed on to the dirty surface which is then rinsed with water and brushed to remove the loosened dirt. These acids are extremely dangerous in inexperienced hands and their use should be left to firms employing trained operatives. They will etch glass and destroy any polish on marble and granite; they may leave unsightly marks on windows, pavings and footpaths. If they come into contact with the skin, they can cause very serious and painful burns. Scaffold boards and poles must be kept well rinsed with water. However, even after thorough rinsing enough acid can collect inside the poles to create a hazard to scaffold workers and cause frosting of unprotected glazing. The ends of all poles, especially horizontal ones, should be plugged to prevent ingress of any liquid.

Among the numerous proprietary chemical cleaners on the market, some, which are very effective on limestone, contain caustic soda. Although the use of this substance is likely in general to leave harmful salts in the building material it may be used under specially restricted conditions. It can cause severe injury to operatives or any passers-by who become splashed with it and it can damage glass, aluminium, galvanised steel and paint. Precautions must be taken accordingly. Before using any of these proprietary cleaners assurance should be obtained that there is no risk of damage to the surfaces to which they are applied and no undisclosed risk to operatives. It is advisable that any cleaner used should have Agrément Certification and be used solely in accordance with any specification in the Certificate.

More information about the dangers involved with chemical cleaners and important first-aid precautions is given in Technical Information Leaflet No. 44, copies of which are available from the Building Research Advisory Service.

Steam cleaning Mains water is pumped to a flash boiler and the steam generated is fed to a lance through which it is played on to the surface. As with the water spray method it is usually necessary to

A Comparison of Methods

Method	Relative speed	Relative cost	Advantages	Disadvantages
Water spray	Slow	Low	No risk of damage to masonry except under frost conditions. No danger to public or operatives. Quiet.	Limestone may develop brown, patchy stains. Water penetration may damage interior finishes, hidden timber and ferrous metals. Some risk of drain blockage. Possible nuisance from spray and saturation of surrounding ground. Often requires supplementing with an abrasive method or high-pressure water lance.
Dry grit-blasting	Fast	High	No water to cause staining or internal damage. Can be used in any season.	Risk of damage to surface being cleaned and to adjacent surfaces, including glass. Cannot be used on soft stone. Possible noise and dust nuisance. Risk of drain blockage. Injurious dust from siliceous materials. For best results, needs to be followed by vigorous water washing.
Wet grit-blasting	Fast	High	Less water than with water spray method. Less visible dust than with dry-grit blasting.	Similar to dry grit-blasting but greater risk of drain blockage. Some risk of staining limestone. Can result in mottled finish if operatives are unskilled.
Mechanical cleaning	Fast	High	No water to cause staining or internal damage. Can be used in any season.	Considerable risk of damage to surface, especially mouldings. Injurious dust from siliceous materials. Hand rubbing may be necessary for acceptable finish.
Hydrofluoric acid preparations	Medium	Low	Will not damage unglazed masonry or painted surfaces. Quiet.	Needs extreme care in handling—can cause serious skin burns, and instant damage to unprotected glazing and polished surfaces. Scaffold pole ends need to be plugged and boards carefully rinsed.
Caustic alkalis	Fast	Low	Rapid cleaning of some types of limestone with minimum use of water.	Needs extreme care in use; can cause serious skin burns and damage to glazing, aluminium, galvanised surfaces and paint. Only preparations covered by an agrément Certificate should be used and only in accordance with the terms of the Certificate. Incorrect use can cause serious progressive damage to masonry.
Steam cleaning	Slow	Medium	No risk of damage to masonry except under frost conditions.	As 'water spray' but with less risk of staining. Not easy to obtain uniformly clean appearance.

assist the removal of dirt with brushes and abrasive stones. Recent experience indicates that it has little to commend its use when compared with other methods, although it has been found that steam can sometimes help to remove deep-seated soiling after acid cleaning.

Materials and cleaning methods

Limestone and marble Water spray has been the long-standing method used for these materials but the subsequent brown staining of limestone which often results may be unacceptable, particularly on light-coloured stone. The stain can be reduced by re-applying a water jet when the stone has dried, and it is unlikely to occur on stone which is washed regularly (every three to five years). Dry and wet grit-blasting have been finding increasing favour for cleaning the harder stones, such as Portland. Soft or polished surfaces are roughened by blasting, the softer the stone the greater the risk of damage. The finished appearance after blasting can be uniform but the finish may be considered 'dead' and un-interesting, although this improves with weathering. A method now in increasing use is a combination of water spray with a very small grit-blasting gun and a high-pressure water lance. Power tools are likely to produce the least acceptable finish.

Sandstone, granite and slate These materials can sometimes be cleaned by water spray but usually it will be necessary to use dry or wet grit-blasting, mechanical means or dilute hydrofluoric acid with or without additions. Caustic alkali should not be used. Rough-textured granite is usually cleaned with dilute hydrofluoric acid but aqueous solutions of ammonium bifluoride have been used successfully. They contain free hydrofluoric acid and must be used with great care. Ammonium salts are liable to harm porous stones, so care must be taken to avoid contamination of other kinds of stone with which the granite may be associated. With these materials mechanical cleaning generates active silica dust with consequent risk of silicosis for the operatives; effective protection is essential.

Concrete, cast stone, rendering and brickwork Finishes based on Portland cement sometimes respond well to cleaning by water spray, as does some brickwork. Where this method either does not work or is undesirable for other reasons, any of the other methods of cleaning that do not use caustic alkalis can be considered. All the materials contain free silica, so effective precautions against dust need to be taken. For renderings, it may be considered preferable to paint the finish rather than attempt to clean it.

Polished surfaces Polished surfaces are usually maintained by washing and/or polishing, but if neglected may need special skills, outside the scope of this digest, to restore their appearance.

Safety Measures

Exterior cleaning ranks as a building operation and all proper safety precautions must be taken. Advice on any safety aspect can be obtained from HM Factory Inspectorate, Baynards House, 1–13 Chepstow Place, Westbourne Grove, London W2.

Buildings of special importance

Particular care should be taken with buildings of architectural or historic interest both in the choice of method of cleaning and in the preliminary protective work to avoid damage to the buildings. Where the cleaning proposed is extensive, or the building to be cleaned forms part of a group of similar buildings, the appropriate Planning Officer should be consulted at the planning stage.

Owners of buildings scheduled under the Ancient Monuments Acts are required to give notice of works affecting the building to the Department of the Environment, Directorate of Ancient Monuments and Historic Buildings, at the following addresses:

For England (Sec B1/22), Fortress House, 23 Savile Row, London WIX 2AA.

For Scotland, SSA/S3 Argyle House, 3 Lady Lawson Street, Edinburgh EH3 9SD.

For Wales (AM/admin), Block 1, Government Buildings, St Agnes Road, Gabalfa, Cardiff.

Extensive cleaning requires such notice and on request the Department will give advice on the treatment of scheduled buildings.

For owners of scheduled buildings in Northern Ireland it would be advisable to give notice to the Ancient Monuments Branch of the Ministry of Finance, Churchill House, Belfast 1.

Repair and renovation of flood-damaged buildings

This digest is intended to help architects, surveyors and builders with the problems they are likely to face when dealing with property damaged by flood water. It describes the possible effects of flooding on materials and structures and the various types of damage that may be caused. Appropriate remedial measures are given but these may be modified in some cases depending on the particular circumstances of flood damage.

Before starting work on a structure that has been flooded, electricity, gas and water services should be tested and isolated if necessary.

Draining

All water trapped in or around the building should be drained or pumped out as soon as possible, drilling drain holes in walls if necessary. Check for water trapped in:

1 Underfloor air ducts.

2 Service access pits.

3 Cavities in cavity walls.

4 Areas under the building where the level of the site concrete or ground is below that of the adjoining ground outside the building.

Cleaning

Mud above dpc

Apart from the normal cleaning-up of mud and silt, any earth, mud or debris that has accumulated against the walls above the damp-proof course must be cleared away as soon as possible otherwise it will hinder the drying of the walls. All airbricks and ventilators should be cleared.

Underfloor spaces

Mud that has found its way under boarded floors should also be removed. The underfloor space should be sprayed with disinfectant for health reasons and the Local Authority should be consulted so that their recommendations can be implemented.

Cavity walls

The flooding of cavity external walls may leave mud bridging the cavity above the damp-proof course which, if not removed, could lead to permanent rising dampness. Where there is such a risk the cavity should be inspected, removing an occasional brick if necessary, and any mud present raked or flushed out. The cavity behind wall linings should be inspected and cleaned out if necessary.

House after flooding showing depth of flood water

Drying

After cleaning, the structure should be heated and ventilated as much as possible; the continuation of warm air ventilation promotes drying and is essential *if further damage is to be minimised.*

1 Keep windows and doors open as much as possible even when a fire is lit or heaters are used.

2 Take up loose floor coverings, dry and store them.

3 Lift floorboards preferably near walls to increase draught under the floor. Consider installation of extra ventilators.

4 Wallpaper may have to be stripped and any wall panelling removed.

5 Keep furniture and pictures away from affected walls otherwise they will slow down the rate of drying.

6 Open cupboard doors.

Brickwork and plaster

Porous building materials absorb large quantities of water during flooding. A one-brick wall, for example, may have absorbed as much as 55 litres per m². This water will take months to dry out. Any salts appearing on the surface of the brickwork or plasterwork should be brushed off dry—if more appear it is a sign that the structure is still drying out. Where both sides of a wall are impervious, for example gloss painted, it may be necessary to remove the covering on one side.

Masonry

The denser types of natural stone absorb very little water and will therefore dry out more quickly but if the masonry has an infilling of porous material, such as a rubble hearting, that has become saturated drying will take a long time.

Timber

All timber must be dried as soon as possible to minimise the risk of fungal attack. The risk is greater the longer it remains moist. New outbreaks of decay are unlikely if the timber is dried within a few weeks.

The risks of timber distorting or splitting from too rapid drying must be balanced against the need to dry out the building as soon as possible. Such damage to timber can be minimized by promoting drying from both faces, for example, by removing panelling from walls or lifting floorboards.

Skirting boards, door frames, sills and joist ends and ground-floor timbers generally attached to, or embedded in, damp walls are in the most vulnerable positions and should be carefully examined. The surface of timber may look and feel dry long before the interior dries. A moisture meter with deep probes should be used to check the drying process.

If the measures already suggested for drying out have been taken, the risk of rot will be greatly reduced, but it is recommended that the underfloor be re-inspected after six months and again in twelve months time. Inspection of timber floors may reveal parts that have been suffering from decay for a long time, though not sufficiently extensive either to have caused structural failure or even to have been noticed before flooding led to detailed examination. Long-standing rot of this kind seen in some buildings has been found to be due to earth piled up against the walls above the damp-proof course. Flooding may accentuate this unnoticed decay unless precautions are taken to eliminate its causes.

Long-term effects on sand/lime bricks ten years after flooding by sea-water

Effect of water on materials

Brick, stone and concrete

Water is unlikely to have any serious effect on these materials unless the flood water contained a high proportion of sea-water when there may be long-term effects such as surface powdering and flaking of soft brickwork.

Lightweight concrete with its relatively high moisture movement may have expanded on wetting and therefore shrink on drying. This may eventually lead to some cracking.

Materials in external walls are unlikely to be damaged by frost as the flooded sections are not severely exposed. Dwarf free-standing boundary walls may suffer frost damage if very wet.

Wall finishes

Strong undercoats of cement and sand, or cement, lime and sand, are unlikely to be affected, but lime–sand or black ash mortars in older houses may become friable. Damage is more likely in houses that have been flooded more than once.

Plasterwork based on calcium sulphate plasters may be soft while wet and harden to its original state on drying but some may remain weak and in some instances re-wetting may have caused a delayed expansion with rippling and buckling of the plaster finish.

Plasterboard and fibreboard are soft while wet but may dry out without much warping or twisting. On ceilings the boards may sag.

Asbestos-cement sheeting is unlikely to have been harmed but because it has been saturated it should be re-decorated as for new asbestos-cement.

Timber

Timber swells and distorts on wetting. When swelling occurs under restraint permanent damage may occur which will show up on drying, for example, as excessive gapping between floorboards. Most types of chipboard swell on wetting and suffer permanent weakening. The risk of decay has already been discussed above.

Floor finishes

Permanent floor finishes other than timber and chipboard are unlikely to have been affected. Timber may have swollen and caused buckling of floorboards and lifting of wood blocks. Where water-sensitive adhesives have been used to fix floor coverings to a concrete screed some loss of adhesion may result. Re-use of affected materials depends on their condition after drying out.

Metals

Metals are unlikely to have suffered much damage unless the flood water was contaminated with salts. In factories where such contamination may have occurred metal surfaces should be washed where accessible as a precaution against accelerated corrosion. Locks and hinges should be oiled to prevent rusting.

Structural damage

Structural damage can occur if there has been severe buffeting by flood waters. Simple immersion is unlikely to cause such damage.

Foundations

Damage to foundations may occur during drying-out if the subsoil is shrinkable clay. This swells when wetted and may crack brickwork. No repointing should be done until the ground has dried out since cracks may close as the ground shrinks. The effects of scouring and erosion will usually be obvious and must be remedied. Such damage may not be confined to the foundations and a detailed examination of the whole structure should be made before deciding on remedial measures.

Structural failure caused by severe buffeting by flood water

Walls

The factor of safety of brickwork is so great that minor cracking can generally be ignored unless this occurs in very narrow piers of brickwork between windows and door openings.

Floors and roofs

Structural damage to floors and roofs is usually the result of serious damage to supporting structures or weaknesses existing before flooding. However, possible weakening of, for example, chipboard may need to be considered.

Concrete solid ground floors will normally be undamaged unless they were already seriously cracked or of weak construction, but there may be long-term troubles from some materials used for hardcore such as burnt colliery shale or chalk.

Paths and driveways

Surfaces should not be reinstated until swollen sub-soils have returned to their normal condition. Hardcore and blinding may have been washed away and need replacement.

Drains

If inspection covers were removed to facilitate the draining of surface water, silt may have built-up in drain runs and caused blockages.

Renovating interiors

Walls

The re-decoration of walls, with replastering where necessary, can follow normal procedures, bearing in mind that if the work has to be carried out before the walls have thoroughly dried the same precautions should be taken as for new work. Porous coatings should be used since they will allow evaporation to continue. Wallpaper should not be applied too soon on damp walls. If mould growth is already present, treat walls with a suitable fungicide before re-decoration.

Timber

The main problem in renovation concerns timber—particularly that in suspended ground floors. Much depends on the original condition of the woodwork before flooding and the rate at which it has subsequently been dried. Wherever possible a sufficient number of the floorboards should be lifted to allow a thorough inspection of the floor joists. If there is any doubt as to the state of dryness of any of the timbers the moisture content should be measured by means of a moisture meter. If this shows a reading of more than 20 per cent, further drying is necessary before any more work is done. (The presence of salt water may cause unreliable readings.) There should be no contact between the ends of the joists and the walls, but if there is it should be broken either by cutting off the ends of the joists or by removing any rubbish that has accumulated in the gap. The opportunity should be taken to replace any decayed timbers by pressure-impregnated timber. If the ground or over-site concrete appears to be damp it would be wise to leave the floorboards off for a time to encourage drying. The importance of thorough drying to avoid decay by fungal growth cannot be too strongly emphasised.

It is seldom practicable to remove door frames, window frames, sills or stair stringers and drying operations must be relied on to reduce the risk of fungal growth.

Valuable timber panelling should be removed to allow drying out. It should be allowed to dry and be re-placed only when the walls have dried otherwise water vapour will be transmitted from the wall to the back of the panelling and any battens or strapping providing conditions favourable to fungal growth.

Panelled doors are unlikely to be affected unless the panels are made of plywood in which the plies are bonded with water-sensitive adhesives.

Flush doors may be more severely damaged and require replacement. Much depends on the details of the design and the materials used. Generally there is no difficulty in deciding upon the course of action required.

Swollen doors and opening lights should not be planed until drying and shrinkage are completed.

Linoleum and other impervious floor coverings should not be relaid on timber floors until they are thoroughly dry; rugs and carpets without rubberised backings may be safely used when the floor surface is dry.

Electrical installations

Electrical installations that have been immersed should be disconnected until tested by an electrician and all appliances should be examined and tested.

Connections

All terminations and other unsealed connections must be exposed, examined and cleaned if necessary. All water must be mopped up and terminations left open until dry. When clean, each connection should be examined for surface tracking across insulation surfaces that may have been produced if the supply had been switched on while the installation was still wet. Where this has occurred the component should be replaced.

Ducts, conduits and cables

Water trapped in ducts or conduits must be removed. Inspection elbows and conduit boxes can be opened to facilitate draining.

Plastics covered cable should not be affected by immersion but rubber insulation may be damaged and need replacing.

Tests

After cleaning and drying the installation should be tested for earth continuity and insulation resistance (as laid down in the current IEE Regulations) and an inspection certificate obtained.

Future arrangements

Since the installation may have to operate in a damp atmosphere for up to a year, the insulation may fail due to tracking in moisture films. The occupier should be advised to look for overheating at socket outlets, sizzling, crackling or buzzing, or emission of smoke or steam. If these occur the electricity supply should be switched off at the main immediately.

Trouble may also arise from the rusting of ferrous metal components which may affect the earth return path in steel conduit installations. Clips around socket tubes in socket outlets may also rust causing poor contact at the pins and possible local overheating. Rust attracts moisture and its formation on the inside surfaces of outlet boxes encourages the retention of moisture.

The electrical installation should be inspected and tested at monthly intervals for the first six months and at least twice in the following six months.

Flooded stocks of building materials

Some builders and builders' merchants will have had stocks of building materials flooded, either on sites in course of development or in their own yards. Much of this material can be used provided certain elementary precautions are taken.

Porous materials such as bricks, stone or tiles that have become saturated with water will require at least a certain amount of drying before use. Those sensitive to frost attack should be temporarily covered in frosty weather, and any that have been lying on frozen ground, at the bottom of stacks for example, should be discarded.

Timber will have absorbed water to an extent dependent on how long it has been immersed. Most absorption occurs at the exposed end grain and in sap wood. The timber must be open-piled and re-dried before use.

Some sheet materials such as asbestos-cement may be little affected, and can be put aside and allowed to dry. Wet plasterboard and fibreboard may be too weakened to withstand handling to permit drying and much of it may be unusable. If wetted, chipboard, strawboard and plywood not resistant to water must be rejected.

Glass stored in crates should be examined as a film of water may have been trapped between the sheets. If so, the sheets should be taken out of the case and dried before being re-stored. Water allowed to remain may set up a chemical reaction causing a surface discoloration of the glass, and this is not easily removable. Other products packed in straw, such as sanitary goods, should also be examined and wet straw removed to prevent possible staining.

Metal sheets should be separated and allowed to dry. Iron and steel goods should be dried as quickly as possible to prevent rusting.

Sea-water flooding

Sea-water flooding creates additional problems. Walls contaminated by the deliquescent salts in sea water may remain permanently damp. The salts also promote severe corrosion of any metal fastenings and are likely to corrode electrical installations.

Timber tends to remain damper when contaminated by sea water, but there is no evidence to suggest an increased risk of rot; the fungicidal effect of the salt appears to compensate for the increased dampness.

Check-list

A summary of points to check when dealing with flood-damaged buildings.

Draining	Drain or pump out any water trapped in:

1 Underfloor air ducts
2 Service access pits
3 Wall cavities
4 Site concrete below ground level

Cleaning

1 Clear mud above dpc
2 Remove mud under boarded floors and disinfect space
3 Rake or flush out mud in wall cavities

Drying   Ventilate structure as much as possible:

1 Keep windows and doors open
2 Dry and store floor coverings
3 Remove wallpaper and wall linings
4 Ensure adequate air flow under suspended timber flooring
5 Keep interior walls clear

Oiling   Oil locks and hinges

Structural damage

1 Check floors and roofs for damage caused by disruption of supporting structures or resulting from previous weaknesses
2 Re-point cracked foundation brickwork *after* ground has dried out
3 Examine whole structure for scouring and erosion and repair damage
4 Repair paths and driveways *after* swollen subsoils have returned to normal

Renovating interiors

1 Use porous coatings on walls
2 Treat any mould growth on walls with fungicide
3 Allow walls to dry out before papering
4 Check moisture content of floor timbers—if appreciably more than 20 per cent continue drying
5 Inspect timber floors for rot and re-inspect regularly for one year
6 Replace decayed timber by pressure-impregnated timber
7 Do not plane swollen doors and opening lights until dry
8 Replace linings and panelling only when walls are dry

Electrical installations and appliances

1 Disconnect installations affected until tested by an electrician
2 Leave unsealed connections open after cleaning and drying. Replace if surface tracking present
3 Drain any water trapped in ducts or conduits
4 Check rubber insulated cable for damage
5 Test system after renovation according to IEE Regulations and re-test regularly for one year
6 Examine and test all affected appliances

Stocks of materials

1 Cover wet porous materials during frost
2 Open-stack timber to re-dry before use
3 Separate sheet materials to dry
4 Remove glass from crates and dry before use
5 Remove wet straw packing from goods such as sanitary ware

Sources of further information

Dampness

Rising damp in walls	Digest 27
Damp-proofing solid floors	Digest 54
Damp-proof courses	Digest 77
Damp-proof courses	Advisory Leaflet 23
Dampness in buildings	Advisory Leaflet 47
Inserting a damp-proof course	Advisory Leaflet 58

Timber and woodwork

Design of timber floors to prevent decay	Digest 18
Prevention of decay in window joinery	Digest 73
Dry rot	Advisory Leaflet 10
Care in the use of timber	Advisory Leaflet 29
Woodworm	Advisory Leaflet 42
Maintaining exposed woodwork	Advisory Leaflet 62

Brickwork

Mortars for bricklaying	Digest 160
Cracking in buildings	Digest 75
Efflorescence and stains on brickwork	Advisory Leaflet 75

Painting

Painting woodwork	Digest 106
Control of lichens, moulds and similar growths	Digest 139
Painting new plaster and cement	Advisory Leaflet 1
Painting woodwork	Advisory Leaflet 25
Painting asbestos-cement	Advisory Leaflet 28
Emulsion paint	Advisory Leaflet 37

Plastering

Plaster mixes for inside work	Advisory Leaflet 9
Plasterboard dry linings for houses	Advisory Leaflet 64

DOE ADVISORY LEAFLETS are guides to good building. They contain practical information on building methods and materials and are available from Her Majesty's Stationery Office, PO Box 569, London, SE1, or any bookseller

Wilful damage on housing estates

This digest reports on some of the findings that have emerged from a short explora-tory study by the Building Research Station of wilful damage on housing estates. The study was confined to the design and technical aspects, it did not attempt the more difficult sociological and psychological problems. The recommendations made are based on some forty interviews and inspections and are applicable to the design of buildings, equipment and layouts, and the selection of materials, fittings and finishes, both at the inception of a scheme and subsequently when maintenance and repairs are undertaken.

General lessons and recommendations

Among the factors which promote vandalism are boredom and lack of discipline among young people, unsettled conditions of occupancy and absence of pride of possession and community spirit among tenants; these factors seem to be most prevalent in high-rise estates, though the precise effect of density is not clear. These adverse factors can be countered to some extent strategically, for example, by the provision of well designed children's playgrounds and other recreational facilities—though regrettably these in their turn can become targets for vandalism—and by the encouragement of tenants' associations, by good housing management, caretaking and main-tenance. Estate layout and building design, particu-larly the selection of materials and finishes, can reduce the incidence of vandalism by offering greater resistance to damage and less 'satisfying' targets, but no matter to what extent the resistance to actual physical damage is increased, no design can be secure against disfigurement. Technology can, how-ever, usefully reinforce the efforts of the psychologist and the sociologist.

Some general recommendations follow. All are com-mon sense but the survey showed the need to state them because they were not always followed in practice, perhaps because of the need to limit first cost, perhaps because designers did not foresee the conditions that would develop on a particular estate. Some specific recommendations are summarised in the tables on pages 223 and 224.

Good lighting and avoidance of hidden corners

Some of the recommendations of Digest 122 *Security* apply also in the prevention or reduction of wilful damage. Clear visibility is a recognised deterrent; this means good lighting of buildings, particularly public staircases and corridors, garage courts and car parks, and the avoidance of hidden corners particularly in entrance halls and under stairs.

Removal of builders' rubbish and safeguarding of plant

Wilful damage is often at its worst when an estate is first occupied. This may be due in part to the social problems involved in 'settling down' and forming a community. But it may also be associated with the fact that unfinished parts of an estate, contractors' plant and builders' rubbish, are attractive both as adventure playgrounds* and as targets for youthful vandals. Digest 122 gives guidance on security on building sites against theft; adoption of its recom-mendations is a first step to countering vandalism on estates where building work is still in progress. Ladders should be safeguarded and where practicable unfinished work should be fenced off from the rest of the estate. Broken bricks, timber offcuts, etc, are handy missiles or weapons and should be cleared from a site before families move in.

A good standard of maintenance

Buildings and site works in a dilapidated state breed vandalism. The dilapidation may start with accidental damage, poor initial design or workmanship, failure to complete a maintenance operation or failure to repair promptly a minor act of wilful damage. The responsibility for such failures falls in part on the original designers and in part on those responsible for management and maintenance.

* A BRS study of children's play on housing estates (National Building Studies Research Paper 39:1966) found that 'Build-ing and demolition sites are utilised as adventure playgrounds, for building huts, lighting fires, or for the sort of freedom where "I can fire my catapult at old tin cans", "I like to play on the workmen's shed . . . you have to climb over a big green gate. . . . On the top of the shed is something like green sandpaper."'

Fig 1 Dark finish on light substrate

Fig 2 Lamp cover at kicking height

Avoid:	Alternatives:	To reduce risk of:
Wall finishes		
Soft-textured	Resist damage or marking : cleanable :	Defacement by writing, scratching or carving
Easily scratched, particularly if of colour contrasting with substrate *see* Fig 1	—special paints and glazes, similar in colour to substrate	
Light colours	—ceramic mosaic	*All are vulnerable to aerosol sprays; some authorities therefore prefer cheap finishes, easily renewed*
	—glazed tiles	
Requiring renewal, but too expensive for frequent renewal	Resist damage or marking ; difficult to clean :	
	—ribbed metal sheet —roughcast —rough-textured bricks	
Materials		
Glass in large panes and vulnerable positions	Windows, doors, signs, etc : transparent plastics (polycarbonate considered best ; acrylic, UPVC and butyrate sheet also available) ; armour-plate glass	Breakage
		Plastics sheets can be removed; risk of being burnt appears to be less than in lighting fittings
	Opinions vary on the use of glass bricks ; though stronger than window glass, they can still be broken and seem to be particularly attractive to vandals	
	Translucent covers to lighting fittings : if inaccessible, use plastics (polycarbonate or butyrate)	*see* Fig 2
		Breakage ; *but may become target for catapult, air-gun or stone-throwing*
Plastics covers to lighting fittings near ground	Glass (preferably armour-plate)	Burning
Plastics and asbestos-cement rainwater pipes below 2 m in height	Cast iron	Breakage
External copper and lead piping	Keep pipe runs within the building	Theft
Soft mortar joints, if accessible	Hard mortar	Scraping out
Design features		
Easy access to flat roofs from adjacent walls or lower buildings, projections giving foothold, rainwater pipes, etc. *see* Fig 3	Wide projections at eaves and top edges ; parapet walls *see* Fig 4	Damage to felt or asbestos-cement roofs and accidents by falling through the latter
Tile-hanging or glass below ground floor window cill level, particularly if adjacent ground is open for children's play *see* Fig 5	Brickwork, blockwork, etc.	Breakage. accidental or deliberate ; removal of tiles
'Up-and-over' garage doors of inadequate strength *see* Fig 3	Good quality doors with lock at floor* Heavy framed, ledged and braced doors with robust hasp, staple and padlock ; no glass*	Youths swinging on them ; distortion ; dislocation of balancing mechanism
	* Alternatively, or in addition, garages to be overlooked from dwellings	

Fig 3 'Up-and-over' converted to 'down-and-under' ; accessible roof

Fig 4 Roof access made difficult—though there is still the rainwater pipe.

Fig 5 Damage may be wilful or accidental

Fig 6 Heavy copings

Avoid:	Alternatives:	To reduce risk of:
Design features (Contd)		
Projecting garage door handles about knee-high	Retractable handle for 'up-and-over' doors; or tee handle locked in vertical position	Kicking off, leading to break-in; access to roof
Lever handles to external doors	Spherical knobs	Breakage *but in old people's dwellings lever handles may be needed*
Painted metal posts, rails, etc, in playgounds or public spaces	Non-ferrous metal; galvanised or plastics-coated steel	Chipping and scratching of paint
Common access areas		
Dark corners in entrance halls and open spaces under stairs	Good artificial lighting, day and night if necessary	General nuisance and accumulation of rubbish
	Locked external doors with telephone communication between tenants and visitors	*Limited experience, effectiveness not proved—subject to vandalism*
	Caretaker's office overlooking entrance	
Vulnerable features in lifts *see also* **Wall finishes**	PVC or other sheet flooring	Damage by fouling *though PVC is damaged by hot tobacco ash*
	Metal control buttons	Burning or prising out plastics to dislocate lift service
	Stop buttons	Damage by wedging doors open, eg by milkmen *but not all authorities agree*
	Provision of WC off lift hall	Fouling of lifts *but WC is itself subject to vandalism*
Vulnerable features in visitors' toilets	Specially designed sanitary fittings; pipework and mechanisms concealed; embedded conduit; concealed fixing of fittings and equipment; recessed head or hexagon socket screws	Deliberate or accidental damage; electric shock or blown fuses; theft
Landscaping features		
Excessive amounts of soft landscaping *see* Figs 7 and 8	Roses or other prickly bushes; hard pavings; planted plots raised and with strong retaining walls; paths in the right places	Shortcutting over beds; damage or theft of plants and turf. *Opinions vary on the effectiveness of raised beds*
Cobbles or granite setts	Large slabs or jointless pavings	Lifting and use as missiles
Ranch fencing in white-painted wood	Vertical pales; horizontal boarding suitably strong and unpainted	Damage to boarding or painted finish by climbing
On low walls—thin concrete or stone copings, particularly with overhang; tile copings; brick-on-edge copings without strengthened angles and ends	Large section *in situ* or precast concrete copings, flush on one or both faces and anchored to wall *see* Fig 6; brick-on-edge with *in situ* concrete angles and ends	Removal
Open spaces too large; 'nooks and crannies' in layout	High standard of lighting; all-night floodlighting in extreme cases	Nuisance

Fig 7 Short cuts over flower beds

Fig 8 Raised flower beds

Avoidance of features which attract youthful adventure and vandalism

A number of design features provide opportunities for adventure and for vandalism and should be avoided. Blocks of lock-up garages may suffer badly from attack if they are hidden from general view; abandoned cars are added attractions. So are flat or low-pitched roofs which have easy access; asbestos-cement sheeting is particularly at risk and provides an accident hazard. Monopitch roofs falling to the rear are not easy of access from the front, especially if protected by a wide overhang, but they may need to be protected at the back. Other design features which provide targets are posts, signs, special lighting fittings, etc, which may be unusual in appearance or become objects for climbing and swinging on. Their design should either be kept simple and unattractive for adventure play or they should be strong enough to withstand it.

Caretaking on mixed estates

Housing estates developed with blocks of flats at high density in urban centres usually have caretakers, but caretaking is often less adequate on lower density estates when blocks of flats are mixed with low-rise housing. In these situations the problem of vandalism and wilful damage can be serious, especially where there is a high proportion of landscaped public open space and hidden corners.

Layout

Damage may be inflicted on flower beds and ornamental grass by people taking short-cuts across them instead of following the formal paths provided; fences may also be damaged in an effort to make a route where none was planned. Raised beds may help to prevent this (Fig 8) but the whole problem could be anticipated when the layout is planned so that paths are provided along routes that users are likely to follow.

Maintenance and appearance criteria

The attitudes of housing authorities to the problem of wilful damage can be broadly classified according to whether the criterion of 'maintenance' or 'appearance' takes precedence. Design and maintenance policies vary between the two schools of thought though they share a common interest in cost. The aim of the 'maintenance' group can be expressed simply as to find means of minimising the combined cost of maintenance, repair and supervision. This may lead to a choice of robust finishes, fittings, etc; high initial cost is acceptable if the reduction in maintenance and other subsequent costs is likely to show an overall saving. Unfortunately, when precautions against wilful damage are intensified beyond a certain point, appearance and amenity standards may drop. The aim of the 'appearance' group is, therefore, to steer a middle course between the unsightliness of wilful damage and the possible bleakness of anti-vandal treatment.

Given some initial damage on a new estate, regardless of whether or not it is made good, vandalism is likely to remain a problem for some time. Eventually, though possibly not until the first full redecoration removes all signs of defacement, maturity and a well-maintained appearance may combine to discourage further attack. Persistence in the repair of damage and removal of defacement is essential if headway is to be made against the problem. Deterioration in appearance can arise from causes other than vandalism, such an accidental damage, misuse or ordinary wear and tear, or weathering, decay, corrosion and other forms of failure; if these are allowed to develop, conditions favouring vandalism can become established in an estate previously free from it, or re-established in one from which it has been eliminated. Comparatively minor faults or incipient failure can provide temptation even to well-suppressed vandalistic tendencies.

The probable incidence of wilful damage in a particular situation is not easy to predict. Technical preventive measures might not, therefore, be adopted in new work unless the most adverse conditions are indicated. If, however, the risk is kept in mind during the design stage, it may be possible to build in protection at little or no extra cost or loss of amenity. The design should not preclude the adoption of vandal-resisting measures later, if found necessary.

As with all matters concerning maintenance, good feed-back from the management and maintenance side to the designers is essential if mistakes are not to be repeated.

Index

This two-part index consists of a *numerical* index of BRE Digest current titles followed by an *alphabetical* subject index. The numerical section shows the location of each digest by volume and page number, whilst the alphabetical section gives the relevant digest numbers for each subject.

It will be seen that some digests appear in more than one volume, thus ensuring that the subject area of each volume is fully covered and repeating a feature which proved its value to users of the first edition of this series. The index is common to all four volumes, Building Materials, Building Construction, Services and Environmental Engineering, and Building Defects and Maintenance. When a reader is seeking a particular volume which is temporarily unavailable, as, for instance, in an office library, consulting the index in one of the other volumes will show if any of the required digests is to be found elsewhere.

Key M = Building Materials, C = Building Construction, S = Services and Environmental Engineering, D = Building Defects and Maintenance.

Numerical list of current titles

Alphabetical subject index